D0880851

WALTER DE LA MARE:

A SELECTION FROM HIS WRITINGS

WALTER DE LA MARE

A Selection from his Writings

made by

KENNETH HOPKINS

FABER AND FABER
24 Russell Square
London

This Selection
first published in mcmlvi
by Faber and Faber Limited
24 Russell Square London WC1
Printed in Great Britain by
Latimer Trend & Co Ltd Plymouth
All rights reserved

PR6007
E3
A6
1956

CONTENTS

7

Contents

Contents

INTRODUCTION

Looking back along the past fifty years it is possible to see the literature of our century—now more than half over—coming into focus. It is a troubled, turbulent literature, born of difficult times; yet—for nothing is wholly consistent, wholly on one plane, wholly in one character—it has its seasons of peace, its places of refreshment.

The fifty years of which I am thinking have given us a handful of books great and original enough to stand with any: such poems as *The Dynasts* and *The Testament of Beauty*; such novels as *All Our Yesterdays* and *A Glastonbury Romance*; such memoirs as *A Foxhunting Man* and *Undertones of War*; these, with others, come readily to mind to speak for the first decades of the century.

But 'great' is a relative term, and a general one. Often it is so loosely used as to lose its native force. Although I believe a comprehensive list of great contemporary writers should include the name of Walter de la Mare, it is not primarily his greatness I want to discuss in this introductory note. As he says in one of his own prefaces, 'Time will soon see to all that'. I will say only that when Time has done its work I believe the reputation of Walter de la Mare will not be all brought down.

Most ages of literature, except perhaps the darkest, produce a few outstanding writers, as ours has done. But it is rarer to find a figure whom all classes of readers join in praising; and whom all classes of readers love. It is a word much abused, love: but hardly abused here. Walter de la Mare is perhaps the only writer of our time, one of the few in any time, for whom countless thousands feel a warm and genuine personal affection. Others command respect, attention; provoke controversy; inspire praise; suffer neglect, misunderstanding, derision; but de la Mare is loved. This is one of the unusual occasions when a writer's success had marched in step with his deserts. To the darker aspects of a literary life—the necessary early struggle apart—de la Mare has remained a stranger. Often enough, we see the wrong fellow going triumphantly forward to his fiftieth impression, and the 'work that will live' enjoying a prospect denied to its author. But at least once in our time, we may say, there was no mistake.

Although he has lived by his pen for fifty years—and that is a way of life almost more precarious than any—it has been de la Mare's fortune to write chiefly (if not quite only) the things he has been moved to write; and—something more than fortune enters here—to write them not much below the level of their conception. Between the ideal and the execution there must always be some loss; this is the writer's basic problem, one that no writer has finally solved. But de la Mare has given almost consistently of his best, and how good that is a handful of remembered titles serves to tell—*Memoirs of a Midget; Peacock Pie; Songs of Childhood; Henry Brocken*. These books, and a dozen others in the list they represent, have entered into the consciousness of a host of readers wherever English is understood; and everywhere they have made those readers the richer. They show, even in their darker passages, that the nobility of the human spirit is not quenched yet, despite man's own best efforts. Taken as a body of work they show, what may be looked for in vain in some writers else unquestionably great, that a man's life may be spent in writings whose only tendency is to good, and whose principal end is to promote happiness. There is not a sentence, not a line in de la Mare that anybody was ever the worse for reading. That's perhaps a negative good, I can't say. I think its effect will be positive. But in any case, this is but a part of the matter. After all, there are plenty of writers who never did anybody any harm. . . . The secret that has given de la Mare his hold on two generations of readers lies deeper than this. It lies in that quality without which neither style, nor wit, nor learning, nor all combined, would suffice. It lies in humanity, in compassion. Compassion, the noblest quality that moves in the heart of man, is everywhere the well-spring in the work of de la Mare. It comes into the smallest poem:

HI!

Hi! handsome hunting man
Fire your little gun.
Bang! Now the animal
Is dead and dumb and done.
Nevermore to peep again, creep again, leap again,
Eat or sleep or drink again, Oh, what fun!

It comes into the tales: consider how, only by the compassion underlying it is such a story as 'In the Forest' bearable at all, it is otherwise so uselessly tragic, so complete in disaster. There is nothing to be done at the end. The telling of such a story can be justified only because the writer's compassion calling forth the reader's adds somehow to the world's stock —which is at no time too large. It comes, this ever-present, never-failing compassion, into work not primarily tragic. By this quality alone is the stylistic *tour-de-force* of *Memoirs of a Midget* made into something the world will not easily forget. That book would always have been a masterpiece; but it might not always have been read. Even masterpieces gather dust; but not this one, I think, because Miss M. is created with the most delicate love and compassion in the whole of twentieth-century literature. She seems the only completely flawless character ever born in fiction. Well, that's a bold thing to say, unless one happens to have read all fiction; but it is the measure of how this perfect piece of writing may move a reader not given to casual superlative.

I will not labour this theme of compassion, although I believe its presence—never obtrusive, often all but concealed—does explain the universality of de la Mare's appeal. For I don't at all suggest that it is the single explanation. There are other factors, of which I may mention one or two.

Introduction

There is style. Now, style is not among the average reader's preoccupations and he might, if challenged, be inclined to suggest that it is something more or less invented for the use of Robert Louis Stevenson and Walter Pater. 'Style' to the every-day reader suggests perhaps a certain artificiality, a contrived effect, a mannered way of writing. Yet that style is the man, like most old adages, remains essentially true. The plain prose of Robert Southey is as much 'style' as the intricate word-spinning of John Donne, or the massive invectives of John Milton. But in de la Mare style is a subordinate quality, no matter how valuable in its own right. It is never an applied decoration, but is integral to the thought. The style was there, we feel, before ever a word appeared on paper. It varies, is modified as occasion calls. It is perhaps as much in the mood as in the language. So:

'The church was brimmed so full of limpid moonlight that at any moment, it seemed, the stone walls, the pulpit, the roof itself might vanish away like the fabric of a dream. Its contents appeared to have no more reality than the reflections in a glass. Every crevice in the mouldings of the arches, every sunken flower and leaf in the mullions of the windows, every knot in the wood of the pew beneath his nose stood out as if it had been blacked in with Indian ink. Every jut and angle, corbel and finial, marble nose and toe and finger seemed to have been dipped in quicksilver. And Philip, his eyes fixed on the faintly golden, winged, ecstatic figure—mutely "shaking her gilded tresses in the air"—whose gaze he pined and yet feared even in imagination to meet, was lost for the time being to the world of the actual. He failed even to notice urgent reminders that one of his legs from knee to foot had gone numb, and that he was stone cold.'

Now this truly is 'fine writing' as the term is conventionally used. It is 'style' as a chosen passage might be from one of the admired masters—except for two little things. The marble nose and toe would have been excluded by a conscious stylist in favour of something more 'poetical'—'torso', perhaps, or 'form'; and nobody in a set 'purple passage' would ever be permitted to have pins and needles. Many stylists could have written the first sentence; few would have ventured to add the last—yet that is what makes the effect of the quotation. We feel that the writer is not losing sight of humanity and its frailties amid these verbal splendours. His language matches the occasion, but he never forgets that the central character is a child; and what, among these moon-bathed ecclesiastical details might a child notice especially?—a cherub's nose.

Here's another effect of style, the right words in the best order:

'Then again Miss Rawlings, like her renowned Aunt Felicia, had always enjoyed a weakness for taking naps in the train, the flowers and plumes and bows in her bonnet nodding the while above her head. The sound of the wheels on the iron lines was like a lullaby, the fields trailing softly away beyond the window drowsed her eyes.'

That starts off briskly enough but it quickly settles into a comfortable sleepiness—though there are not sixty words in all—and the second sentence is a marvel of subtle suggestion.

These are details, and in a short Introduction they cannot be multiplied. Style, moreover, lies in something more than this. It lies as much in the approach as in the execution. Consider 'Pigtails, Ltd.', a story in this collection. The tone is everywhere light, and often bantering. Some of the touches are frankly absurd: the several fantastic village Funds, the phaetons and gigs by which Miss Rawlings was frequently all but run over. The writer knows that phaetons went out when railways came in, but he doesn't care; and he probably thinks it a pity. So he dashes away, putting into his story (as Southey long ago recommended) as much as his story will hold, until he has given us a charming, tender, *true*, and lovable bit of fantasy. But—

The deeper note is never quite silent, although it sounds so faintly. Miss Rawlings is a living woman, and not a caricature; she wins by turns our compassion, our respect, and our affection. This story has a deceptive lightness; it is 'great fun'. But, read it again. It is as much a criticism of life as the sombrest of the pages of Thomas Hardy himself.

Miss Rawlings is a 'character', but she's not the less real on that account and this power of making real something or someone in a story which is itself outside normal reality is not a common one. Kipling has it: we know wolves and tigers don't talk, but while reading *The Jungle Book* we agree that they do. So with the least probable of de la Mare's characters —the Royal Monkeys, or the widely dissimilar Lispet and Lispett who, although they never really appear at all, are yet sufficiently 'live' at the end. This gallery of strange yet consistently credible characters is a large one. Take, for example, the old Count in 'The Count's Courtship'. He figures only in two stories, neither of them of great length. We are not told his age, or his size in shoes or the colour of his eyes. Indeed, we are told very little directly about him; yet we see him clearly enough, a little faded, a little out of fashion, but a gentleman of the old school just the same, his dignity a thought pathetic, his linen the merest fraction frayed. These figures are drawn with reticence, and perhaps that is why they are so 'like'—as a silhouette is 'like' because it takes no count of inessentials. It is the bone structure that dictates the outward appearance. In written description, few words are best, for the multiplication of detail confuses. Choosing those few words rightly, that is the difficulty. It is a difficulty de la Mare almost always surmounts.

There is another reason for de la Mare's wide appeal, and perhaps a more obvious one than those I have glanced at above. This is, simply, the essential ordinariness of his subject matter: he's interested in birds, and sticky buns, and people kissing under trees, and July mornings, and old women gathering firewood, and watched-pots somehow boiling at last, and spiders' webs and pebbles and peaches and ships-in-bottles. So are ordinary people everywhere. His themes—a few exceptions apart—have been 'rubbed by a hundred

rhymesters, battered a thousand times', but it makes no matter. Once again, a shifting of the viewpoint, a modification
in the approach, and we are given the old magic renewed. I
believe this is the true secret. We are not looking for something new; the old beauty, the old love, the old truth, suits us
very well. But in de la Mare's hands it's given a twist, an
unfamiliar setting, a shifting of emphasis: and we see it again
with a child's wonder, through a child's eyes. Indeed, perhaps
it is not the subject matter that is renewed, but ourselves: we
have, he shows us:

> *At lip, miraculous, life's wine,*
> *At hand, its wondrous bread.*

In our time few people can assemble an extensive library; they
have, mostly, neither the space to house nor the money to buy
large quantities of books. A full set of de la Mare's works
makes a long row on the shelf; by these Selections I have tried
to provide a short cut, a sort of interim report, the chance to
dip into this book or that, an invitation to taste the wine and
try the bread. Such selections as these I believe do not super-
sede the long row, but serve to send new readers to it. The
reader will not, I hope, suppose that he need look no further.
For then he would indeed be missing something.

Love, for example, is one of the most ambitious anthologies
ever attempted. It is, somehow, not a compilation at all, although it contains passages from several hundreds of writers.
The genius of Walter de la Mare for work of this kind—and
it is genius, no less—has made *Love* a work as four-square and
integral as a house, which contains thousands of separate
bricks, and is yet itself an undivided thing. I have given a
short extract from the Introduction to *Love*; but the reader
of my chosen passage must not suppose he no longer has
occasion for the whole work. That Introduction alone, apart
from the anthology it illuminates, is an essay of fifty thousand
words, of which what I have given is but a taste. Again,
nothing but the complete work can justly represent *Memoirs*

of a Midget, and although there are beauties enough in an enlarged detail, only with the whole canvas in view can one appreciate the scale, balance and humanity of the conception, and the triumphant miracle of its execution.

What I have attempted, then, in the Selections which follow is to give a broad outline of de la Mare's work, showing so far as my limits allow the several aspects of his genius. His tales and poems are the most widely known of his writings; few readers, I suppose, have entirely missed 'The Listeners' and 'Peacock Pie' and 'Seaton's Aunt', and surely every reader who has enjoyed even so small an acquaintance with de la Mare will be willing to explore further. Here is a chapter from *Henry Brocken*, a book which perhaps our reader has missed. It is a unique book, a poet's book; a book which for fifty years has 'numbered good intellects'; to read it is to meet with an experience no other book of our time can afford. To read *The Return* is to meet with another, and a bitterer; for *The Return* gives us a frightening glimpse into the cunning soul of evil and shows us how at every step we tread nearly through the crust between us and an unspeakable abyss. The achievement of *The Return*, surely, is in taking us so near to the edge of reason and yet bringing us safely home. Here too are examples of those perceptive essays on books and writers whose unspectacular judgments may be found—on closer inspection—to give a view of letters more satisfying than the cries of the iconoclasts.

And there are the poems. To them we must always come back with gratitude and love. Many of them we have known from childhood, and yet they lose neither freshness nor grace. It is thirty years since I first learned 'Nod' by heart, yet I have copied it into the present volume with delight wholly undiminished. Who could forget, or tire of the beautiful dead lady of the West Country; or the grave melancholy of 'Very old are the woods'; or cease to enjoy the bright, breathless dancing of the three jolly farmers?

There are hundreds of poems; I can give but a handful here. They display an astonishing range of music, a wide variety of occasion and mood. They speak memorably for us on most of life's encounters: on death and birth; on trouble and summer and sleeping and stroking the cat. Trivial things enough?—but they make up the burden of our days. There is much that may be expressed in a mere four lines:

THE OLD AUTHOR

The End, *he scrawled, and blotted it. Then eyed*
Through darkened glass night's cryptic runes o'erhead.
'*My last, and longest book.*' *He frowned; then sighed:*
'*And everything left unsaid!*'

'Everything?' No, not quite everything, I think.

KENNETH HOPKINS

PROSE SELECTIONS

From THE RETURN

She came out into the sunlight, and they went through the gate together. She walked on quickly, and without speaking, over the bridge and past a cottage whose stooping hollyhocks displayed their last flowers above a low flint wall. Skirting a field of stubble, she struck into the woods by a path that ran steeply up the hillside. And presently they came to a glen where the woodmen of years ago had felled the trees, leaving a green hollow of saplings in the midst of their towering neighbours.

'There,' she said, holding out her hand to him; 'now we are alone. In only a few hours the sun will be there,' she pointed to the tree-tops to the west already tinged with autumn, 'and then you will have to go. For good, for good—you your way, and I mine. What a tangle and mystery is this life of ours. Could I have dreamt we should ever be talking like this, you and I? Friends of an hour. What will you think of me? Does it matter? Don't speak. Say nothing—poor face, poor hands! If only there were something to look to—to pray to!' She bent over his hand and pressed it to her breast. 'What worlds we have seen together, you and I. And now—another parting.'

Her dark clear eyes searched his face, as might an anxious mother's her child's, as though in search of a reassurance no mortal lips can bestow.

They talked, and fell silent, and talked again; without sadness or reproach, feigning a confidence neither could feel, concealing the desolation of their hearts. She even mocked at themselves—at this change. 'Why,' she said, 'and yet without it, would you ever even have dreamed once a poor outcast of a Frenchman went to his restless grave for me—for me! Need we understand? Were we told to pry? Who made us human must be human too. Why must we be so cautious, take such care, make such a fret? This *soul*? I know it, I know it; it is all we have. "To save", they say, poor creatures. No, never to *spend*. And so they daren't for a solitary instant lift it on a finger from its cage. Well, we have; and now, soon, back it must go, back it must go, and try its best to whistle the day out. And yet, even this glimpse of freedom has a little shaken its— its monotony. It's true, you see. They have lived a long time; these Worldly Wisefolk. They learned prudence before they were weaned. . . .

'There, you must be hungry?' she asked him, laughing in his eyes. 'Of course, of course you are—scarcely a mouthful since that strange supper of ours; our first and our last. And you haven't slept a wink, except like a tired-out child after its first party, in that old garden chair. I sat and watched, and yes, almost hoped you'd never wake again! In case—in case! Come along, see, down there! I can't go home just yet. There's an absurd little inn. We'll go and sit down there—as if we were really trying to be romantic! I know the woman quite well. We can talk there—just this one day out.'

They sat at a little table in the garden of 'The Cherry Tree', the twisted lichenous branches around them burdened with their ripening apples. And Grisel tried to persuade him to eat and drink. 'For to-morrow we die,' she said, her hands trembling, her face veiled as it were with a faint mysterious light.

'There are dozens and dozens of old stories, you know,' she said, leaning on her elbows, 'dozens and dozens, meaning only us. You must, you *must* eat. Look, just an apple. We'll be Adam and Eve. We have to say *good-bye*. And faintness will double the difficulty.' She touched his hand as if to compel him to smile at her. 'There, I'll peel it. And this is Eden; and

22

soon it will be the cool of the evening; and then, oh yes, the voice will come. My dear, what nonsense I am talking. Never mind.'

They sat on in the quiet sunshine; and a garden-spider slid softly through the air and with busy claws set to weaving its net; and those small late-summer ghosts the robins flitted whistling restlessly from tree to tree.

A pale-faced child came out of the porch of the inn into the garden and, battered wooden doll in its arms, stood silently watching them. But when Grisel smiled at her and tried to coax her over, she burst out laughing and ran back into the house.

Lawford stooped forward on his chair with a groan. 'You see,' he said, 'the whole world mocks me. You say "this evening". Need it be, must it be *this* evening? If you only knew how far they have driven me. If you only knew what we might only detest each other for saying and for listening to. The whole thing's dulled and staled. Who wants a change-ling? Who wants a painted make-believe? Who does not loathe the would-be converted? Well, I have been converted to Sabathier's God. Should we be sitting here talking like this if it were not so? I can't—I can't go back.'

She rose and stood with her hand pressed over her mouth, steadily watching him.

'Won't you understand?' he continued. 'I too am an out-cast now—a felon caught red-handed, come in the flesh to a hideous and righteous judgment. I hear myself saying all these things; and yet, Grisel, I love you. I love you with all the dull best I ever had. Not now, though. I daren't ask for now, Grisel. I can, I would begin again. God knows my face has changed enough even as it is. Think of me as that poor wan-dering ghost of yours. How easily I could hide away—in your memory; and just wait, wait for you. In time. Even this wild futile madness too would fade away—in time. Then I could come back. May I try?'

'I can't answer you,' she almost whispered. 'I can reason no more. And yet, talk, defer, forget as I may, I know that must is must. Right and wrong, who knows what *they* mean, except that one's to be done and one's to be forsworn. Or—forgive the truest thing I have ever said—or else we lose the savour of both. Oh, and I know, too, you would soon weary of me.

'I know you, Monsieur Nicholas, better than you can ever know yourself, though you *have* risen from your grave. You follow a dream: no voice or face or flesh and blood. And not to do what that merciless raven within you cries you *must*, would be in time to hate the very sound of my footsteps. You shall go back, poor turncoat; and face the daylight, the utterly more difficult, bald, and heartless daylight, as together we faced the dark. Life, after all, is only a little while. And though I have no words to tell what are and must be foolish reasons because they are not reasons at all but ghosts of memory, I know now in my very heart that to face the worst is your only hope of peace. Should I have staked so much on your realizing that, and now throw all away—surrender? Don't let us talk any more. I'll walk half the way with you, perhaps. Perhaps I will walk *all* the way! I think my brother guesses— at least *my* madness. I've talked and talked him nearly past his patience. And then, when you are quite safely, oh yes, quite safely and soundly gone, then I shall go away for a little, so that we can't even hear each other speak. Except in dreams. "Life!" Once I used to think it was much too plain a tale to have so strange an ending. And with us the powers beyond have played a newer trick. That's all. Another hour, and we will go. Till then, there's just the solitary walk home; and only the dumb old haunted house, that hoards as many ghosts as we ourselves, to watch our coming.'

Evening began to shine between the trees. They seemed to stand in flames, with a melancholy rapture in their uplifted boughs above their fading coats. The fields of the garnered harvest shone with a golden stillness, a-whir with shimmering flocks of wild birds. And those that had sung their rapture in the spring had begun to sing again amid the same leaves, grown older too to give them harbourage. . . .

Herbert was sitting in his room when they returned, nursing an extra large teacup on his knee while he pretended to be reading, his elbow propped on the table.

'Here's Nicholas Sabathier, my dear, come to say good-bye to us,' said Grisel. She stood silent for a moment, her face turned towards the clear green-reflected twilight of the open window. There was a loveliness in it that a spiritual weariness can give even to one not conspicuous for its beauty. 'I have promised to walk part of the way back with him. But I think first we must have some tea. No; he flatly refuses to be driven. We are going to walk.'

The two friends were left alone, face to face with a rather difficult silence; a certain degree of nervousness apparent, so far as Herbert was concerned, in that odd aloof sustained air of impersonality that had so baffled his companion in their first talk together.

'Your sister said just now, Herbert,' blurted Lawford at last, ' "Here's Nicholas Sabathier come to say good-bye". Well, I—I want you to understand that it *is* Sabathier, the worst he ever was. And also that it *is* "good-bye".'

Herbert slowly turned. 'I don't quite see why "good-bye", Lawford. And—honestly, there is nothing to explain. We have chosen to live such a very out-of-the-way life,' he went on, as if following up a train of thought, 'my sister and I. The truth is, if one wants to live one's own life, there's no time for many friends. And just steadfastly regarding your neighbour's tail as you follow it down into the Nowhere—it's that that seems to me the deadliest form of hypnotism. One must simply go one's own way, doing one's best to free one's mind of cant—and I dare say clearing some excellent stuff out with the rubbish. One runs that risk. And the consequence is that I don't think, however foolhardy it may be to say so, I don't think I care a groat for any opinion as human as my own, good or bad. My sister's a million times a better woman than

I am a man. What possibly could there be, then, for *me* to say?'
He turned with a nervous, almost reluctant smile. 'You understand one another. Why should it be good-bye?'

Lawford glanced involuntarily towards the door that stood
in shadow duskily ajar. 'Well,' he said, 'we have talked, and
we think it must be that. Until, at least, I can come as quietly
as that old ghost you told me of. It might not, then, be so very
long to wait.'

Their eyes met fleetingly across the still, listening room.
'The more I think of it,' Lawford pushed slowly on, 'the less
I understand the frantic purposelessness of all that has happened to me. Until I went down, as you said, "a godsend of
a little Miss Muffet", and the inconceivable farce came off, I
was *fairly* happy, fairly contented to dance my little wooden
dance and to wait till the showman should pack me away into
his box again with his other puppets. And now—well, here I
am. The whole thing has gone by and left but little open trace
of its visit. Here I am for all my friends to swear to; and yet,
Herbert, if you'll forgive my troubling you with this stuff
about myself, not a single belief, or thought, or desire remains unchanged. You will remember all that, I hope. It's
not, of course, the ghost of an apology, only the bare facts.'

Herbert rose and paced slowly across to the window. 'The
longer I live, Lawford, the more I curse this futile gift of
speech. Here am I, wanting to tell you, to say out frankly
what, if mind could appeal direct to mind, would be merely
as the wind passing through the leaves of a tree with just one
—one multitudinous rustle, but which, if I tried now to put
it into words—well, daybreak would find us still groping
on. . . .' He turned, a peculiar wry smile on his face. 'It's a
dumb world: but there we are. And some day you'll come
again.'

'Well,' said Lawford, as if with an almost hopeless effort to
turn thought into such primitive speech, 'that's where we
stand, then.' He got up suddenly, like a man wakened in the
midst of unforeseen danger. 'Where is your sister?' he cried,

looking into the shadow. And as if in actual answer to his entreaty, they heard the clinking of the cups on the old, green lacquer Chinese tray she was at that moment carrying into the room. She sat down on the window seat and put the tray down beside her. 'It will be before dark even now,' she said, glancing out at the faintly burning skies.

They had trudged on together with almost as deep a sense of physical exhaustion as that of harvesters who have been labouring the fields since dawn. And a little beyond the village, before the last, long road began that led in presently to the housed and scrupulous suburb, she stopped with a sob beside an old scarred milestone by the wayside. 'This—is as far as I can go,' she said. She stooped, and laid her hand on the cold moss-grown surface of the stone. 'Even now it's wet with dew.' She rose again and looked strangely into his face. 'Yes, yes, here it is,' she said, 'oh, and worse, worse than any fear. But nothing now can trouble you again of that. We're both at least past that.'

'Grisel,' he said, 'forgive me, forgive me. I *can't* go on.'

'Don't think, don't think,' she said, taking his hands, and lifting them to her lips. 'It's only how the day goes; and it has all, my one Dear, happened scores and scores of times before —mother and child and friend—and lovers that are all these too: like us. We mustn't cry out. Perhaps it was all before even we could speak—that this sorrow came. Take all the hope and all the future: and then may come our chance.'

'What's life to me now. You said the desire would come back; that I should shake myself free. I could if you would help me. I don't know what you are or what your meaning is, only that I love you; care for nothing, wish for nothing but to see you and think of you. A flat, dull voice keeps saying that I have no right to be telling you all this. You will know best. I know I am nothing. I ask nothing. If we love one another, what is there else to say?'

'Nothing, nothing to say, except only good-bye. What

could you tell me that I have not told myself over and over again? Reason's gone. Thinking's gone. Now I am only sure.' She smiled shadowily. 'What peace did *he* find who couldn't, perhaps, like you, face the last good-bye?'

They stood in utter solitude a while in the evening gloom. The air was sluggish and cold as some grey unfathomable untraversed sea. Above them uncountable clouds drifted slowly across space.

'Why do they all keep whispering together?' he said in a low voice, with cowering face. 'Oh if you knew, Grisel, how they have hemmed me in; how they have come pressing in through the narrow gate I left ajar. Only to mock and mislead. It's all dark and unintelligible.'

He touched her hand, peering out of the shadows that seemed to him to be gathering between their faces. He drew her closer and touched her lips with his fingers. Her beauty seemed to his distorted senses to fill earth and sky. This, then, was the presence, the grave and lovely overshadowing dream whose surrender made life a torment, and death the nearer fold of an immortal, starry veil. She broke from him with a faint cry. And he found himself running and running, just as he had run that other night, with death instead of life for inspiration, towards his earthly home.

PIGTAILS, LTD.

How such a very peculiar notion had ever come into Miss Rawlings's mind, even she herself could not possibly have said. When had it come? She could not answer that question, either. It had simply stolen in little by little like a beam of sunshine into a large room. Not, of course, into an empty room, for Miss Rawlings had many, many things to think about. She was by far the most important person in the Parish, and everyone—from Archdeacon Tomlington and his two curates, Mr. Moffatt and Mr. Timbs, down to little old Mrs. Ort, the humpbacked charwoman who lived in the top attic of a cottage down by Clopbourne (or, as they called it, Clobburne) Bridge—everyone knew how *practical* she was.

But once that sunny beam had begun to steal into Miss Rawlings's mind and into her life, it had lightened up with its dangerous gold everything that was there. It was nevertheless an extremely fantastic notion, because it could not possibly be true. How *could* Miss Rawlings ever have lost a little girl if there had never been any little girl to lose? Yet that exactly was Miss Rawlings's idea. It had flitted into her imagination like a nimble, bright-feathered bird. And once it was really there, she never hesitated to talk about it; not at all. 'My little girl, you know,' she'd say, with an emphatic nod and a pleasant smile on her broad face. Or rather, 'My little gal'—for she always pronounced the word as if it rhymed with Sal, the short for Sarah. This too was an odd thing; for Miss Rawlings had been brought up by her parents with the very best education, and seldom mispronounced even such words as 'Chloe' or 'Psyche' or 'epitome' or 'misled'. And so far as I know—though that is not very far—there is hardly a word of one syllable in our enormous language (except shall

and pal) that is pronounced like Sal; for Pall Mall, of course,
is pronounced Pell Mell. Still, Miss Rawlings did talk about
her little girl, and she called her her little gal.

It never occurred to anybody in the Parish—not even to
Mr. Timbs—to compare the Little Gal to a gay little bird or
to a beam of sunshine. Mrs. Tomlington said, indeed—and
many other persons in the Parish agreed with her—it was
nothing but a bee in Miss Rawlings's bonnet. But whether or
not, partly because she delighted in bright colours, and partly
because, in fashion or out, she had entirely her own taste in
dress, there could not be a larger or brighter or flowerier bonnet for any bee to be *in*. Apart from puce silk and maroon
velvet and heliotrope feathers and ribbons, and pompons and
rosettes, Miss Rawlings's bonnets always consisted of handsome, spreading flowers—blue-red roses, purple pansies,
mauve cineraria—a dizzying little garden for any bee's amusement. And this bee sang rather than buzzed in it the whole
day long.

You might almost say it had made a new woman of her.
Miss Rawlings had always been active and positive and good-
humoured and kind. But now her spirits were so much more
animated. She went bobbing and floating through the Parish
like a balloon. Her *interest* in everything seemed to have first
been multiplied by nine, and then by nine again. And eighty-
one times anything is a pretty large quantity. Beggars, blind
men, gypsies, hawkers, crossing-sweepers positively smacked
their lips when they saw Miss Rawlings come sailing down
the street. Her heart was like the Atlantic, and they like rowboats on the deep—especially the blind men. As for her dona-
tions to the parochial Funds, they were first doubled, then
trebled, then quadrupled.

There was first, for example, the Fund for giving all the
little parish girls and boys not only a bun and an orange and
a Tree at Christmas and a picnic with Veal and Ham Pie and
Ice Pudding in June, but a Jack-in-the-green on May-day and
a huge Guy on November the fifth, with squibs and Roman

Pigtails, Ltd.

candles and Chinese crackers and so on. There was not only the Fund for the Delight of Infants of Every Conceivable Description; there was also the Wooden-Legged Orphans' Fund. There was the Home for Manx and Tabby Cats; and the Garden by the River with the Willows for Widowed Gentlewomen. There was the Threepenny-Bit-with-a-Hole-in-It Society; and the Organ Grinders' Sick Monkey and Blanket Fund; and there was the oak-beamed Supper Room in the 'Three Wild Geese' for the use of Ancient Mariners—haggis and toad-in-the-hole, and plum-duff and jam-roly-poly—that kind of thing. And there were many others. If Miss Rawlings had been in another parish, it would have been a sad thing indeed for the cats and widows and orphans and organ monkeys in her own.

With such a power and quantity of money, of course, writing cheques was very much like writing in birthday books. Still, it is not easy to give too much to a Fund; and few people make the attempt. Miss Rawlings, too, was a practical woman. She knew perfectly well that (wheresoever it may end) charity must begin at home, so all this time she was keeping what the Ancient Mariners at the 'Three Wild Geese' called a 'weather eye' wide open for her lost Little Gal. But how, it may be asked, could she keep any kind of eye open for a lost Little Gal, when she didn't know what the lost Little Gal was like? And the answer to that is that Miss Rawlings knew perfectly well.

She may not have known where the absurd notion came from, or when, or why; but she knew that. She knew what the Little Girl looked like as well as a mother thrush knows what an egg looks like; or Sir Christopher Wren knew what a cathedral looks like; or Mr. Peace a gold watch. But as with the thrush and Sir Christopher, a good many little things had happened to Miss Rawlings first. And this quite apart from the old wooden doll she used to lug about when she was seven, called Quatta.

One morning, for example, Miss Rawlings had been out

31

in her carriage and was thinking of nothing in particular, nothing whatsoever, when not very far from the little stone bridge at Clobburne she happened to glance up at a window in the upper part of a small old house. And at that window there seemed to show a face with dark bright eyes watching her. Just a glimpse. I say 'seemed', for when in the carriage Miss Rawlings rapidly twisted her head to get a better view, she discovered either that there had been nobody there at all, or that the somebody had swiftly drawn back, or that the bright dark eyes were just two close-together flaws in the diamond-shaped bits of glass. In the last case what Miss Rawlings had seen was mainly 'out of her mind'. But, if so, it went back again and stayed there! It was excessively odd, indeed, how clear a remembrance that glimpse left behind it.

Then Miss Rawlings, like her renowned aunt Felicia, had always enjoyed a weakness for taking naps in the train, the flowers and plumes and bows in her bonnet nodding the while above her head. The sound of the wheels on the iron lines was like a lullaby, the fields trailing softly away beyond the window drowsed her eyes. Whether asleep or not, she would generally close her eyes and *appear* to be napping. And not once, or twice, but three separate times, owing to a scritch of the whistle or a sudden jolt of the train, she had rapidly opened them again to find herself staring out—rather like a large animal in a small field—at a little girl sitting on the opposite seat, who, in turn, had already fixed *her* eyes on Miss Rawlings's countenance. In every case there had been a look of intense, patient interest on the little girl's face.

Perhaps Miss Rawlings's was a countenance that all little girls are apt to look at with extreme interest—especially when the owner of it is asleep in a train. It was a broad countenance with a small but powerful nose with a round tip. There was a good deal of fresh colour in the flat cheeks beneath the treacle-coloured eyes; and the hair stood like a wig beneath the huge bonnet. Miss Rawlings, too, had a habit of folding her kid-gloved hands upon her lap as if she were an image.

None the less, you could hardly call it only a 'coincidence' that these little girls were so much alike, and so much like the face at the window. And so very much like the real lost Little Gal that had always, it seemed, been at the back of Miss Rawlings's mind.

I don't mean at all that there was any kind of ghost in Miss Rawlings's family. Her family was far too practical for that; and her mansion was most richly furnished. All I mean is that all these little girls happened to have a rather narrow face, a brown pigtail, rather small dark-brown bright eyes and narrow hands, and, except for the one at the window, they wore round beaver hats and buttoned coats. No; there was no ghost *there*. What Miss Rawlings was after was an absolutely real Little Gal. And her name was Barbara Allan.

This sounds utterly absurd. But so it had come about. For a long time—having talked about her Little Gal again and again to the Archdeacon and Mrs. Tomlington and Mr. Moffatt and other ladies and gentlemen in the Parish—Miss Rawlings had had no name at all for her small friend. But one still, summery evening, there being a faint red in the sky, while she was wandering gently about her immense drawing-room, she had happened to open a book lying on an 'occasional' table. It was a book of poetry—crimson and gilt-edged, with a brass clasp—and on the very page under her nose she had read this line:

Fell in love with Barbara Allan.

The words ran through her mind like wildfire. Barbara Allan—it was *the* name! Or how very like it! An echo? Certainly some words and names *are* echoes of one another—sisters or brothers once removed, so to speak. Tomlington and Pocklingham, for example; or quince and shrimp; or angelica and cyclamen. All I mean is that the very instant Miss Rawlings saw that printed 'Barbara Allan' it ran through her heart like an old tune in a nursery. It *was* her Little Gal, or ever so near it; as near, that is, as any name can be to a thing—viz., crocus, or comfit, or shuttlecock, or mistletoe, or pantry.

Pigtails, Ltd.

Now if Miss Rawlings had been of royal blood and had lived in a fairy-tale—if, that is, she had been a Queen in Grimm—it would have been a quite ordinary thing that she should be seeking a lost Princess, or badly in need of one. But, except that her paternal grandfather was a Sir Samuel Rawlings, she was but very remotely connected with royalty. And yet, if you think about it, seeing that once upon a time there were only marvellous Adam and beautiful Eve in the Garden —that is, in the whole wide world—and seeing that all of Us as well as all of the earth's Kings and Queens must have descended from them, *therefore* all of Us must have descended from Kings and Queens. So too with bold Miss Rawlings. But—unlike Mrs. Tomlington—she had not come down by the grand staircase.

Since, then, Miss Rawlings did not live in a fairy-tale or in Grimm, but was a very real person in a truly real Parish, her friends and acquaintances were all inclined in private to agree with Mrs. Tomlington that her Little Gal was nothing but a bee in her bonnet. And that the longer it stayed there the louder it buzzed. Indeed, Miss Rawlings almost began to think of nothing else. She became absent-minded, quite forgetting her soup and fish and chicken and French roll when she sat at dinner. She left on the gas. She signed blank cheques for the Funds. She pointed out Sunsets to blind beggars, and asked after deaf ones' children. She gave brand-new mantles and dolmans away to the Rummagers; ordered coals from her fishmonger; rode third-class with a first-class ticket; addressed a postcard to Mrs. Tomfoolington—almost every kind of absent-minded thing imaginable.

And now she was always searching—even in the house sometimes; even in the kitchen-quarters. And her plump country maids would gladly help too. 'No, m'm, she ain't here', 'No, m'm, we ain't a-seed her yet'. 'Lor, yes'm, the Room's all ready'.

Whenever Miss Rawlings rose from her chair she would at once peer sharply out of the window to see if any small crea-

ture were passing in the street beyond the drive. When she
went awalking she was frequently all but run over by cabs
and vans and phaetons and gigs, because she was looking the
other way after a vanishing pigtail. Not a picture-shop, not a
photographer's could she pass without examining every single
face exhibited in the window. And she never met a friend, or
the friend of a friend, or conversed with a stranger, without,
sure enough, beginning to talk about Young Things. Puppies
or kittens or lambs, perhaps, first, and then gradually on to
little boys. And then, with a sudden whisk of her bonnet, to
Little Girls.

Long, long ago, now, she had learned by heart the whole
of 'Barbara Allan':

> *She had not gane a mile but twa,*
> *When she heard the dead-bell ringing,*
> *And every jow that the dead-bell gied,*
> *It cryed,* Woe to Barbara Allan!

> '*O mother, mother, make my bed!*
> *O make it saft and narrow!*
> *Since my love died for me to-day,*
> *I'll die for him to-morrow.*'

Oh, dear, how sad it was; and you never knew! Could it
be, could it be, she cried one day to herself, that the dead
lovely Barbara Allan of the poem had got by some means
muddled up in Time, and was in actual fact *her* Little Gal?
Could it be that the maiden-name of the wife of Miss Allan's
father had been Rawlings!

Miss Rawlings was far too sensible merely to wonder
things. She at once inquired of Mr. Moffatt—who had been
once engaged to her dearest friend, Miss Simon, now no more
—whether he knew anything about Barbara Allan's family.
'The family, Felicia?' Mr. Moffatt had replied, his bristling
eyebrows high in his head. But when, after a visit to the
British Museum, Mr. Moffatt returned with only two or three

pages of foolscap closely written over with full particulars of the ballad and with 'biographical details' of Bishop Percy and of Allan Ramsay and of Oliver Goldsmith and of the gentleman who had found the oldest manuscript copy of it in Glamis Castle, or some such ancient edifice, and of how enchantingly Samuel Pepys's friend Mrs. Knipp used to sing him that air— but nothing else, Miss Rawlings very reluctantly gave up all certainty of this. 'It still might be my Little Gal's family,' she said, 'and on the other hand it might not.' And she continued to say over to herself, with infinite sorrow in her deep rich voice, that tragic stanza:

> *She had not gane a mile but twa,*
> *When she heard the dead-bell ringing,*
> *And every jow that the dead-bell gied,*
> *It cryed,* Woe to Barbara Allan!

And 'Oh, no! Not Woe', she would say in her heart.

Soon after this Miss Rawlings fell ill. A day or two before she took to her bed she had been walking along Combermere Avenue, and had happened to see the pupils of the Miss Miffinses' Young Ladies' Seminary taking the air. Now the two last and smallest of these pupils—of the Crocodile, as rude little boys call it—were walking arm in arm with the nice English mistress, chattering away like birds in a bush. Both of them were rather narrow little creatures, both wore beaver hats beneath which dangled brown pigtails. It was yet one more astonishing moment, and Miss Rawlings had almost broken into a run—as much of a run, that is, as, being of so stout and ample a presence, she was capable of—in order to get a glimpse of their faces.

But, alas and alack, the wrought-iron gates of the School were just round the corner of Combermere Avenue, and the whole Crocodile had completely disappeared into the great stone porch beyond by the time she had come in sight of the two Monkey-Puzzles (or auricarias) on the lawn, and the brass curtain-bands to the windows.

Pigtails, Ltd.

Miss Rawlings stood and gazed at these, for the moment completely forgetting polite manners. The hurry and excitement had made her hot and breathless—and the wind was in the east. It dispirited her, and, instead of ringing the bell and asking for the Miss Miffinses, she had returned home and had at once written an invitation to the whole school to come to tea the following Sunday afternoon. In a moment of absent-mindedness, however, she had left the note on her little rosewood secrétaire beside the silver inkstand that had belonged to Sir Samuel. And two days afterward—on the Friday, that is, the month being February—she had been seized with Bronchitis.

It was a rather more severe attack than was usual for Miss Rawlings, even in foggy November, and it made Miss Rawlings's family physician a little anxious. There was no immediate danger, he explained to Nurse Murphy; still care is care, oh yes. And, Miss Rawlings being so rich and so important to the Parish, he at once decided to invite an eminent Consultant to visit his patient—a Sir James Jolliboy Geoghelan, who lived in Harley Street and knew more about Bronchitis (Harley Street being also in a foggy parish) than any other medical man in Europe or in the United States of America (which are *not* usually foggy places).

Fortunately Sir James took quite as bright and sanguine a view of his patient as did Miss Rawlings's family physician. There Miss Rawlings lay, propped up against her beautiful down-pillows with the frills all round, and a fine large pale-blue-ribboned Bed Cap stood up on her large head. She was breathing pretty fast and her temperature, according to both the gentlemen's thermometers, was 102·6. As for her pulse, Sir James fastened his eyes so close upon the Bed Cap that he forgot to count it; and he laid down her wrist without a word.

A large copper kettle was ejecting clouds of steam from the vast cheerful fire in the vast brass and steel grate, with the Cupids in the chimneypiece. There were medicine bottles on the little table, and not only Nurse Murphy stood on the other side of the bed, but Nurse O'Brien also. And the more solemn *she* looked the more her face appeared to be creased up in a gentle grin.

Miss Rawlings panted as she looked at them all. Her eye was a little absent, but she too was smiling. For if there was one thing Miss Rawlings was certain to be, it was to be cheerful when most other people would be inclined to be depressed. As she knew she was ill she felt bound to be smiling. She even continued to smile when Sir James murmured, '*And* the tongue?' And she assured Sir James that, though it was exceedingly kind of him to call, it wasn't in the least necessary. 'I frequently have bronchitis,' she explained, 'but I never die.'

When Sir James and the family physician had gone downstairs and were closeted together in the gilded library, Sir James at once asked this question: 'What, my dear sir, was our excellent patient remarking about a Miss Barbara Allan? Has she a relative of the name?'

At this Miss Rawlings's family physician looked a little confused. 'No, no; oh dear, no!' he exclaimed. 'It's merely a little fancy, a caprice. Miss Rawlings has a notion there is a little girl belonging to her somewhere—probably of that name, you know. Quite harmless. An aberration. In fact, I indulge it; I indulge it. Miss Rawlings is a most able, sagacious, energetic, philanthropic, practical, generous, and—and —humorous lady. The fancy, you see, has somehow attached itself to the *name* "Barbara Allan"—a heroine, I believe, in one of Sir Walter Scott's admirable fictions. Only that. Nothing more.'

Sir James, a tall man, peered down at Miss Rawlings's family physician over his gold pince-nez. 'I once had a patient, my dear Dr. Sheppard,' he replied solemnly, in a voice a good deal deeper but not so rich as Miss Rawlings's, 'who had the amiable notion that she was the Queen of Sheba and that I was King Solomon. A *most* practical woman. She left me three hundred guineas in her will for a mourning ring.' He thereupon explained—in words that his patient could not possibly have understood, but that Dr. Sheppard understood perfectly—that Miss Rawlings was in no immediate danger and that she was indeed quite a comfortable little distance from Death's Door. Still, bronchitis *is* bronchitis; so let the dear lady be humoured as much as possible. 'Let her have the very best nurses, excellent creatures; and all the comforts!' He smiled as he said these words, as if Dr. Sheppard were a long-lost brother. And he entirely approved, not only of the nice sago-puddings, the grapes, the bee-ootiful beef-juice (with toast *or* a rusk), the barley water *and* the physic, but of as many Barbara Allans as Miss Rawlings could possibly desire. And all that he said sounded so much like the chorus of some such old sea-song as 'Yeo-ho-ho', or 'Away to Rio', or 'The Anchor's Weighed', that one almost expected Dr. Sheppard to join in.

Both gentlemen then took their leave and, Dr. Sheppard having escorted Sir James to his brougham, for this was before the days of machine carriages, the two nurses retired from the window and Miss Rawlings sank into a profound nap.

In a few days Miss Rawlings was much, much, much better. Her temperature was 97·4, her breathing no more than twenty-four or -five to the minute. The flush had left her cheeks, and she had finished three whole bottles of medicine. She devoured a slice from the breast of a chicken and even enjoyed her sago-pudding. The nurses *were* pleased.

But, if anything, Miss Rawlings's illness seemed to have increased her anxiety to find Barbara Allan as quickly as ever she could. After all, you see, we all of us have only a certain number of years to live, and a year lasts only twelve calendar months, and the shortest month is only twenty-eight days, excluding Leap Year. So if you badly want to do anything it is better to begin at once, and go straight on.

The very first day she was out in Mr. Dubbins's invalid chair she met her dear friend Mr. Moffatt in Combermere Grove, and he stood conversing with her for a while under the boughs of almost as wide a spreading chestnut-tree as the

village blacksmith's in the poem. Mr. Moffatt always looked
as if he ought to have the comfort of a sleek bushy beard. If
he had, it is quite certain it would have wagged a good deal
as he listened to Miss Rawlings. 'What I am about to do, my
dear Mr. Moffatt, is advertise,' she cried, and in such a powerful voice that the lowest fronds of the leafing chestnut-tree
over her head slightly trembled as they hung a little listlessly
on their stalks in the spring sunshine.

'Advertise, my dear Felicia?' cried Mr. Moffatt. 'And what
for?'

'Why, my dear old friend,' replied Miss Rawlings, 'for
Barbara Allan, to be sure.'

Mr. Moffatt blinked very rapidly, and the invisible beard
wagged more than ever. And he looked hard at Miss Rawlings's immense bonnet as if he actually expected to see that
busy bee; as if he even feared it might be a Queen Bee and
would produce a complete hive.

But after bidding him good-bye with yet another wag of
the bonnet and a 'Yes, thank you, Dubbins,' Miss Rawlings
was as good as her word. She always was. Three days afterwards there appeared in *The Times* and in the *Morning Post*
and in the *Daily Telegraph*, and five days later in the *Spectator*,
the following:

WANTED as soon as possible, by a lady who has lost her
as long as she can remember, a little girl of the name (probably) of Barbara Allan, or of a name that *sounds* like Barbara Allan. The little girl is about ten years old. She has a
rather three-cornered shaped face, with narrow cheek-
bones, and bright brown eyes. She is slim, with long fingers, and wears a pigtail and probably a round beaver hat.
She shall have an *exceedingly* happy home and Every Comfort, and her friends (or relatives) will be amply rewarded
for all the care and kindness they have bestowed upon her,
for the first nine years or more of her life.

You should have seen Miss Rawlings reading that advertisement over and over. Her *Times* that morning had a per-

fume as of the spices of Ambrosia. But even Miss Rawlings could not have hoped that her advertisement would be so rapidly and spontaneously and abundantly answered. The whole day of every day of the following week her beautiful wrought-iron gates were opening and shutting and admitting all kinds and sorts and shapes and sizes of little girls with brown eyes, long fingers, pigtails, and beaver hats, *about* ten years of age. And usually an Aunt or a Stepmother or the Matron of an Orphanage or a Female Friend accompanied each candidate.

There were three genuine Barbara Allans. But one had reddish hair and freckles; the second, curly flaxen hair that refused to keep to the pigtail-ribbon into which it had been tied; and the third, though her hair was brown, had grey speckled eyes, and looked to be at least eleven. Apart from these three, there were numbers of little girls whose Christian name was Barbara, but whose surname was Allison, or Angus, or Anson, or Mallings, or Bulling, or Dalling, or Spalding, or Bellingham, or Allingham, and so on and so forth. Then there were Marjories and Marcias and Margarets, Norahs and Doras and Rhodas and Marthas, all of the name of Allen, or Allan, or Alleyne, or Alyn, and so on. And there was one little saffron-haired creature who came with a very large Matron, and whose name was Dulcibella Dobbs.

Miss Rawlings, with her broad bright face and bright little eyes, smiled at them all from her chair, questioned their Aunts and their Stepmothers and their Female Friends, and coveted every single one of them, including Dulcibella Dobbs. But you must draw the line somewhere, as Euclid said to his little Greek pupils when he sat by the sparkling waves of the Ægean Sea and drew triangles on the sand. And Miss Rawlings felt in her heart that it was kinder and wiser and more prudent and proper to keep strictly to those little girls with the three-cornered faces, high cheek-bones, 'really' brown eyes, and truly appropriate pigtails. With these she fell in love again and again and again.

Pigtails, Ltd.

There was no doubt in the world that she had an exceedingly motherly heart, but very few mothers could so nicely afford to *give it rein*. Indeed, Miss Rawlings would have drawn the line nowhere if it had not been for the fact that she had only Ten Thousand Pounds or so a year.

There were tears in her eyes when she bade the others Good-bye. And to everyone she gave, not one bun, not one orange, but a *bag* of oranges and a *bag* of buns. And not merely a bag of ordinary Denia oranges and ordinary currant buns, but a bag of Jaffas and a bag of Bath. And she thanked their Guardianesses for having come such a long way, and would they be offended if she paid the fare? Only one was offended, but then her fare had cost only 3d.—2d. for herself, and 1d. (half-price) for the little Peggoty Spalding she brought with her. And Miss Rawlings paid *her* sixpence.

She kept thirty little ten-year-olds altogether, and you never saw so many young fortunate smiling pigtailed creatures so much alike. And Miss Rawlings, having been so successful, withdrew her advertisements from *The Times* and the *Morning Post* and the *Daily Telegraph* and the *Spectator*, and she bought a most beautiful Tudor house called Trafford House, with one or two wings to it that had been added in the days of Good Queen Anne, and William and Mary, which stood in entirely its own grounds not ten miles from the Parish boundary. The forest trees in its park were so fine —cedars, sweet chestnuts, and ash and beech and oak—that you could only get a tiny glimpse of its chimneys from the entrance to the drive.

Things *are* often curious in this world, and coincidences are almost as common as centipedes. So Miss Rawlings was more happy than surprised when, on looking over this mansion, she counted—and to make sure counted again—exactly thirty little bedrooms, with some larger ones over for a matron, a nurse, some parlour-maids, some housemaids, some tweeny-maids, and a boy to clean the button-boots and shoes. When her legal adviser explained to her that this establishment, what

with the little chests-of-drawers, basins and ewers, brass candlesticks, oval looking-glasses, dumpy beds, three-legged
stools, dimity curtains, woolly rugs, not to speak of chif-
foniers, whatnots, hot-water bottles, soup ladles, and so on
and so forth—not to mention a uniform with brass buttons
for the man with whiskers at the park gate—would cost her
at least Six Thousand a year, that bee in Miss Rawlings's bonnet buzzed as if indeed it *was* a whole hive gone a-swarming.

'Well, now, my dear Mr. Wilkinson,' she said, 'I made a
little estimate myself, being a *business* woman, and it came to
£6,004 10s. How reasonable! I shall be at least four pounds-
ten in pocket.'

So, in a few weeks everything was ready—new paint, new
gravel on the paths, geraniums in the flower-beds, quilts as
neat as daisies on a lawn on the dumpy beds, and the thirty
Barbara Allans sitting fifteen a side at the immensely long oak
table (where once in Henry VIII's time monks had eaten their
fish on Fridays), the matron with the corkscrew curls at the
top and the chief nurse in her starched cap at the bottom. And
Miss Rawlings seated in the south bow-window in an old oak
chair, with her ebony and ivory stick and her purple bonnet,
smiling at her Barbara Allans as if she had mistaken Trafford
House for the Garden of Eden.

And I must say every single pigtail of the complete thirty
bobbed as merrily as roses in June over that first Grand Tea—
blackberry jelly, strawberry jam, home-made bread, plum-
cake, the best beef-dripping for those who had not a sweet or
a milk tooth, Sally Lunns, heather honey, maids-of-honour,
and an enormous confection of marchpane, with cupids and
comfits and silver bells and thirty little candles standing up in
the midst of the table like St. Paul's Cathedral on the top of
Ludgate Hill in the great city of London. It was a lucky thing
for the Thirty's insides that Grand Teas are not everyday
teas.

And so, when all the thirty Pigtails had sung a Latin grace
put out of English by Mr. Moffatt and set to a tune composed

by a beloved uncle of Miss Rawlings's, who also was now no more, the Grand Tea came to an end. Whereupon the Thirty —looking themselves like yet another Crocodile with very fat joints—came and said good night to Miss Rawlings, though some of them could scarcely speak. And as Miss Rawlings knew that not *all* little girls liked being kissed by comparative strangers, she just shook hands with each, and smiled at them as if her motherly heart would almost break. And Dr. Sheppard was Medical Adviser to the thirty little Pigtailers, and Mr. Moffatt came every other Sunday to hear their catechisms.

Miss Rawlings had never been much attached to rules and regulations for other people, though she kept faithfully to a few for herself. She loved everyone to be free and everything to be easy, considering how hard most things are. And this was the Order of the Day with the Pigtails in their Home.

At half-past seven in summer, and at nine in winter, the boy in buttons rang an immense bell, its clapper tied round with a swab of cotton-wool to prevent it from clanging too sonorously. This great quiet bell was not only to waken from their last sweet dreams the slumbering Pigtails in their little beds, but to tell them they had yet another half-hour between the blankets before they had to get up. Then hairbrushes, toothbrushes, nailbrushes, as usual. Then 'When morning gilds the skies', and breakfast in the wide white room with the primrose curtains looking out into the garden. And if any Pigtail happened to have been not quite so good as usual on the previous day, she was allowed—if she asked for it—to have a large plateful of porridge with or without salt—for a punishment. No less than ninety-nine such platefuls were served out in the first year—the Pigtails were so high-spirited. Still, it can be imagined what a thirtyfold sigh of relief went up when breakfast on December 31st was over and there hadn't been a hundredth.

From 9 a.m. to 12 p.m. the Pigtails were one and all exceedingly busy. Having made their beds, they ran out into the garden and woods—some to bathe in the stream, some to listen to the birds, some to talk, and some to sing; some to paint, some to play, and some to read, and some to dance; some just to sit; and some high up in a beech tree to learn poems, to make up poems, even to read each other's. It all depended on the weather. The sun shone, the rooks cawed, the green silken leaves whispered; and Miss Rawlings would stand looking up at them in their verdurous perch as fondly as a cat at a canary. There was not at last a flower or a tree or an insect or a star in those parts, or a bird or a little beast or a fish or a toadstool or a moss or a pebble, that the little Pigtails did not know by heart. And the more they knew them, and the more closely they looked at them, the more they loved them and the more they knew them—round and round and round and round.

From twelve to one there were 'Lessons'. Then dinner, and tongues like jackdaws raiding a pantry for silver spoons. In the afternoon those who went for a walk toward the stranger parts—went for a walk. Some stayed at home in a little parlour and sang in chorus together like a charm of wild birds. Some did their mending and darning, their hemming and feather-stitching, and some did sums. Some played on the fiddle, and some looked after their bullfinches, and bunnies, and bees, and guinea-pigs, and ducks. Then there were the hens and the doves and the calves and the pigs to feed, and the tiny mother-less lambs, too (when lambs there were), with bottles of milk. And sometimes of an afternoon Miss Rawlings would come in and sit at a window just watching her Pigtails, or would read them a story. And Dr. Sheppard asseverated not once but three times over that if she went on bringing them sweet-meats and candies and lollipops and suckets to such an *extent*, not a single sound white ivory tooth of their nine hundred or so would be left in the Pigtails' heads. So Miss Rawlings kept to Sundays.

At five was tea-time; jam on Mondays, Wednesdays, and

Fridays; jelly on Tuesdays, Thursdays, and Saturdays; and both on Sundays. From six to seven there were 'Lessons', and when the little Pigtails were really tired, which was always before nine, they just skipped off to bed. Some of them had munched their supper biscuits and were snug in bed, indeed, even before the rest had sung the evening hymn. And the evening hymn was always 'Eternal Father'—for being all of them so extremely happy they could not but be 'in peril on the sea' just as sailors are, for happiness may fly away like birds in corn, or butterflies before rain. And on Sundays they sang 'Lead, Kindly Light' too, because Miss Rawlings's mother had once been blessed by the great and blessed Cardinal Newman. And one Pigtail played the accompaniment on the fiddle, and one on the sweet-tongued viola, and one on the harpsichord; for since Miss Rawlings had read 'Barbara Allan' she had given up pianofortes. And then, sleepy and merry and chattering, they all trooped up to bed.

So this was their Day. And all night, unseen, the stars shone in their splendour above the roof of Trafford House, or the white-faced moon looked down upon the sleeping garden and the doves and the pigs and the lambs and the flowers. And at times there was a wind in the sky among the clouds, and sometimes frost in the dark hours settled like pollen wheresoever its cold brightness might find a lodging. And when the little Pigtails awoke there would be marvellous cold fronds and flowerets on their windowpanes, and even sometimes a think crankling slat of ice in their water-jugs. On which keen winter mornings you could hear their teeth chattering like monkeys cracking nuts. And so time went on.

On the very next June 1st, there was a prodigious Garden Party at Trafford House, with punts on the lake and refreshments and lemonade in a tent in the park, and all the Guardianesses and Aunts and Stepmothers and Matrons and Female Friends were invited to come and see Miss Rawlings's little Pigtails. And some brought their sisters, and some their nieces and nephews. There were Merry-go-Rounds, Aunt Sallies,

Pigtails, Ltd.

Frisk-and-Come-Easies, A Punch and Judy Show, a Fat Man, a fortune-teller, and three marvellous acrobats from Hong-kong. And there were quantities of things to eat and lots to see, and Kiss-in-the-Ring, and all broke up after fireworks and 'God Save the Queen' at half-past nine.

The house, as I keep on saying, was called Trafford House, but the *Home* was called 'The Home of all the Little Barbara Allans and Suchlike, with Brown Eyes, Narrow Cheek-bones, Beaver Hats, and Pigtails, Ltd.' And it was 'limited' because there could be only thirty of them, and time is not Eternity.

And now there were only three things that prevented Miss Rawlings from being too intensely happy to go on being alive; and these three were as follows: (a) She wanted to live always at the House; but how could the Parish get on without her? (b) What was she going to do when the Pigtailers be-came twelve, thirteen, fourteen, fifteen, sixteen, seventeen, and so forth, and Grown-Up? And (c) how could she ever possibly part with any of them or get any more?

For, you see, Miss Rawlings's first-of-all Barbara Allan was aged ten, and had somehow managed to stay ten. But because I suppose things often go right in this world when we are not particularly noticing them, and don't know how, all these difficulties simply melted away like butter in the sun.

In the first place, Miss Rawlings did at last—in 1888, to be exact, one year after Queen Victoria's first Jubilee—did, I say, at last go to live at the Home of All the Little Barbara Allans and Suchlike, with Brown Eyes, Beaver Hats, and Pigtails, Ltd. She was called The Matron's Friend, so as not to under-mine the discipline. When her Parish wanted her, which was pretty often, the Parish (Thirty or Forty strong) came to see her in her little parlour overlooking the pond with the punts and the water-lilies.

Next—though how, who can say?—the little Pigtails some-how did not grow up, even though they must have grown older. Something queer happened to their Time. It cannot have been what just the clocks said. If there wasn't more of it, there was infinitely more *in* it. It was like air and dew and sunbeams and the South Wind to them all. You simply could not tell what next. And, apart from all that wonderful learning, apart even from the jam and jelly and the Roast Beef of Old England, they went on being just the right height and the right heart for ten. Their brown eyes never lost their light and sparkle. No wrinkles ever came in their three-cornered faces with the high cheek-bones, and not a single grey or silver hair into their neat little pigtails—that could at any rate be seen.

Next, therefore, Miss Rawlings never had to part with any of them or look or advertise for any more.

Yet another peculiar thing was that Miss Rawlings grew more and more like a Pigtail herself. She grew younger. She laughed like a schoolgirl. Her face became a little narrower, even the cheek-bones seemed not to be so wide. As for her bonnets, as time 'went on' they grew up instead of broadwise. And when she sat in Church with the Thirty, in the third pew down from Mrs. Tomlington's, you might almost have supposed she *was* a widish pigtail, just a little bit dressed up.

It is true that in the very secretest corner of her heart of hearts she was still looking for the one and only absolute little Barbara Allan of her lifelong daydream; but that is how things go. And the thought of it brought only a scarcely perceptible grave glance of hope and inquiry into her round brown eyes. And underneath—oh, dear me, yes—she was almost too happy and ordinary and good-natured and homely to be telling this story about at all.

We all die at last—just journey on—and so did Miss Rawlings. And so did the whole of the Thirty, and the Matron, and the Chief Nurse, and Mr. Moffatt, and Dr. Sheppard, and the man with whiskers at the park gates, *and* the boy who cleaned the button-boots; parlour-maids, tweeny-maids, Mrs. Tomfoolington, and all. And if you would like to see the Old House and the little graves, you take the first turning on the

Pigtails, Ltd.

right as you leave the Parish Church on your left, and walk on until you come to a gatepost beyond the milestone.

A path crossing the fields—sometimes of wheat, sometimes of turnips, sometimes of barley or clover or swedes—leads to a farm in the hollow with a duckpond, guinea-fowl roosting in the pines at evening, and a lovely old thatched barn where the fantailed doves croon in the sunshine. You then cross the yard and come to a lane beside a wood of thorn and hazel. This bears a little east, and presently, after ascending the hill beyond the haystack, you will see—if it is still there—the Home of All the Little Barbara Allans and Suchlike, with Brown Eyes, Beaver Hats, and Pigtails, Ltd.

And not very far away is a little smooth-mown patch of turf with a beautiful thatched wall around it, which Mr. Moffatt consecrated himself. And there, side by side, sleep the Little Thirty, with their pigtails beside their narrow bones. And there lie the tweeny-maids, the parlour-maids, the man with whiskers at the park gate, and the boy who cleaned the button-boots. And there lies Miss Rawlings, too. And when the last trump sounds, up they will get as happy as wood-larks, and as sweet and fresh as morning mushrooms. But if you want to hear any more about *that*, please turn to the Poems of Mr. Wm. Blake.

From BEHOLD THIS DREAMER

The Moon

I dreamed many years ago that above a wide stretch of flattish land—hummocks of sea-darkened sand, indented with shoaling-water—no fewer than three moons were in the heavens: one to the east, one to the west, and the third at her zenith. For astronomy, no more than any other science, is slavishly respected in sleep. But, in view of all that she has done for me, even my three dream moons were a poor tribute to the earth's faithful yet fickle satellite. A gifted young poet recently assured me that an image now so trite and so incorrigibly romantic as the moon should henceforth be taboo in English verse My dream, then, was no more than as old-fashioned a piece of Victorianism as a robin on a Christmas card. Still, the abrupt snapping of her earthly ties and her escape into space (quite apart from any jarring effects on her guardian-planet) would even to the most prosaic of us be an irreparable disaster. In the earth's destiny she was the happiest of afterthoughts, the oddest of grace-notes, the most magical of things 'thrown in'.

The light and heat of the sun, like air and water, are a human necessity. The moon is in the nature of a luxury. She is sweetheart rather than wife. She is our night-light. The sun excites, challenges, daunts, dazzles, dazes, may even all but stun the mind with radiance. It sucks self outwards; its heat resembles a fourth skin. In its vast shimmering mantle of gold, it pours life into us.

> *With open mouth he drank the sun*
> *As though it had been wine!*

'Doth not the glory of the Sun pay tribute to your sight? Is not the vision of the World an amiable thing?' Not so the moon. Like a spy with a bull's-eye, she silently discloses what she shines upon. She pacifies, invites us *in*. Her light gnaws away shadow; and glides, smooth and softly as a serpent, from stone on to stone. Caught, yet unaware of being so, our instincts and our sentiments are instantly affected by her presence. 'The Sea! The Sea!' we may shout at sight of an ocean basking in splendour beneath the sun; but what barbarian would go bawling into the night to welcome the moon? We tread softly; look and think with caution; as if to be in keeping with this stealthy and motionless lustre. The preternatural is lurking near, is skulking abroad. And a beauty, of bearing, or character in things, indetectable in daylight, now lies in wait for us. Not only is every flower alone in moonlight, and many refuse to bloom until her hour draws near, not only is the air sweet and heavy with smells and odours, and every rose chilled with dew resembles a rose dreaming of itself; but even so gross and coarse a plant as the vegetable marrow, when its great thorny leaves are dusked over with the moon's silver, becomes not only singularly beautiful, but as individual an organism as a basking alligator.

Unlike her lord and master, a Bluebeard who, in her sluggish rotations, never allows her out of his sight, the moon presides rather than rules over the earth. Even at her most brilliant she reflects, we are told, less than half a millionth of his luminousness, and gives as little heat, I fancy, as would to the hand a lighted candle some half-a-mile away. Yet, as human-animals, we can no more evade returning her stare than Criseyde could escape that of Troilus, or a king his cat's. Now she will dazzle an eye that can yet face her out; anon, her gaze is as calm as it is hypnotic. When the heavens are gracious she may be a marvel of beauty in every one of her gradual phases—from that slender half-loop of silvered ivory in the serene of evening, to her last white parched and ghostly relic adrift in the blue of noonday. Harvest moon (which I once mistook for a rounded haystack when she was capping a hill on the horizon), or Hunter's moon, or May-day's, or January's, blanching an earth shag and grey with hoar frost or mantled in driven snow—how choose between them? She is mistress of so many moods and caprices.

As when, for example, having risen an hour or two before a faintly veiled and starry summer midnight, she slowly ascends out of the east, as if she were carrying her own lantern, and *shows*, as it were, the lovely vault of space its beauty; or as when her full circle is stealthily and funereally devoured by the monster called Eclipse; or as when, dwindled and all but evilly bright, she gazes from the heights of winter with the ferocity of some heraldic lynx. Or yet again, as when, fallen towards her setting, she casts on the pallid woods and meadows a light as spectral as that of a phosphoric fish in a dark larder. And hers too is the charming device of enticing into her service every planet or major star she passes on her way.

She pacifies the peaceful—wood, hill and water; gives wings and a tumultuous sky to the wildest gale; smiles down from a pale blue sky of soapsud clouds as benignly as some old family Nannie on the children of men—although candour must add that she can be a little dull and commonplace when gibbous, and rather too sweetly sentimental on the marine parade. She bestows loveliness and magic even on the lovely: 'How sweet the moonlight sleeps upon this bank!' She can win back from the darkness their reds and blues into the flowers, its dyes into a Persian carpet; can etherealize the ugly; bestow grace on the commonplace; and will adore her own splintered reflection, as Tchekhov declared, in every unflattering scrap of broken crockery or glass. Her beams, on some old discoloured wall, green bridle-path or dingle in the woods, make stealthy shadows, jet black and soft as velvet, but not shade.

Only the very timid or guilty *fear* her light, and only the furtive would shun it. A bad conscience has an assignation with her; and the earth itself may seem apprehensive of her unflinching gaze. She can intensify darkness; give magic to the bewitched; terror to vacancy; horror to the haunted; an edge to the spectral. Her presence in the sky or even in a room deepens solitude; prepares for the ghostly. And no wonder the tide of unreason also obeys her influence. The crazy, the insane, are also descr bed as 'lunatics': persons, according to the Law, who manifest lucid intervals, as indeed she does herself. And, although authoritative evidence is conflict ng, even one's own experience may suggest that it is not merely an old wives' tale which declares that the mentally afflicted show increasing disquietude and unease at the approach of full moonlight.

Fish, flesh, and fowl, it is said, go bad more rapidly then than by day. In early childhood I was warned to shield my sleeping face from her direct rays. And not without reason, apparently. A friend who ventured to challenge the full moon by sleeping on deck in the tropics, his countenance bathed in her reflected beams, paid for it, he tells me, with the most severe and most protracted headache of his lifetime—moonstruck. Even the most popular of fallacies could hardly account for that. But what we are not taught in print is held to be hardly worth the learning. We pay less and less court than our grandfathers to our only satellite, discredit her wiles, and ignore her sweet influences. Of old, the country people whose books were running brooks, throughout the round of the seasons—killing, culling, felling, sowing, the taking of medicines and the care of the sick—kept a continually heedful eye on her phases. But this was in the darker ages, and before knowledge became Science.

Although, again, the moon is so close a neighbour, only some thirty days' distance in a chaser aeroplane (eighty being fixed on by Jules Verne as an astonishing minimum for a journey round the world), nothing on earth, except its ice-caps and vast deserts, remotely resembles her realm: with its instantaneous extremes of all but absolute cold, of violent heat and wild glaring radiance; with her enormous craters and prodigious volcanic ramparts; her pocked and arid plains; her unbroken silence, innocent of any twilight, of any odour or fragrance or even of earth's perpetual falling of fine dust; and, above all, her ink-black skies continually frequented, even at noon-day, by a myriad untwinkling stars.

That man should have worshipped the divinity of the Sun or of the Stars is no marvel. What state and circumstance in all its glory could be more divine? Nor is it to be wondered at that he has paid obeisance to, held secret and savage rites under, feared, and saddled superstitions on the Moon. It is she indeed, more closely even than the planets and the stars, whom we associate with sleep and with our dreams. Yet what an oddity of a parasite the creature is. That viewless tethered enormous sterile mass, whether or not torn from the watery hole that is now the Pacific Ocean, refusing to divulge the secret of her hidden side, and reiteratedly revealed to our gaze and telescopic curiosity by the vast bull's-eye of the sun as she skulks on her interminable and circuitous journey through space![1]

Amateur worshippers, however, at the shrine of Astarte, with her mysteries, must be almost as rare nowadays as they are likely to be lukewarm; and 'the implacable Aphrodite' went out of literary fashion with Algernon Charles Swin-burne. The astrologer, as in the days of Defoe, it is true, is put-ting the stars to his own privy use again, and the intelligent pay due attention to his predictions. But our modern ten-dency to introspection—a far more common, and, perhaps, more perilous hobby—is not much concerned with the subtle influences on our minds and moods of the things of nature. At a chance glimpse through window-glass or spectacles of that slim familiar crescent returned again into the west, we

---

[1] According to Hans Hoerbiger, who originated the Cosmic Ice Theory, the moon was once a solar planet, and was gradually seduced from her inter-martian orbit until at length—thirteen to fifteen thousand years ago—she became Terra's servile and serviceable satellite. The disaster thus inflicted on the earth's inhabitants would be excelled if in times to come she is gradually attracted nearer and nearer to the earth until she is finally shattered to pieces on its breast.

may be a little uneasy (it is a personal confession), and at once hasten out into the open to rattle the money in our pockets, inwardly and indulgently at yet another of our little 'superstitions'. Shallow superstitions they may be—valueless as mere lip service; but even at that, they may spring out of a realization of wonder and mystery, and from the conviction that our senses are not our only trustworthy witnesses in this world, but that nature itself resembles a veil over some further reality of which the imagination in its visionary moments seems to achieve a more direct evidence. Just as the name for a thing that we love and delight in binds it closer to our minds and hearts—a bird, a wild flower, a butterfly, a fellow creature— so with the ancient belief that chace and stream, rocky seacoast and unpeopled valley may be haunted by divine presences, whether or not we think of them as dryad, siren, naiad, or are content with a far less evocative phrase, 'the spirit of place'.

All things stale and lose their virtue, the best and worst, the simple and complicated, the plain and beautiful, impulse as well as artifice, unless we attend to them; give to them as much at least as they can bestow. Not that a forced ardour can restore the tinge of strangeness to the familiar which at least once in life was the secret of its charm. Yet it would never be a loss to ponder an instant on the colours of an apple before we peel it; or on the exquisite green-bronze iridescence of a starling's plumage before we dismiss its owner as a pest. No hunter surely, not even Nimrod himself—unless, like Othello, the pitiable prey of jealousy—could kill any creature at the very moment when he was spellbound with admiration of its beauty, and therefore of its mystery.

From LOVE

Marriage

In official quests for information we are usually required (not to express our feelings, but) to state our age, our sex, and whether we are married or single. It would be difficult to give more information in answers so brief. The first two suggest a general notion of our appearance, something of our probable outlook on life, the duration at least of our earthly experience, and, in certain respects, of its kind. As for the third answer—well, bachelor is a word commonly tinged with the waggish; and spinster—in spite of the many priceless maiden aunts there have been in the world, in spite of the wise and sagacious old nuns, and all the fairy godmothers—is one as often as not shrugged off with a smile of amused compassion. Yet if Shakespeare had entitled one of his comedies 'The Merry Spinsters of Twickenham', it would suggest a racy merriment enough; and any *Old Maid's Tale* might be well worth reading.

Still, the bridge between 'single' and 'married' spans life's most crucial Rubicon. It is one singularly easy to cross, but not to retraverse. No other venture in life promises so much, may achieve even more, or prove so disastrous. None the less, the customary English wedding is apt to conceal its gravity. Like our merry Christmas, it is a medley of the Christian and the pagan, and may fail to suggest anything in the nature of a Mystery.

It seldom resembles the illumination depicting the tranquil Garden of Love in the *Roman de la Rose*, or the lyrical festivities on the panels of the old marriage chests. And the difference between them is not merely one of attire. Still it is a joyous occasion. A few tears have been shed at the forgotten solemnity and significance of the Service, thoughts have been thought, memories have come flocking into mind, sweet or bitter, tinged with melancholy, gratitude or regret; the human contents of the two aisles have been critically compared; the Address has been welcomed inversely to its duration; the bride has borne the bell away; the martial strains from the 'Dream' peal up out of the organ. And now the tables are groaning under their burden of presents, champagne and wedding cake; the bridegroom's Hat has been found; the symbolic confetti have been distributed; the car is at the door. The most decisive event in the lives of the two 'young people', of 'the happy pair', is over. Honeymoons are delicious. The Captains and the Kings, or their equivalents, depart. We have washed our hands, and follow them.

A wedding is a feminine rite, and most men in its coils are secretly with the little girl who declared, 'I'm a proper woman-'ater, like my Mum.' Like starlings, unlike pe-wits, women are usually least attractive *en masse*—or in a 'murmuration'. The mystery (which they notoriously fail to detect in one another) either abandons them or takes on a complexion unbeguiling even to their loyalest devotees. And this may apply in particular even to the groom and his best man. Coleridge's 'guest' who 'beat his breast' (at one of the most famous of little country *and* seaside weddings) is an outstanding exception to this general rule. He may have preferred the loud bassoon to the *vox humana*, talk to pure poetry, or was in love with one of the bridesmaids. Still, the more fashionable, expensive and expansive the modern wedding, the less somehow it may seem to have had either Eros or Romance for its guiding star. That Romance, I mean, which, his wedding over, and with the help of a 'shilling to the willing guard' which secured a 'front *coupé*', was ensured for the hero of *The Angel in the House*. Still, if many waters cannot quench love, neither should a multitude of wedding-guests. Why is it then that in the following passage from the *History of Jack of Reading*, of

1570, there seems to be a hint at what a wedding should signify usually absent from the newspaper report of our own day, even when the bride's mother has given a helping hand?

'The bride being attired in a gown of sheep's russet, and a kirtle of fine worsted, attired with a "billement" of gold, and her hair as yellow as gold, hanging down behind her, which was curiously combed and plaited, she was led to church between two sweet boys, with bride laces and rosemary tied about their silken sleeves. There was a fair bride-cup of silver gilt carried before her, wherein was a goodly branch of rosemary, gilded very fair, hung about with silken ribands of all colours. Musicians came next, then a group of maidens, some bearing great bride-cakes, others garlands of wheat finely gilded; and thus they passed into the church.'

And at night, as was the custom in those days, the bride and groom went happily to their naked beds. Mere words again may be part of the charm here—russet kirtle, yellow as gold, sweet boys, bride-cup, goodly—all of an older fashion, and, like the rosemary, with a romantic gilding of which the participants cannot have been aware. Sir John Suckling's 'Ballad of a Wedding', which here and there has shocked the niceness of some anthologists, is less idyllic. But was there ever a more winning and enviable bride?

There are marriages of convenience; marriages intent on an heir, a housekeeper, or a home; on comfort or companionship; the outcome of pique or mere caprice. But 'the pang of all the partings gone', the supreme and overmastering desire of any two humans who are in love with one another is to be together and alone, in a shared and mutual solitude. That (in much) is what weddings are for. It is attained and safeguarded in marriage. How well and happily then should it be spoken of, how profound should be its appeal to our common humanity. But this is not always so. Though the polite and the sceptical may refrain their hearts and keep them low, it is a common source of ribaldry and cynicism. To judge from the

old popular ballads and comic songs, and from the jokes—
with jealous, tattling, nagging, crafty, ageing wife for Aunt
Sallie, or timid, gulled, rich, old, hen-pecked drunken husband, and mischief-making mother-in-law (never father- or
sister-in-law)—this very *eureka*, marriage, that ensures and
legalizes this craved-for felicity, is an unfailing short cut to
mockery and laughter, broad, 'blue' and shrill.

Even from beyond an open window one could guess when
this particular topic is being discussed by the company within
merely from the quality of the crowings and cacklings, their
guffaws and cachinnations. This relaxation may of course be
in the nature of a safety valve; possibly it is the rock salt that
keeps sound hearts sweet, and preserves the rest from putre-
faction. For when, say, in a music hall, the next item on the
programme shifts from love and marriage to the love*lorn*, to
love lost, to the full moon, to partings for ever and a day, to
home sweet home, to mother and child (seldom, if ever, to
father and child), the tears of helpless amusement that coursed
down one cheek are rapidly superseded by those of sentiment
or sentimentality, and begin to trickle down the other. Marie
Lloyd gives place to Annie Laurie. It is human nature so to do.
And we mustn't decide on the depth even of a duckpond by
the ripples on its surface.

Most of us are much of a muchness in this. This may be
because we are more serious-minded, and more often concerned with first and last things, than we prefer to appear to
be. It is none the less a curious fact that very few inspired
wedding hymns are among the 'Ancient and Modern'—that
containing the reference to 'the awful Father' and 'The voice
that breathed o'er Eden', with 'O perfect Father', one of the
best of them and written as recently as 1883, being those most
commonly in use. In his *Songs of Praise Discussed*, Dr. Percy
Dearmer refers to another wedding hymn; and that not the
least remarkable. It was the composition of the Joseph Proud
who helped to form the Swedenborgian 'New Church', and
then, 'breaking into song', wrote no fewer than 300 hymns in

three months. This was very sharp practice, since one might assume that even Martin Tupper's *Proverbial Philosophy* can hardly have been the cream of less than half a lifetime. Joseph Proud's cataract of hymns contains this ambling stanza, its matter rather out of keeping with its manner:

> *Where then is the rapturous pair*
>   *Who conjugal pleasures possess?*
> *'Tis found with the man and the fair*
>   *Whose only delight is to bless;*
> *Whose only love is so ardent a flame*
>   *That nothing can equal its fire;*
> *Whose will is in all things the same,*
>   *The same is their every desire.*

None the less, to guard this ardent flame from danger, to secure this mutual delight, and to keep this 'will' in happy equipoise, the sacrament of marriage was originated, although as an ecclesiastical institution in England it is not many centuries old. What does it impose to this end? In the 'Solemnization of Matrimony', five grave declarations are made, and two supreme promises are exchanged; one of them to love and cherish, the other to love, honour, and obey.[1] Although these promises must be frequently and full-heartedly made by the young, inexperienced, impulsive, passionate and wilful, they are to remain binding for life, and they involve everything that the makers of them are, have, shall as time goes by become, and shall also acquire. The promise to obey has of recent years been challenged and may now be waived. It is one-sided and may seem humiliating and exacting, and yet this is a promise that depends for its keeping less on the feel-

---

[1] It may be remarked that a marriage at a register office—in which the parties must declare, in prescribed words, 'that they take each other as husband and wife'—must be solemnized with open doors and in the presence of two witnesses. No religious service is permitted. The latest rules governing the registration of buildings for this purpose were set out as recently as 1909.

ings than the will. We teach a child to obey, we can only hope it will love. Without having even been called upon to make any promises to do so, we most of us obey the Law; indeed ignorance of it is no defence against the charge of having broken it.

In the Church catechism, on the other hand, the 'young person' declares, 'My duty towards my neighbour is to love him as myself, and to do to all men as I would they should do unto me.' A promise may be here implicit, but it is not expressed. For the unsociable Englishman this is an onerous duty, since his *amour propre* is usually active and faithful. But pure Narcissism is a very unusual malady, and love of self implies physical comforts rather than spiritual well-being; the protection of our pride, our vanity and our purse-strings rather than the insistence on the exercise of our highest faculties. It is as different from the Love promised in the Marriage Service as self-respect is from veneration. In spite of its intention, that is, it is more likely to bring the Levite to mind than the good Samaritan.

A promise converts a duty into a trust. The fulfilment of a duty rests with conscience and character; the keeping of a promise with the spirit and the heart. Our duties are seldom pleasures, and, as we know only too well, may prove too much for us. We should hate a solemn promise to be so. A neglected duty will or should distress us. A broken solemn promise, if it was within our fulfilment, should cut us to the quick, and may lie beyond even our own absolution.

In a Court of Law we swear before God to tell the truth, the whole truth and nothing but the truth: but we shall not then be called upon to answer Pilate's inquiry. There, facts are at issue, not principles or convictions. In the promise to love until death there is no such restriction or reservation. In making it, we may believe that we know our own mind, and may be confident that we shall never change it. But in view of the past and of others can we be as certain that life will never change us? Here, if only by implication, we avow that we can. Is any such avowal more than an aspiration? We can promise to do our best, but not so assuredly to control our feelings, though we may the exhibition of them. The heart realizes that it is erratic and often at enmity with the mind. So long as it stands fast, the constancy is not only effortless, it is as inevitable as the drawing of the breath and the beating of the heart.

When it begins to waver and we to cease to care; when what we gave willingly is no longer ours to give; when the mysterious wellspring of love no longer flows—what then? We are promising to remain in a rare state of being which has befallen us unsought, may have proved transitory in the past (if Juliet has succeeded to Rosaline), and compared with which any usual rapture is a will-o'-the-wisp and enthusiasm a flash in the pan. Being human, our love too will depend in part on our continuing to be loved. That failing, it may not necessarily wane, but it will be less stable, and also of far less value to her to whom it was given. It may then become a tragic burden even to ourselves; and a love once really lost is past the *wit* of man at any rate to recover.

We can be surer too of our minds than of our bodies. The more there is of the physical in any love, the more precarious its continuance is likely to be. That again is a double danger. The kiss asked for is not quite of the same quality on either side as the kiss freely given, whether it is Lesbia's first or ten-thousandth. The essence of love consists in giving, not in making demands. These, and how transparent even the subtlest may be, soon become a fret. Love is innocent of motive and design. Even an affection that has Duty for a step-mother is rather cold commons.

We enter into love, or love enters into us, as purely and happily as the song of birds into the hush of daybreak. A new sun has risen upon our narrow horizon and our whole world lies gilded and shining in its beams. That love may steadily burn on in us until we draw our last breath.

Love

The tides shall cease to beat the shore,
The stars fall from the sky;
Yet I will love thee more and more
Until the day I die, my dear,
Until the day I die.

But however desirable its objects may be, however ardent in
conviction, is such a love as a pure and solemn promise really
within the bounds of mortal assurance? 'Out upon it, I have
loved three whole days together!' . . . What if the fair weather
doesn't hold, and the ship proves unseaworthy? Should we as
confidently promise even to be hungry to-morrow morning,
or angry in the afternoon? Can we be certain to continue even
to like, to value, or to want anything or anybody? We can
pledge ourselves to do our utmost to this end, to 'explore
every avenue', to 'leave no stone unturned'; but it is as hazardous to undertake not to fall out of love as it would to bind
ourselves not to fall into it. Love between man and woman
is a more sensitive plant than this implies. It is too a common
human weakness that the assured is not invariably preferred
to the hoped-for. If, again, possession is nine points of the
law, how many is it of love? Positive ownership implies both
sovereignty and submission. Even if these are mutual, it has
its dangers. Monarchy must not edge into monopoly. We
must be content with our share. The rationing of physical
necessities has many advantages. But we should not welcome
the rationing of beauty or kindness, or of thinking or even of
the 'expectation of life' itself. If one were positively certain
even of paradise, would one at once depart from this wicked
world? Marriage promises the paradise of an imperishable
love. But every promise is confined within its own limits—of
how much and of what kind. Once in these longing eyes of
ours there was a fervent illimitable *speculation*.

Most of us, in a flash of originality, have compared marriage to a lottery; but we cannot be certain either of the price
or the value of the tickets. And how many of us are likely to

prove prizes? Marriage is intended as a cage, and it is hoped that the love-birds may be happy. Church, State, convention, and the general convenience ensure that its exit shall be narrow and its bars secure. The 'bonds' are still bonds even though they seem light as thistledown and prove no more a hindrance to love than his metre is to a poet, or to a painter the limits of his canvas. Love will add every conceivable grace; just as the poet does—of rhythm, music and cadence to his metre. And the artist gilds his frame.

The philosopher of Evolution, who defined a kiss as a gustatory pleasure, declared that to monogamy humanity owes the development of the passion of love. An ideal marriage should have the same gradual and happy outcome. But that is not its only purpose. Marriage was ordained for three excellent 'causes': for the procreation of children, for a remedy against sin, and for the mutual society, help and comfort of the man and woman it links together. Children are, or at least used to be, what honeycomb is to the bear—an irresistible bait. They have been the means of saving many marriages from shipwreck. But if, fruitful or barren, that love should fail, and the mutual society become no longer either a help or comfort? What then?

But even if, apart from its social advantages, it were always a failure, no *less* of a failure might be any alternative. 'Free love' has a resemblance to free verse; which is apt to fall short of poetry, and for the finest poetic purposes to be too loose rather than really free. Any other true and faithful alliance remains unsanctified, and is—in both of the two contradictory meanings of the word—egregious. Birds in cages are no friends of the wild. They refuse to be charmed by the passionate song from the myrtle grove. Birds of the wild have to risk cold winters. And the love-child, alas, faces the handicap of the charity brat.

'What do you think of marriage?' inquires the Duchess of Malfi of her steward, Antonio, a few moments before she declares her love for him. 'I take it,' he replies,

Love

> *as those that deny purgatory;*
> *It locally contains or heaven or hell.*
> *There's no third place in't . . .*

And what does a man get from marriage?

> *Only the bare name*
> *Of being a father, or the weak delight*
> *To see the little wanton ride a cock-horse*
> *Upon a painted stick, or hear him chatter*
> *Like a taught starling.*

'Third place', of course, there may be, in spite of Antonio, even though not all husbands become fathers.

Still, one of the crucial problems of human society and human happiness lies in the question of how far marriage is a help or a hindrance to a mutual love and its continuance. One of the commonest reasons, apart from other human frailties, why it falls short of perfection is that the promise *had* to be made, was kept with joy for a time and then broken, and not necessarily either light-headedly or light-heartedly. A broken promise may sometimes be repaired; and may then, if love managed the mending of it and supplied the cement, look almost as good as new. Also human nature is infinitely accommodating. How else could one endure stark solitude? —that irremediable burden of self; that poor patient ass, the body; that all-too-familiar face; that squirrel-cage of a mind; that slovenly treasure-house Memory; that one creature with whom one is compelled to share one's bed, even to the last bed of all?

But in no circumstances can we remain at any extremity either of passion, happiness or misery. A love stagnant is a love in decay. It is living, or dying. In any shared life there is bound to be some conflict. To fight it out may prove more or less fatal to one of the contestants and grievous for both. Only compromise with the aid of its last two syllables can make peace. Love doesn't *make* peace. It gives it, as the flame even of a candle, of an intense, however narrow, activity, gives both light and heat.

Is then this lifelong promise to love and cherish, which is made by those who are not, by the way, called on to vow that they love already, in the main a boon and a blessing: even though *as* a promise it was wildly hazardous? And is it in fact usually and consistently kept?

Trustworthy evidence is not easy to obtain. Humanity is reluctant to proclaim its failures on the housetop, and at its best refuses to make a song of its successes. Coventry Patmore's *Angel in the House* is indeed the only lyrical and rapturous epic that I know of in English on the theme of married love—and its sale exceeded a quarter of a million copies. Was it so welcomed by its Victorian readers merely as a tribute to the might-have-been? That seems unlikely. And what would be its success to-day? Neither the Church nor the Government Departments responsible for the general well-being of the community issue an annual questionnaire (similar to the lucid and solicitous document devoted to the collection of Income Tax), to be completed by every husband and wife; and containing such instructions as: 'In the event of the percentage of love (that on the day of betrothal being taken as 100) having in the specified period fallen below that stated in B (3) above, enter here (in block capitals) (a) the cause of decrease, (b) a graph denoting rapidity of recession, (c) the effect of this, ascertainable or apparent, (d) the likelihood of a further decline, (e) the anticipated percentage for ensuing period . . .' and so forth. The inquiry would be informative enough, but it would not be a popular innovation. Newspaper reports, those of the Divorce and the Police Courts, and the pages of Whitaker provide rather arid statistics. I chanced recently too on a paper written by a general practitioner which had been based on the confidences of his women patients. It was extremely depressing.

Two human beings passionately in love with one another are usually conspicuous of course; and, no less usually, is extreme incompatibility of temper. But reliable evidence after some years of their wedded life of the degree in which one's own personal friends continue to be happy, or otherwise, *because* they are married, is not easy to acquire; and even angels might here fear to tread. The only recent summary that has come my way is Arnold Bennett's.

'Personally,' he says, in his *Mental Efficiency*, 'I should estimate that not in one per cent even of romantic marriages are the husband and wife capable of *passion* for each other after three years. So brief is the violence of love! In perhaps thirty-three per cent passion settles down into a tranquil affection—which is ideal. In fifty per cent it sinks into sheer indifference, and one becomes used to one's wife or one's husband as to one's other habits. And in the remaining sixteen per cent it develops into dislike or detestation.'

This is a compact little piece of arithmetic; it seems to be innocent of prejudice. Its value depends on the range of the inquiry, the degree of intrusiveness, and the precise content of its 'passion' and 'violence'. But this, perhaps, is splitting hairs. Nothing is said about age, or relative ages, or circumstances, or profession, or character; or of how much and what kind of love went to the making of the marriages referred to. What, as it stands, does it finally tell us? Is it favourable to the making of the promise and to the likelihood of its being kept, or is it not?

We may first ask ourselves if a period of three whole years out of a married life, even of thirty, should be described as 'brief'. Hardly, if it were spent in penal servitude. Two and a half hours of rapturous happiness every day for thirty years—nearly four hours indeed, if we ignore night and sleep: how many people have that good fortune in any state of life? Even to be sure of one's own poor best at any job for a single hour of every day! Indeed, in spite of the tone of this little summary, its percentaging is on the whole rather grateful and comforting. It was made by a shrewd and 'realistic' observer of life who was an accomplished novelist, the novelist of *The*

67

Old Wives' Tale and *The Card*. It should be level rather than sanguine; 666 human beings out of a thousand in an 'ideal' state, no fewer than twenty in *excelsis*—that, surely is a compliment to wedlock. Nor are we in the Doldrums even yet. Becoming used to anything or to anybody, whether it is roast beef or roses, one's bed or one's newspaper, the children or the cook, need not imply 'sheer indifference'. 'Habits', according to that generous philosopher, William James, are in much the bread and salt of life, and some may be its honey. To become merely tepidly 'used to' them—to a little music, to a little gossip, to a little Bridge, to a little violent argument —is a reflection on oneself rather than on one's habits. But norms and averages are a lifeless and deceptive method of dealing with human nature even in a world which appears to have become more stereotyped even than it used to be. No one ever fell in love with a norm. Statistics serve for stature, colour of eyes, incomes, cars and refrigerators, but hardly for passion, happiness, detestation, or suicide. The last time Mary Coleridge saw William Cory, he told her: 'My father was ten years older than my mother. He let her fall out of his arms when she was a baby. Picking her up, he said, "Never mind, darling! I'll marry you some day." ' And he kept his word. I once myself had a friend who, when she went as bridesmaid to her bosom friend's wedding, vowed she would never marry any other man than the bridegroom. Many years went by; the wife died; and marry him she did. In both cases constancy persisted, first without bonds, then with them. Are such little romances extremely exceptional? With Donne, we may fail to pierce love's 'hidden mystery', but may still question his summary 'So lovers dream a rich and long delight, But yet a winter-seeming summer's night'. And as Arnold Bennett admits, a serene, nocturnal, summer twilight of affection may follow the dream. Are we not asking too much of human nature to expect a perpetual noonday?

And how about the *un*married? If, though this will be mainly guesswork, we compare the relations between the husbands and wives of our acquaintance with those of two brothers living together, all things in common between them; or of two sisters; or of brother and sister; of widow or widower with one child, of two friends of the same sex, of man and woman unwedded; what then? It is amusing to conjure up minute households of each kind, and then to make comparisons. Is the arrangement, as in Arnold Bennett's summary, likely to be as often ideal, or one of indifference or detestation? We hear a good deal of the cat-and-dog life; less of the life spent cat with cat, or dog with dog.

To a child, weeping his heart out in solitude at school, home seems a paradise beyond even John Bunyan's imagining; but keep him in as a punishment during his holidays, and it at once becomes a prison. Even the most fervent yet untravelled lover of England can hardly have failed during these last three years of enforced confinement to pine for pastures new. So too at times it may be with every wedded lover. The promiseless ménage of any kind, on the other hand, which must also be subject to misunderstandings, dissension, and estrangement, has a less urgent reason for deciding on compromise, or a return to amity, than have the married. *No* love of course but must regret the briefest of resentment. But human nature, again, is blessedly adaptable, and often for sweeter motives than self-interest. There is too a delicious joy in 'making it up'—the giving to a wasted day a sunny morrow. 'The falling out of faithful friends renewing is of love.' Few words in the language could hint at a more corrosive misery and desolation—roof, board, and bed—than a 'loveless marriage'. And yet, if love brought no more than the tenderness of reconciliation, the balm of insight and forgiveness, and the renewal of fidelity, it would still remain the ransom of the world.

Precisely how prolonged, again, is any violence of self-love in the solitary bachelor, old maid, or egoist likely to prove? And what is the usual outcome of wedding, say, Money? Or pleasure, or Society, or Science, or art, or a vocation?—

situations, when a neglected wife is the sufferer, much in vogue in Hollywood. And must we estimate any impassioned love solely, or even chiefly, by its duration? Apart from the marriage which is an all-but-indissoluble sacrament, it may, perhaps, be less of a disaster to fall out of love than to be incapable of falling into it again. Still, however fickle we may be, constancy appeals straight to our hearts. We are charmed by those faithful monogamists, duck and drake. The wildly and hotly impulsive have far fewer admirers. We may sympathize with the righteous man who refuses to 'put up with' a wife once loved whom he now regards as unworthy of him, or who has wronged him, or whose temper is out of keeping with his own—a worse offence, in Milton's eyes, than adultery. But something more valuable even than sympathy may go out to the man who faces out even this calamity, unless or until it engulfs its causer also, and she can no longer put up with *him*.

Without any further descent into statistics,[1] it would seem that the promises made in marriage, however precarious they may appear to be, are not only a tribute to love but often effective; though it must be admitted that exceptions nowadays abound to prove the rule. And yet even a 'tranquil

[1] In respect to the United Kingdom, that is. Max Nordau estimated that three out of four modern marriages are in no sense true love marriages; Georg Hirth, nine out of ten. In a book published in 1861, by Julien Lemer, *L'Amour par les Grands Ecrivains*, occurs the desolating summary, 'Usually in a marriage for love, hate takes its place. I have seen it with my own eyes.' Other people have seen with their own eyes that a marriage made without love may invite it in. An Austrian, Dr. Antos Gross-Hoffinger, a century ago investigated no fewer than three hundred marriages, chosen at random and from diverse classes. He was 'never able to satisfy himself' that 'happy marriages are anything but extremely isolated exceptions to the general rule'. 'About one-half of all marriages are absolutely unhappy.' A second experiment may prove more fortunate; and there is no question that a deep and passionate love may recur in a single lifetime. The edict of the Courts of Love notwithstanding, even an ardent love for two women at the same time is not impossible. Indeed this was a little miracle of divided allegiance that I myself accomplished when I was nine!

affection' between any particular man and woman may be hard to comprehend. We glance at the wedding rings on the fingers of our fellow passengers in a railway carriage, then at their faces, and may marvel afresh at the resilience, good humour and divine hospitality of the human heart. If that is so, how perilous is the attempt, not to comprehend, but to intervene in love's misunderstandings, quarrels, ruptures, jealousies, entanglements. Let some other hand pick up the first stone. 'Would you advise me to marry?' a friend of Dr. Johnson's once asked him. 'I would advise no man to marry, sir,' was his retort, 'who is not likely to propagate understanding.' Alas, he and his beloved Tetty were childless. 'I married for ambition,' confessed Jane Welsh Carlyle. 'Carlyle has exceeded all that my wildest hopes ever imagined of him, and I am miserable.' Nor even if a true love be the only incentive, will it bring nothing but happiness—and Sir Walter Raleigh has expatiated on the false. That depends far less on others than on ourselves.

Every love is unique; every marriage is unique. We take upon ourselves too easy and arrogant a censorship when we sit in judgement on any fellow creature unless we not only believe that our judgement is impeccable but that we are also in possession of the secrets of another heart. It makes for wisdom and modesty if, instead, we keep a close watch upon our own, arraigning ourselves no less for loving too little than for loving 'not wisely but too well'—the self-deceived, remorseful, death-confronting and noble Othello's—and Shakespeare's—words. But what, whether or not, of the self-sufficient for whom 'there is no joy but calm'?

'The greatest thing in the world', Montaigne declared, 'is to know how to belong to oneself.' He also said that to achieve a beneficent self-friendship is 'the summit of human wisdom'. None the less a paternoster was never far from his lips; and he affirmed that 'He who in nowise liveth for others hardly knoweth how to live for himself.' Indeed, of his friend, La Boétie, he said:

71

'There was I know not what predestined and inescapable force which affected his union (with me). We sought for one another before we set eyes on one another and because of the reports that each had heard of each. I think that by some ordinance of heaven we embraced one another by our names. And at our first encounter . . . we found ourselves so taken one with the other, so mutually bound that thenceforward nothing could be nearer than I to him and he to me. Our spirits, his and mine, were so closely yoked together . . . that not only did I know his soul as I knew mine, but I would certainly have trusted myself more willingly to his hands than to my own.'

Other friends, other lovers, other husbands and wives have similarly testified. Late in Montaigne's life, and within a year or two of his death, there came into it Mlle. Marie de Jars de Gournay, who, when she was only eighteen, had fallen in love with his *Essays*. When at length they met, he immediately and joyfully accepted her as his daughter by adoption. And 'truly', as he says, she was

'. . . by me beloved with more than a fatherly love . . . there is nothing in the world I esteem more than her. . . . If childhood may presage any future success, her mind shall one day be capable of many notable things and, amongst others, of the perfection of this thrice-sacred amity whereunto we read not, her sex could yet attain. . . . The exceeding vehemency with which she loved me . . . is an accident most worthy of consideration.'

To be at ease with and the lenient master of our own mind, and in no other service; to be equable, tolerant, assured of our balance, and confident in our sanity; to be able to wander from room to room of the house of life—absolute right-of-way denied to every other living soul, and with a tranquil meditative eye for every familiar memorial around us, for every object of beauty, and possibly of virtue, and yet not one too keenly prized; the portraits of faithful friends not too fervently needed smiling serenely on us from its walls; with no exacting phantom of bewitchment to whisper 'I am absent' or 'I come!'; our windows lit with the ordinary and undisquieting light of day; to let our hopes be a sound investment rather than a hazardous speculation; to keep our heart secure in our own breast; imagination in song but not at liberty; to think, design and do what we will and not what we must, the sport neither of enthusiasm nor caprice—what better means of dealing with earthly existence, its shocks and treacheries, could prudence devise or sagacity secure?

None the less, as Bacon says, 'A man would die, though he were neither valiant nor miserable, onely upon a weiriness to doe the same thing so oft over and over.' For many people life is too hard, too densely occupied to admit even a choice of variety. Almost self-forgetfully they toil on. For others a more or less comfortable and shallow indifference suffices. They are neither hot nor cold. The self-satisfied, self-immured egotist resembles a silkworm unable to free itself from its cocoon.

This brings to mind Sir Henry Wotton's famous poem:

> *How happy is he born and taught*
> *That serveth not another's will;*
> *Whose armour is his honest thought,*
> *And simple truth his utmost skill—*

and who is content with a love of God, that is free from passion and all heartache. It is a safeguard of the soul, but how little of it it seems to spend. Is it the mind or the heart that is speaking; or is it an ideal duet? Whether by accident or design, this poem is followed in *The Oxford Book of English Verse* by Wotton's lines 'Upon the Death of Sir Albert Morton's Wife':

> *He first deceased; she for a little tried*
> *To live without him, liked it not, and died.*

That, of course, refers to a woman. But it pierces something deep within us that his happy paragon left unscathed. Moreover, in poetry written by men, no aspiration, desire, *pis aller* or threat of an impassioned love recurs more frequently than that of death. It is as if by some paradoxical instinct of the mind Love divines that death alone can ensure a final severance or a unification beyond our mortal bodies to attain.

But although this strange conviction is common in humanity, high and low, love, even of the least of things, tends to be infinitely more self-creative and all-vivifying than destructive. It is a *life*-giving inspiration.[1]

Nothing in this world at any rate can be done well, or with much satisfaction, unless there is at the least some zeal and zest in the doing of it. And Zeal is Love's housekeeper. She carries the keys. Even a machine that achieves a reiterated mechanical perfection was itself once the invention of a creative or inventive zest. Nor can anything be even perceived with the eye and the intelligence without some active hospitality; and that we usually give only to what we care for. We may, of course, be coldly and calculatingly aware of the use of a thing for our own purpose and profit; but this use with this end in view is a neglect of its most valuable asset—

---

[1] Not that this affects the truth of Isaac Watt's declaration, 'It is the gentle and harmless, the peaceful, benevolent and compassionate man, who is the object of universal esteem and love.' Less so the enthusiast, the fanatic, the evangelist, the impassioned artist, the martyr to love's throes. The joys of a domesticated (and wedded) recluse are related in a charming and talkative poem by Henry Erskine:

> *A book—my slippers—and a field to stroll in—*
> *My garden-seat—an elbow chair to loll in.*

And in his *Discorsa della Vita Sobria* the centenarian Luigi Cornaro, who died in 1565, ridicules (in his eighties), those who dismiss old age as a living death. 'Peace and joy', he declares, 'never quit me.' He has just completed a most amusing comedy, 'full of blameless wit'. For playmate he has a grandson not yet five; and he sings away, accompanied by the instruments of the elder ones, in a voice, 'better, clearer and louder than ever'. Nor, he concludes, while confessing to bygone 'years of disorder', would he exchange his age for 'the youth of such as live in the service of their passions'. There are of course degrees of service, and one of them is slavery.

its essential self. How much more wastefully is this so when the thing in question is alive! The statement 'He is only making use of me' involves an unmitigated outrage against 'me' and a rapacious 'he'. So mill-owners, mine-owners, and chimney-sweeps once made pitiless use of children of only four to nine years old. To line their pockets they both wasted and laid them waste. Some of their victims came up at length out of the darkness of the pit, pallid, dwarfed and half-imbecile. Now and again 'Dick, Joe, Ned or Jack', beaten and half-starved, would get stuck in a chimney and suffocated.

These are extremes; but no vestige of love or even admiration was ever thus misled. The continued use of any thing, and no less of a fellow creature, may at length of course deeply endear it to us. Its virtues and graces steal into view. It becomes at length familiar; and familiarity may bring to birth feelings the complete opposite to contempt. 'So might we talk of the old familiar faces.' We sadly miss it when it is gone, and shall indeed when we ourselves are going. But time and habit may confer even on the ugly and faulty a sort of quiet patina of affection—a more lasting beauty than most. In general, however, 'getting used' to anything can hardly but imply some detraction. It has ceased to surrender the perpetual novelty of its own being. For this reason it is an advantage to get used to what we detest—and even, it may be, to our own worst defects! And this, although the adjuration in our childhood that we should soon become used to Fortune's slings and arrows may have proved far too optimistic. Life and beauty have a value infinitely beyond their mere usableness. Love, which steadfastly refuses merely to use, does its utmost to guard and preserve both; hate to destroy them. Only necessity can excuse any such kind of sacrifice, a Nature red in tooth and claw; and only then if what is good is sacrificed to what is better—though this was not true of the greatest sacrifice of all. The flesh-eaters and the fox-hunter had best not reason too closely about their needs and their hobby. In spite of the Good Shepherd in the parable and of William

Love

Blake, we most of us like mutton better than sheep; they the chase than foxes. It is the *pet* lamb that need have no dread of Easter.

What hideous things, indeed, solely for profit man has made of excellent materials simply for want of a decent regard for them. It was not with eyes as dull as this that the old Chinese craftsmen and mystics put to their serene and profound purposes their clay and bronze and jade. Use your frog 'an if you loved it' was Izaak Walton's advice to the angler; but it is prettier if it is addressed to the painter. Mere attention and skill will alone work wonders, but it is something more than these that a man of sense gives to his horse and his dog, to his tools and work. So with a writer and with the words he uses. His mere craftsmanship will be wanting in one of its essences until, as well as taking care *with* them, he cares *for* them; and it is love that finds out the way. The fountain of devotion to his work flows from within. 'He learns how it's done by doing it.'

All this, of course, is tediously commonplace. Indifference, none the less, to so simple a truth is the supreme defect of the machine-made and the machine-minded, when the sole criterion is mere 'use'. Life without the giving and receiving of love is in a worse state than that of a flower without water, since it continues in a mockery of its own existence after it is dead.

And how conscious of this even mute matter may make us. There are sensitives or psychics who (after the manner of witch-doctors, water-diviners, and those reputed to have the second sight) believe they can detect the presence or the influence of the praeternatural. And the ghost-story decoys and seduces us in vain if we are insusceptible to its symptoms. I was even assured many years ago by a resident alienist in an asylum for the insane that he could tell if the room he entered had been recently vacated by a lunatic. And few of us are insensitive to the presence of—at least—embodied evil. Similarly, though not more explicably, we may recognize the

Love

loved, and lovable and the loving. They carry with them an aura or penumbra; and our sensitive tentacles grope out in its direction; since even physical energy may range beyond the termination of the nerves.

However that may be, there are streets, villages, and even towns, which are overcast with the unfriendly and the inhospitable; institutions breathing and bristling with antagonism; houses which, as soon as the door is opened, seem to reek of the acidity of hatred and strife, or to be festering with the mildew of indifference; just as a human face may be pocked, as it were, by the fret of a lifetime of the world's contempt; coated with continuous doses of a kind of viscous admiration; or parched with the misery of offering, with few bidders, what no one should sell. Anger, it is said, secretes a positive poison in the skin.

There are no less happy-seeming, friendly, welcoming houses, churches, gardens, hill and river, woods, valleys, combes and coves of the sea. They exhale an atmosphere of benignancy and consolation, as the sea itself its ozone. So may one find oneself at times—after perhaps a surfeit of the usual social commerce, the rote-manners, the tired extravagances, the stuffy witticisms, the naughtinesses, the brittle talk—in an affectionate family, as unlike that of the Barretts of Wimpole Street as some old inn is from a private hotel. It is like chancing in old days on a roast-chestnut-man's barrow with its crackling coke in one of London's November fogs.

It is indeed as difficult to dissociate love, in all its kinds and phases, from living, as sex from being. On our valuation of it depends our valuation of most things else. The stark assertion, 'I hate everything', reveals an intensification of the ego so extreme that fatuity rather than insanity appears to have been its impulse. Whereas 'I love everything', though we may mock at its diffuseness and suspect it of sentimentality, at least suggests an expansion, limited only by the range and quality of the thought and being behind it.

77

Love

. . . O what a thing is Thought!
Which seems a dream; yea, seemeth nought,
Yet doth the mind
Affect as much as what we find
Most near and true; sure Men are blind,
And can't the forcible reality
Of things that secret are within them see.

Thought! Surely thoughts are true;
They please as much as things can do:
Nay things are dead
And in themselves are severed
From souls; nor can they fill the head
Without our thoughts. Thoughts are the real things
From whence all Joy, from whence all Sorrow springs.

What else, at the very least, are the pagan divinities, the
woodland nymphs, the sylphs, the Shades, Pan, Eros, demon,
seraph, archangel, but the ethereal embodiments of power
and of ideas?

There are those in whom the love of God is so pervasive
that even an atheist, however acid his contempt of both subject and Object, must agree that it is all-sufficing. There are
those also in whom affection for a fellow-creature, whether
that of St. Augustine for his friend, of Henry King for his
wife, of the nine-year-old Byron for Mary Duff, or Chaucer's
for the daisy, or a child's for her rag doll, is so generous and
tender that even an angel might be tempted to envy. And it is
the love, not its object, that is, again, the sovereign test.

'We needs must love the highest when we see it,' said
Guinevere, 'not Launcelot nor another.' If the 'needs must'
means the ought-to, well and good; if it means that on recog-
nizing the 'highest' we cannot help ourselves, then even better; but the mastery and mystery of love are best revealed in
the love for a highest or deepest which may be radiantly
apparent to itself yet concealed from others. Cophetua's

nobles praised the beggar-maid's ankles, her eyes, hair and 'lovesome mien'; it was her 'sweet and angel grace' that persuaded Cophetua to make her his queen. Her 'poor attire', in fact, is her only recorded disability; and it ranks in bathos with Enoch Arden's costly funeral. The honour and glory, of course, was her love for the king. Such is the idiom of all the old folk tales, including 'Mollie Whuppie'. And the rags should have been *his* wear. For if there is one thing certain about love it is the humility of its celestial aspiration:

> My love is of a birth as rare
> As 'tis for object strange and high:
> It was begotten by Despair
> Upon Impossibility . . .

and these are the words of the poet of 'Time's winged chariot', of 'your quaint honour' and of that 'fine and private place'.

'Yes,' may be the reply, 'but as often as not a poem is the revelation merely of a rare and ecstatic moment even in the life of a man of so ardent and individual an imagination as Andrew Marvell's. And he himself in a different mood could declare in "The Garden",

> Two paradises 'twere in one
> To live in Paradise alone.

The imaginative are notoriously fickle—butterflies intent on a transitory self-satisfaction, not on the well-being of the hive. The retrospective testimony of a lifetime expressed in a sober, workaday prose would be far sounder and more trustworthy evidence. "Wilt thou show the whole wealth of thy wit in an instant? I pray thee understand a plain man in his plain meaning." '

Well, many witnesses in the pages that follow solicit this understanding; and they would be echoed by countless others who have never entrusted their feelings to print. Among those who have, Havelock Ellis in his Studies in the *Psychology of Sex* cites the author of the *Essay on the Principles of Popula-*

tion and *The Nature and Progress of Rent*; neither of them sub-jects likely to appeal to the Muses. However great the pleasures conferred on him by his intellect, declared Malthus, there is scarcely a man who does not recall and contemplate the period of his life when he 'experienced the genuine delight of virtuous love' as that 'which he would most wish to live over again'. Nietzsche, too, considered that this 'angelic instinct' is not only life's 'greatest stimulant', but that it affects the esti-mate of whatever else is of value, gives strength, enhances the lover, and is the dominant, if secret, incentive of Art. Carl von Bonstetten maintains that every explanation of love—as 'a force analogous to electricity, or as a kind of magnetism, or as a variety of chemical affinity, or as a vital tropism'—is nothing more than a way of expressing its mystery and mag-nitude. The dying Laplace dismissed even his *Traité de Mé-canique Céleste* as 'only trifles'. 'There is nothing real in the world but love.' And Comte: one may weary of thought and action; but in spite of all its tortures, its bitterest pangs, 'there is nothing real in the world but love'. 'To lack love', said the old Chinese sage, Mencius, 'is to lack wisdom.'

'They say that God is love,' said Samuel Butler, 'but life and love are co-extensive . . . "God is life" is not far off saying "God is love".' All healthy instinct, he declared, is for love between the sexes, even if all reason is against it. There may be individual intuitions, innate convictions, deeper even than reason against it: a natural austerity, genuine Puritanism, re-ligious fervour, a passion for chastity. Love conflicts with worldly ambition, it entails the loss of freedom and self-sufficiency. 'It cheateth business,' says Bacon; hinders practical ends, wastes time and substance, and dissipates energy. Bacon had 'gods' of his own choosing, and preferred a different order of affection.

But reason, intuition and self-interest apart, it is a morbid prudery that repudiates and disparages the body—a thing of such miraculous craftsmanship and aptitudes!—since, surely, whatever its oddities and absurdities may be, its earthiness and animalness, it is here our only highway to the treasury of the actual, and our only direct means of communication with our fellow-creatures. It is easy and amusing, too, to mock at Nature, with her insensate craving to increase and multiply—aphis to hippopotamus, schizomycete to the banyan tree. But her irresponsive smile is as enigmatic as that of the Sphinx. Eating, drinking, laughing, weeping, sneezing, yawning, kissing, sleeping, dreaming—what imbecilities such things are if thinking cares to make them so! Daintiness can never tiny its mouth too much at them, and fastidiousness is capable of an inexhaustible indigestion.

But quite apart from the body and its wiles and drawbacks, hard things have been said about love, and many of them will be found in this book. They express the revulsion, lamentations, disenchantment and woe of the embittered or thwarted. A contrasting catalogue of its ills and wells, like Burton's on marriage, was a favourite amusement of the Elizabethan poets. The scorned, the rejected, the inveigled, the victimized, the betrayed and the surfeited—all have a bone to pick with Cupid, and fling back the broken arrow in his face. And even the truest love, a love all loving-kindness and long-suffering, may be tried almost beyond human endurance. It may exhaust the heart and cause an intensity of suspense and desolation never experienced by the indifferent and the cold. And then

> *The heart must pause to breathe,*
> *And Love itself have rest.*

While my father was away at the war, I marked off each day with a knife on a piece of wood. He had started when it was scarcely light beneath the trees. I was very sleepy so early in the morning while he ate his breakfast, and as I watched him on the other side of the lighted candle drinking his steaming tea in his saucer, my eyes kept rolling back of themselves because I was so tired. And everything in the room was plain one moment and the next all blurred and wavering. The baby was asleep in the cradle. The wind was still roaring in the tops of the trees, but the candle burned clear, because the wind did not come down in the house.

When my father opened the door I saw that the grass was strewn with green leaves, and falling leaves were in the air, and the wind overhead sounded like water, though the tree trunks hardly swayed even, down here. But it was not raining when he started, only the leaves were wet with rain and the bark of the trees was darkened with wet. I asked him to bring me back a long rifle. He kept rubbing his hands over his face and blinking his eyes and listening to the wind as if he heard the guns. Two or three times he came back to say good-bye to my mother. And when at last he didn't come back he kept turning his face, looking over his shoulder at us. There was no sun shining yet that morning, but the bright light of the sky gleamed on the wet leaves. I asked mother if father was glad to be going to the war. But she was crying over the baby, so I went out into the forest till dinner.

My mother was more cheerful at dinner, and we had some hot soup. After dinner I chopped up some wood in the shed. It made me very hot and excited chopping up the wood. It was getting dark when I came back, carrying the logs. It seemed that the wind grew more angry in the twilight, and although it still roared like the mill-water in the village, yet it whistled too, and the leaves kept dropping, heavy with rain. And now it was not clear, but cold and misty round the hut. I went in with the logs.

Mother was sitting in the wooden chair with the baby in her arms. She looked as if she was pretending. I went close and stared at her, and found that she was fast asleep. The baby was asleep too, but it scarcely seemed to be really breathing—it was like a moth fluttering on a pin; its face was quite pale and still in its sleep, but its cheeks were very red. I thought I would make a fire again without asking mother's leave, so as to be more cheerful; besides, I could feel the cold air oozing through the crannies of the timbers, and it was getting so dark I could see only the white things in the room. The rushing sound of the wind never ceased at all.

As soon as the flames began to spring up, and the sparks to crack out of the wood, my mother woke up. She looked at me with a curious face; but soon she remembered that she had been asleep, and she enjoyed the warmth of the fire.

On the next day I woke up where I had fallen asleep by the hearth, and it was a very quiet morning. I looked out of the window, and saw the sun shining yellow between the branches; and many of the boughs were now all but bare. But the fallen leaves lay thick on the ground as far as I could see, and some of them were still quite large and green. I was glad my father was gone away, because now I could do just as I pleased. I did not want the trouble of lighting the fire, so I went out into the forest, and down to visit the snares. There was a young hare caught by the leg in one, and the leaves were all round him. His eyes were bleeding, and not very bright. I killed him with a crack on the neck as I had seen father kill the hares, and carried him back by his hind legs. The leaves made an incessant rustling as I walked through them. I could see the blue sky above the trees; it was very pale, like a ribbon. I stood still a minute, carrying the hare, and listening to find if I could hear the guns. But I heard only a bird singing and a rushing sound, as if a snake were going away under the leaves. Sometimes I came to branches blown down to the ground, and even now, here and there, a leaf would fall slowly through the air, twirling, to be with all the rest. I enjoyed my broth for dinner very much, and the hare lasted for three days, with some turnips.

I asked mother how long father would be away. She said she could not tell. And I wondered how they would carry back his body if he was killed in the war.

I stayed out in the forest nearly all that day because the baby kept on crying. It was dark, and the window was lit up when I came home, and still the baby was fretting. Its eyes were gone dull, and it would not go to sleep in the night, though mother kept walking up and down, crooning and mumbling to it, and rocking it in her arms. She said it was very ill, and she held it pressed close to her. I asked her if it was going to die, but she only walked a little faster, and, as I was very sleepy, we did not talk much that night. The baby was still crying when I woke up, but not so loud. It was bleating small and shrill; like a young lamb, I told mother. I felt very refreshed after my sleep, and very hungry. I lit the fire and boiled the kettle, and put the plates on the table, and the loaf.

After breakfast I told mother I was going down to the old pool to fish, and that I would bring her some fish for dinner. But she looked at me and called me to her.

'The baby is dreadfully ill', she said, 'and we must go without the fish. Feel its poor thin hot hands. That's the fever. Do you love it? Then take it in your arms.'

But I shook my head. It looked very ugly because its face was all puckered up, and it just wailed and wailed like a gnat in the air.

'I think I would *like* to go fishing, Mother,' I said, 'and I promise you shall have the biggest I catch.'

But she kept on persisting that the baby was too ill to wait, that it was very queer, and that I must go for the doctor in the village. It wasn't so very far, she said, and I could fish to-morrow.

'But it *is* far,' I told her; 'and it doesn't look so very bad; and it might be windy and cold to-morrow. It's only crying,' I said. And I ran out before she could catch me.

But I did not catch any fish. I suppose they would not bite because I had been wicked. So I tied up my lines and came home about three in the afternoon. As I stood at the door waiting before going in, I heard a sound far away, and then, in a while, again, through the forest. And I knew it was the guns and cannons on the other side of the forest. The baby was not crying now, when I went in. But my mother did not turn her head to speak to me. She was kneeling beside its old rocking-cradle, some of her hair hanging down on her shoulders.

'I'll go for the doctor now, Mother; but the guns are firing; you can hear them now if you come and listen at the door.'

But when I told her about the guns, she began to cry out loud, and hid her face in the coverlet on the cradle. I watched her a little while, and I could hear the cannons going off quite plainly now; only far away, like a drum when you put your hand on it.

I got very hot standing still, so I put my tackle on the hook and sat down by the hearth.

'Shall I go for the doctor now, Mother? It'll be dark before I get back.'

Mother turned on me very wild. 'Oh, you coward, you coward,' she said. 'Dark—it's dark enough for me!'

She startled me very much by saying this and I felt very uncomfortable. I went nearer and looked. The baby's face was white, and its eyelids were like white wax. Its lips were the colour of its hands, almost blue.

'Is it dead, Mother?' I asked. But she did not answer me, only shook her shoulders. I walked away and looked out of the door. First I felt hot and then my back shivered. And I began to cry too, because I had not gone in the morning for the doctor. I did not dry my eyes because the tears ran quite hot down my cheeks, and I could hear them dripping off my chin upon my jacket. I liked to have the door open, although it was cold and grey in the afternoon.

My mother came to the doorway and drew me close to her as if she were sorry, with her hand clutching my head. I could not cry any more now, but stood still; and even then the guns and cannons went on firing. And sometimes birds silently flew between the trees away from the sound. I wondered if father was fighting near the cannons.

The next day it was so cold again my mother made me a jacket out of an old coat of father's. It was just hemmed up, and I wore it instead of my other jacket when I went out. She had drawn the coverlet over the baby's face, so that it now lay in a kind of little house in its cradle. I thought I would please mother, so found the place and read out of the Bible about Herod; but the candle burned very sooty and smoky, so that I could not read very well, and left out the long words.

The next morning mother told me to go down to the village and tell the sexton that the baby was dead so that it could be buried in the churchyard.

I started out with my switch, about ten o'clock. It was a warm day; so I was wearing my old jacket again, and the air smelled of the leaves, which were withered and yellow and brown. I went on, whistling; but it was more than five miles to the village. The robins were singing on the twigs, and I saw some crows flying in the sky. It was so quiet in the forest, that the cannons seemed to shake the air with their sound.

And while I was walking along, not very fast, and looking out for wild berries, I heard a noise in the distance of men running, and then the sound of a rifle quite near, and a scream like a rabbit, but much more loud and awful. I hid behind a tree, and when the forest was quiet again I ran home as quick as I could. But I did not like to tell my mother that I had been frightened of the soldiers, because she had called me a coward already. So I said instead that the sexton was nowhere to be found in the village, that he must have gone to the war himself, and that no one would come for fear of the soldiers.

She looked me full in the face with her eyes. She looked so earnestly and so hard at me that I could not help moving my shoulder a little. And at that she turned away, and I felt very wretched because I knew that she had seen it was a lie. But I did not say anything.

All the while I sat there my eyes would not keep from looking at the cradle. I was very hungry. But since mother was putting on her shawl I knew that she was going out presently. Then, I thought, when she is gone, I will eat as much as ever I can. There were some bones in the cupboard well worth picking, I knew. When mother had put on her shawl and her bonnet, she lifted the baby out of the cradle.

'I must carry it to the churchyard myself,' she said, but more to herself than to me. There were no tears in her eyes; they were dark all round.

'Won't you kiss your little brother, Robbie?' It was wrapped up in her wedding shawl, which she had sometimes shown me of an evening, out of the chest. I began to cry when I kissed its forehead. It was as cold as a stone, as a piece of dough, and looked very heavy, yet thin, and its face was quite still now.

'Take care of the house, Rob,' she said. 'Don't go out; and bolt the door after me.'

I watched her hasten off along the narrow path between the trees. There was a light like crimson in the forest, and I knew that the sun would soon be setting. It was silly of her not to have gone earlier. It was very quiet now; and I was afraid it would soon be dark.

Soon she was out of sight, and only the trees seemed to come a little nearer and stand still. I left the door open, went into the room and put the candlestick on the table. I kicked the log till it began to flame. Then I went to the cupboard and took out the loaf and the bones, and a few puckered old apples. I ate from the dish, sitting by the hearth, looking out of the door. When I had finished I fell asleep for a little while.

By and by I opened my eyes. It was darker, and I saw some animal looking in at the door. I jumped up, and the animal ran away. Then I shut and barred the door and put some more wood on the fire until it was blazing high up the chimney. But I did not like to look over my shoulder towards the square window; it was so dark and silent and watchful out there. I could not hear the cannons now, either because they weren't sounding or because the flames made a loud bubbling noise as they ran up and waved. I did not dare to let them fall quiet, to only the red embers, so I kept on putting wood on the fire as fast as it burned away.

Mother did not come back, and it seemed I was sitting in front of the warm hearth in a dream that would never come to an end. All was still and motionless, and there was no ordinary sound at all that I could hear in the forest, and even the cannons were more muffled now and further away. I could not cry, though I felt very angry at being left alone, and I was afraid. Besides, I didn't know what I would say to mother when she came back—about the food. Yet I longed for her too, and got a pain with it, and felt that I loved her, and was very sorry for my wickedness.

I fell asleep unawares. When I awoke it was broad daylight. I felt very glad and relieved to see the light, even though mother had not come back. It seemed to me that some noise had awakened me. Presently there came a groan at the doorway. Kneeling down and peeping through a crevice between the planks, I saw my father lying there on the doorstep. I took down the bar and opened the door. He was lying on his stomach; his clothes were filthy and torn, and at the back of his shoulder was a small hole pushed in in the cloth. There was dark, thick blood on the withered leaves. I tried to see his face, but couldn't very well. It was all muddy, bleared and white, and he groaned and swore when I touched him. But he didn't know who I was, and some of what he said didn't seem to me to have any sense.

He asked for some water, but I could not turn him over so that he could drink it. And it was all spilt. I told him about the baby dying, but he didn't show that he could hear anything. And just as I finished I heard mother coming back from the churchyard. So I ran out and told her that it was father.

From MEMOIRS OF A MIDGET

Still the slow train bumped on, loath to drag itself away from the happy harvest fields. Darkness was near when we ourselves alighted at our destination, mounted into a four-wheeled cab, and once more were in motion in the rain-laid dust. On and on rolled Pollie and I and our luggage together, in such ease and concealment after the hard wooden seats and garish light that our journey began to seem—as indeed I wished for the moment it might prove—interminable. One after another the high street lamps approached, flung their radiance into our musty velvet cabin, and went gliding by. Ever and again the luminous square of a window beyond the outspread branches of a tree would float on. Then suddenly our narrow solitude was invaded by the bright continuous flare flung into it from a row of shops.

Never before had I been out after nightfall. I gazed enthralled at the splendours of fruit and cakes, silks and sweetmeats packed high behind the glass fronts. Wasn't I myself the heiress of £110 a year? Indeed I was drinking in Romance, and never traveller surveyed golden Moscow or the steeps of Tibet with keener relish than I the liquid amber, ruby, and emerald that summoned its customers to a wayside chemist's shop. Twenty—what a child I was! I smile now at these recollections with an indulgence not unmixed with envy. It is Moscow survives, not the artless traveller.

After climbing a long hill—the wayside houses steadily thinning out as we ascended—the cab came to a standstill. The immense shapeless old man who had so miraculously found our way for us, and who on this mild August evening was muffled up to his eyes in a thick ulster, climbed down backwards from his box and opened the door. At the same moment as if by clockwork, opened another door—that of the last house on the hill. I was peering out of the cab, then, at my home; and framed in that lighted oblong stood Mrs. Bowater. All utterly different from what I had foreseen, this much smaller house, this much taller landlady, and—dear me, how fondly I had trusted that she would not for the first time set eyes on her lodger being *carried* into her house. I had in fancy pictured myself bowing a composed and impressive greeting to her from her own hearthrug. But it was not to be.

Pollie lifted me out, settled me on her arm, and my feet did not touch *terra firma* again until she had ascended the five stone steps and we were within the passage.

'Lor, miss; then here we are,' she sighed breathlessly, then returned to the cabman to pay him his fare. Even dwarfed a little perhaps by my mourning, there I stood, breathed upon by the warm air of the house, in the midst of a prickly door-mat, on the edge of the shiny patterned oilcloth that glossed away into the obscurity from under the gaslight in front of me; and there stood my future landlady. For the first time, with head thrown back, I scanned a countenance that was soon to become so familiar and so endeared. Mrs. Bowater's was a stiff and angular figure. She, too, was in black, with a long, springside boot. The bony hands hung down in their peculiar fashion from her elbows. A large cameo brooch adorned the flat chest. A scanty velvet patch of cap failed to conceal the thin hair sleekly parted in the middle over the high narrow temples. The long dark face with its black, set eyes, was almost without expression, except that of a placid severity. She gazed down at me, as I up at her, steadily, silently.

'So this is the young lady,' she mused at last, as if addressing a hidden and distant listener. 'I hope you are not over-fatigued by your journey, miss. Please to step in.'

To my ear, Mrs. Bowater's was what I should describe as a low, roaring voice, like falling water out of a black cloven rock in a hillside; but what a balm was its sound in my ear, and how solacing this dignified address to jaded nerves still smarting a little after my victory on the London, Chatham, and Dover Railway. Making my way around a grandfather's clock that ticked hollowly beside the door, I followed her into a room on the left of the passage, from either wall of which a pair of enormous antlers threatened each other under the discoloured ceiling. For a moment the glare within and the vista of furniture legs confused my eyes. But Mrs. Bowater came to my rescue.

'Food was never mentioned,' she remarked reflectively, 'being as I see nothing to be considered except as food so-called. But you will find everything clean and comfortable; and I am sure, miss, what with your sad bereavements and all, as I have heard from Mr. Pellew, I hope it will be a home to you. There being nothing else as I suppose that we may expect.'

My mind ran about in a hasty attempt to explore these sentiments. They soothed away many misgivings, though it was clear that Mrs. Bowater's lodger was even less in dimensions than Mrs. Bowater had supposed. *Clean*: after so many months of Mrs. Sheppey's habits, it was this word that sang in my head. Wood, glass, metal flattered the light of gas and coal, and for the first time I heard my own voice float up into my new 'apartment'; 'It looks *very* comfortable, thank you, Mrs. Bowater; and I am quite sure I shall be happy in my new abode.' There was nothing intentionally affected in this formal little speech.

'Which being so,' replied Mrs. Bowater, 'there seems to be trouble with the cabman, and the day's drawing in, perhaps you will take a seat by the fire.'

A stool nicely to my height stood by the steel fender, the flames played in the chimney; and for a moment I was left alone. 'Thank God,' said I, and took off my hat, and pushed back my hair. . . . Alone. Only for a moment, though. Its mistress gone, as fine a black cat as ever I have seen appeared in the doorway and stood, green-eyed, regarding me. To judge from its countenance, this must have been a remarkable experience.

I cried seductively, 'Puss.'

But with a blink of one eye and a shake of its forepaw, as if inadvertently it had trodden in water, it turned itself about again and disappeared. In spite of all my cajoleries, Henry and I never were to be friends.

Whatever Pollie's trouble with the cabman may have been, Mrs. Bowater made short work of it. Pollie was shown to the room in which she was to sleep that night. I took off my bodice and bathed face, hands, and arms to the elbow in the shallow bowl Mrs. Bowater had provided for me. And soon, wonderfully refreshed and talkative, Pollie and I were seated over the last meal we were to share together for many a long day.

There were snippets of bread and butter for me, a little omelette, two sizes too large, a sugared cherry or two sprinkled with 'hundreds and thousands', and a gay little bumper of milk gilded with the enwreathed letters, 'A Present from Dover'. Alack-a-day for that omelette! I must have kept a whole family of bantams steadily engaged for weeks together. But I was often at my wits' end to dispose of their produce. Fortunately Mrs. Bowater kept merry fires burning in the evening—'Ladies of some sizes can't warm the air as much as most,' as she put it. So at some little risk to myself among the steel fire-irons, the boiled became the roast. At last I made a clean breast of my horror of eggs, and since by that time my landlady and I were the best of friends, no harm came of it. She merely bestowed on me a grim smile of unadulterated amusement, and the bantams patronized some less fastidious stomach.

My landlady was a heavy thinker, and not a copious— though a leisurely—talker. Minutes would pass, while with dish or duster in hand she pondered a speech; then perhaps her long thin lips would only shut a little tighter, or a slow, convulsive rub of her lean forefinger along the side of her nose would indicate the upshot. But I soon learned to interpret these mute signs. She was a woman who disapproved of most things, for excellent, if nebulous, reasons; and her silences were due not to the fact that she had nothing to say, but too much.

Pollie and I talked long and earnestly that first evening at Beechwood. She promised to write to me, to send me all the gossip of the village, and to come and see me when she could. The next morning, after a sorrowful breakfast, we parted. Standing on the table in the parlour window, with eyes a little wilder than usual, I watched her pass out of sight. A last wave of her handkerchief, and the plump-cheeked, fair-skinned face was gone. The strangeness and solitude of my situation flooded over me.

For a few days, strive as she might, Mrs. Bowater's lodger moped. It was not merely that she had become more helpless, but of far less importance. This may, in part, be accounted for by the fact that, having been accustomed at Lyndsey to live at the top of a high house and to look down on the world, when I found myself foot to foot with it, so to speak, on Beechwood Hill, it alarmingly intensified the *sense* of my small stature. Use and habit, however, and the relative merits of myself and of the passing scene gradually readjusted themselves with a proper respect for the former. Soon, too, as if from heaven, the packing-case containing my furniture arrived. Mrs. Bowater shared a whole morning over its unpacking, ever and again standing in engrossed consideration of some of my minute treasures, and, quite unaware of it, heaving a great sigh. But how to arrange them in a room already over-occupied?

A carpenter of the name of Bates was called in, so distant a relative of Mrs. Bowater's apparently that she never by nod, word, or look acknowledged the bond. Mr. Bates held my landlady in almost speechless respect. 'A woman in a thousand,' he repeatedly assured me, when we were grown a little accustomed to one another; 'a woman in *ten* thousand. And if things hadn't been what they was, you may understand, they might have turned out different. Ah, miss, there's one looking down on us could tell a tale.' I looked up past his oblong head at the ceiling, but only a few flies were angling round the chandelier.

Mrs. Bowater's compliments were less indirect. 'That *Bates*,' she would say, surveying his day's handiwork after he was gone, 'is all thumbs.'

He was certainly rather snail-like in his movements, and spent most of his time slowly rubbing his hands on the stiff apron that encased him. But I minded his thumbs far less than his glue-pot.

Many years have passed, yet at the very whisper of his name, that inexpressible odour clouds up into my nose. It now occurs to me for the first time that he never sent in his bill. Either his memory failed him, or he carpentered for love. Level with the wide table in the window recess, strewn over with my small Persian mats, whereon I sat, sewed, read, and took my meals, Mr. Bates constructed a broad shelf, curtained off on three sides from the rest of the room. On this wooden stage stood my four-poster, wardrobe, and other belongings. It was my bedchamber. From table to floor he made a staircase, so that I could easily descend and roam the room at large. The latter would have been more commodious if I could have persuaded Mrs. Bowater to empty it a little. If I had *kept on* looking at the things in it, I am sure I should have gone mad. Even tact was unavailing. If only there had been the merest tinge of a Cromwell in my character, the baubles that would have been removed!

There were two simpering plaster figures—a Shepherd and Shepherdess—nearly half my height on the chimney-piece, whom I particularly detested; also an enlarged photograph in a discoloured frame on the wall—that of a thick-necked, formidable man, with a bush of whisker on either cheek, and a high, quarrelsome stare. He made me feel intensely self-conscious. It was like a wolf looking all day into a sheep-fold. So when I had my meals, I invariably turned my back on his portrait.

I went early to bed. But now that the autumnal dusks were shortening, an hour or two of artificial light was necessary. The flare of the gas dazzled and stupefied me, and gave me a kind of hunted feeling; so Mrs. Bowater procured for me a couple of fine little glass candlesticks. In bed I sometimes burned a wax-light in a saucer, a companionable thing for night-thoughts in a strange place. Often enough I sat through the evening with no other illumination than that of the smouldering coals, so that I could see out of the window. It was an endless source of amusement to withdraw the muslin curtains, gaze out over the darkened fields beyond the roadway, and let my daydreams wander at will.

At nine o'clock Mrs. Bowater would bring me my supper —some fragments of rusk, or of bread, and milk. My food was her constant anxiety. The difficulty, as she explained, was to supply me with *little* enough to eat—at least of cooked food: 'It dries up in the winking of an eye.' So her cat, Henry, fared more sumptuously than ever, though the jealous creature continued to reject all my advances, and as far as possible ignored my existence. 'Simple victuals, by all means, miss,' Mrs. Bowater would admit. 'But if it don't enjoy, the inside languishes; and you are not yet of an age that can fall back on skin and bone.'

The question of food presently introduced that of money. She insisted on reducing her charges to twenty shillings a week. 'There's the lodging, and there's the board, the last being as you might say all but unmentionable; and honesty the best policy though I have never tried the reverse.' So, in spite of all my protestations, it was agreed. And thus I found myself mistress of a round fifty-eight pounds a year over and above what I paid to Mrs. Bowater. Messrs. Harris, Harris and Harris were punctual as quarter-day: and so was I. I 'at once' paid over to my landlady £13 and whatever other sum was needful. The 'charity' my godmother had recommended began, and, alas, remained at home. I stowed the rest under lock and key in one of my grandfather's boxes which I kept under my bed. This was an imprudent habit, perhaps. Mrs. Bowater advocated the Penny Bank. But the thought of my money being so handy and *palpable* reassured me. I would count it over in my mind, as if it were a means to salvation; and became, in consequence, near and parsimonious.

Occasionally when she had 'business' to transact, Mrs. Bowater would be off to London. There she would purchase for me any little trifle required for the replenishment of my wardrobe. Needing so little, I could afford the finest materials; my sovereign was worth at least sixty shillings. Rather than 'fine', Mrs. Bowater preferred things 'good'; and for this 'goodness', I must confess, she sometimes made rather alarming sacrifices of appearance. Still, I was already possessed of a serviceable stock of clothes, and by aid of one of my dear mother's last presents to me, a shiny Swiss miniature workbox with an inlaid picture of the Lake of Geneva on the lid, I soon became a passable needlewoman.

I love bright, pure colours, and, my sweeping and dusting and bedmaking over, and my external mourning for my father at an end, a remarkable festive figure would confront me in my cheval glass of an afternoon. The hours I spent in dressing my hair and matching this bit of colour with that! I would talk to myself in the glass, too, for company's sake, and make believe I was a dozen different characters. I was young. I pined for life and companionship, and having only my own —for Mrs. Bowater was rather a faithful feature of the landscape than a fellow being—I made as much, and as many, of myself as possible.

Another question that deeply engaged my landlady was my health. She mistrusted open windows, but strongly recommended 'air'. What insidious maladies she spied around me! Indeed that September was unusually hot. I sat on my table in the window like a cricket in an oven, sorely missing my high open balcony, the garden, and the stream. Once and again Mrs. Bowater would take me for a little walk after sunset. Discretion to her was much the better part of valour; nor had I quite recovered from my experiences in the train. But such walks—though solitary enough at that hour of the day—were straggly and irksome. Pollie's arm had been a kind of second nature to me; but Mrs. Bowater, I think, had almost as fastidious a disinclination to carrying me as I have to being carried. I languished for liberty. Being a light sleeper, I would often awake at daybreak and the first call of the birds. Then the hill—which led to Tyddlesdon End and Love (or Loose) Lane—was deserted. Thought of the beyond haunted me like a passion. At a convenient moment I intimated to Mrs. Bowater how secure was the street at this early hour, how fresh the meadows, and how thirsty for independent outings her lodger. 'Besides, Mrs. Bowater, I am not a child, and who could see me?'

After anxious and arduous discussion, Mr. Bates was once more consulted. He wrapped himself in a veritable blanket of reflection and all but became unconscious before he proposed a most ingenious device. With Mrs. Bowater's consent, she being her own landlady and amused at the idea, he cut out of one of the lower panels of her parlour door a round-headed opening just of an easy size to suit me. In this aperture he hung a delicious little door that precisely fitted it. So also with the door into the street—to which he added a Bramah lock. By cementing a small square stone into the corner of each of the steps down from the porch, he eased *that* little difficulty. May Heaven bless Mr. Bates! With his key round my neck, stoop once, stoop twice, a scamper down his steps, and I was free— as completely mistress of my goings-out and of my comings-in as every self-respecting person should be.

'That's what my father would have called a good job, Mr. Bates,' said I cordially.

He looked yearningly at me, as if about to impart a profound secret; but thought better of it. 'Well, miss, what I say is, a job's a *job*; and if it *is* a job, it's a job that should be made a job *of.*'

As I dot the i's and cross the t's of this manuscript, I often think—a little ruefully—of Mr. Bates.

As soon as daybreak was piercing into my region of the sky, and before Mrs. Bowater or the rest of the world was stirring, I would rise, make my candlelit toilet, and hasten out into the forsaken sweet of the morning. If it broke wet or windy, I could turn over and go to sleep again. A few hundred yards up the hill, the road turned off, as I have said, towards Tyddlesdon End and Loose Lane—very stony and steep. On the left, and before the fork, a wicket gate led into the woods and the park of empty 'Wanderslore'. To the verge of these deserted woods made a comfortable walk for me.

If, as might happen, any other wayfarer was early abroad, I could conceal myself in the tussocks of grass and bushes that bordered the path. In my thick veil, with my stout green parasol and inconspicuous shawl, I made a queer and surprising figure no doubt. Indeed, from what I have heard, the ill fame of Wanderslore acquired a still more piquant flavour in the town by reports that elf-folk had been descried on its outskirts. But if I sometimes skipped and capered in these early outings, it was for exercise as well as suppressed high spirits. To be prepared, too, for the want of such facilities in the future, I had the foresight to accustom myself to Mrs. Bowater's steep steps as well as to my cemented-in 'Bateses', as I called them. My only difficulty was to decide whether to practise on them when I was fresh at the outset of my walk, or fatigued at the end of it. Naturally people grow 'peculiar' when much alone: self pity plays with self, and the mimicry fades.

These little expeditions, of course, had their spice of danger, and it made them the more agreeable. A strange dog might give me a fright. There was an old vixen which once or twice exchanged glances with me at a distance. But with my parasol I was a match for most of the creatures which humanity has left unslaughtered. My sudden appearance might startle and perplex them. But if few were curious, fewer far were unfriendly. Boys I feared most. A hulking booby once stoned me through the grass, but fortunately he was both a coward and a poor marksman. Until winter came, I doubt if a single sunshine morning was wasted. Many a rainy one, too, found me splashing along, though then I must be a careful walker to avoid a sousing.

The birds renewed their autumn song, the last flowers were blossoming. Concealed by scattered tufts of bracken where an enormous beech forked its roots and cast a golden light from its withering leaves, I would spend many a solitary hour. Above the eastern tree-tops my Kent stretched into the distance beneath the early skies. Far to my left and a little behind me rose the chimneys of gloomy Wanderslore. Breathing in the gentle air, the dreamer within would stray at will. There I kept the anniversary of my mother's birthday; twined a wreath for her of ivy-flowers and winter green; and hid it secretly in a forsaken blackbird's nest in the woods.

Still I longed for my old home again. Mrs. Bowater's was a stuffy and meagre little house, and when meals were in preparation, none too sweet to the nose. Especially low I felt, when a scrawling letter was now and then delivered by the postman from Pollie. Her spelling and grammar intensified my homesickness. Miss Fenne, too, had not forgotten me. I pored over her spidery epistles till my head ached. Why, if I had been so rash and undutiful, was she so uneasy? Even the texts she chose had a parched look. The thought of her spectacling my minute handwriting and examining the proof that I was still a child of wrath, gave my pride a silly qualm. So Mrs. Bowater came to my rescue, and between us we concocted replies to her which, I am afraid, were not more intelligible for a tendency on my landlady's part to express my sentiments in the third person.

This little service set her thinking of Sunday and church. She was not, she told me, 'what you might call a religious woman', having been compelled 'to keep her head up in the world, and all not being gold that glitters'. She was none the less a regular attendant at St. Peter's—a church a mile or so away in the valley, whose five bells of a Sabbath evening never failed to recall my thoughts to Lyndsey and to dip me into the waters of melancholy. I loved their mellow clanging in the lap of the wind, yet it was rather doleful to be left alone with my candles, and only Henry sullenly squatting in the passage awaiting his mistress's return.

'Not that you need making any *better*, miss,' Mrs. Bowater assured me. 'Even a buttercup—or a retriever dog, for that matter—being no fuller than it can hold of what it is, in a manner of speaking. But there's the next world to be accounted for, and hopes of reunion on another shore, where, so I understand, mere size, body or station, will not be noticeable in the sight of the Lamb. *Not* that I hold with the notion that only the good so-called will be there.'

This speech, I must confess, made me exceedingly uncomfortable.

'Wherever I go, Mrs. Bowater,' I replied hastily, 'I shall not be happy unless you are there.'

'D.V.,' said Mrs. Bowater grimly, 'I will.'

Still, I remained unconverted to St. Peter's. Why, I hardly know: perhaps it was her reference to its pew rents, or her description of the vicar's daughters (who were now nursing their father at Tunbridge Wells), or maybe even it was a stare from her husband which I happened at that precise moment to intercept from the wall. Possibly if I myself had taken a 'sitting', this aura of formality would have faded away. Mrs. Bowater was a little reassured, however, to hear that my father and mother, in spite of Miss Fenne, had seldom taken me to church. They had concluded that my absence was best for both me and the congregation. And I told her of our little evening services in the drawing-room, with Mrs. Ballard, the parlourmaid, Pollie, and the Boy on the sofa, just as it happened to be their respective 'Sundays in'.

This set her mind at rest. Turn and turn about, on one Sunday evening she went to St. Peter's and brought back with her the text and crucial fragments of Mr. Crimble's sermon, and on the next we read the lessons together, and sang a hymn. Once, indeed, I embarked upon a solo, 'As pants the hart', one of my mother's favourite airs. But I got a little shaky at 'O for the wings', and there was no rambling, rumbling chorus from my father. But Sunday was not my favourite day on Beechwood Hill. Mrs. Bowater looked a little formal with stiff white 'frilling' round her neck. She reminded me of a leg of mutton. To judge from the gloom and absentmindedness into which they sometimes plunged her, quotations from Mr. Crimble could be double-edged. My real joy was to hear her views on the fashions and manners of her fellow-worshippers.

Well, so the months went by. Winter came with its mists and rains and frosts, and a fire in the polished grate was no longer an evening luxury but a daily need. As often as possible I went out walking. When the weather was too inclement, I danced for an hour or so, for joy and exercise, and went swimming on a chair. I would entertain myself also in watching through the muslin curtains the few passers-by; sorting out their gaits, and noses, and clothes, and acquaintances, and guessing their characters, occupations, and circumstances. Certain little looks and movements led me to suppose that, even though I was perfectly concealed, the more sensitive among them were vaguely uneasy under this secret scrutiny. In such cases (though very reluctantly) I always drew my eyes away: first because I did not like the thought of encroaching on their privacy, and next, because I was afraid their uneasiness might prevent them coming again. But this microscopic examination of mankind must cease with dusk, and the candle-hours passed rather heavily at times. The few books I had brought away from Lyndsey were mine now nearly by heart. So my eye would often wander up to a small bookcase that hung out of reach on the other side of the chimney-piece.

One supper-time I ventured to ask Mrs. Bowater if she would hand me down a tall, thin, dark-green volume, whose appearance had particularly taken my fancy. A simple enough request, but surprisingly received. She stiffened all over and eyed the bookcase with a singular intensity. 'The books there', she said, 'are what they call the dead past burying its dead.'

Spoon in hand, I paused, looking now at Mrs. Bowater and now at the coveted book. '*Mr.* Bowater', she added from deep down in herself, 'followed the sea.' This was, in fact, Mr. Bowater's début in our conversation, and her remark, uttered in so hollow yet poignant a tone, produced a romantic expectancy in my mind.

'Is——' I managed to whisper at last: 'I hope Mr. Bowater isn't *dead*?'

Mrs. Bowater's eyes were like lead in her long, dark-skinned face. She opened her mouth, her gaze travelled slowly until, as I realized, it had fixed itself on the large yellowing, photograph behind my back.

'Dead, no'; she echoed sepulchrally. 'Worse than.'

By which I understood that, far from being dead, Mr. Bowater was still actively alive. And yet, apparently, not much the happier for that. Instantaneously I caught sight of a rocky, storm-strewn shore, such as I had seen in my *Robinson Crusoe*, and *there* Mr. Bowater, still 'following the sea'.

'Never, never,' continued Mrs. Bowater in her Bible voice, 'never to darken these doors again!' I stole an anxious glance over my shoulder. There was such a brassy boldness in the responsive stare that I was compelled to shut my eyes.

But Mrs. Bowater had caught my expression. 'He was, as some would say,' she explained with gloomy pride, 'a handsome man. *Do* handsome he did never. But there, miss, things being as they must be, and you in the green of your youth— though hearing the worst may be a wholesome physic if taken

with care, as I have told Fanny many a time. . . .' She paused to
breathe. 'What I was saying is, there can be no harm in your
looking at the book if that's all there's to it.' With that she
withdrew the dry-looking volume from the shelf and laid it
on the table beside my chair.

I got it down, opened it in the middle (as my father had
taught me, in order to spare the binding), opened it on a page
inkly black as night all over, but starred with a design as
familar to me as the lines of the palm on my hand.

'But, oh! Mrs. Bowater!' I cried, all in a breath, running
across, dragging back the curtain and pointing into the night;
'look, look, it's there! It's Orion!'

There, indeed, in the heavens beyond my window, straddling the dark, star for star the same as those in the book,
stood the Giant, shaking his wondrous fires upon the air.
Even Mrs. Bowater was moved by my enthusiasm. She came
to the table, compared at my direction chart with sky, and
was compelled rather grudgingly to admit that her husband's
book was at least true to the facts. Stooping low, I read out a
brief passage. She listened. And it seemed a look of girlhood
came into the shadowy face uplifted towards the window. So
the stars came into my life, and faithful friends they have remained to this day.

Mrs. Bowater's little house being towards the crest of the
hill, with sunrise a little to the left across the meadows, my
window commanded about three-fifths of the southern and
eastern skies. By day I would kneel down and study for hours
the charts, and thus be prepared for the dark. Night after
night, when the weather was fair, or the windy clouds made
mock of man's celestial patternings, I would sit in the glow of
the firelight and summon these magic shiners by name—
Bellatrix, huge Betelgeuse, Aldebaran, and the rest. I would
look at one, and, while doing so, watch another. This not
only isolated the smaller stars, but gradually I became aware
that they were one and all furtively signalling to *me*! About
a fortnight later my old Lyndsey friend, the Dogstar, topped

the horizon fringe of woodland. I heard myself shout at him across the world. His sudden molten bursts of crimson betwixt his emeralds and sapphires filled me with an almost ridiculous delight.

By the middle of December I had mastered all the greater stars in my region, and with my spyglass a few even of the Gammas and Deltas. But much of the zenith and all the north was closed to me, and—such is human greed—I began to pine beyond measure for a sight of Deneb, Vega, and the Chair. This desire grew unendurable, and led me into a piece of genuine foolhardiness. I determined to await the first clear still night and then to sally out and make my way, by hook or crook, up to my beech-roots, from which I should be able to command a fair stretch of the northern heavens. A quiet spell favoured me.

I waited until Mrs. Bowater had gone to her bedroom, then muffled myself up in my thickest clothes and stole out into the porch. At my first attempt, one glance into the stooping dark was enough. At the second, a furtive sighing breath of wind, as I breasted the hill, suddenly flapped my mantle and called in my ear. I turned tail and fled. But never faint heart won fair constellation. At the third I pressed on.

The road was deserted. No earthly light showed anywhere except from a lamp-post this side of the curve of the hill. I frisked along, listening and peering, and brimming over with painful delight. The dark waned; and my eyes grew accustomed to the thin starlight. I gained the woods unharmed. Rich was my reward. There and then I begged the glimmering Polestar to be true to Mr. Bowater. Fear, indeed, if in a friendly humour, is enlivening company. Instead of my parasol I had brought out a carved foreign knife (in a sheath at least five inches long) which I had discovered on my parlour what-not.

The whisperings of space, the calls of indetectable birds in the wastes of the sky, the sudden appearance of menacing or sinister shapes which vanished or melted themselves into mere stocks or stones as I drew near—my heart gave many an anguished jump. But quiet, and the magnificence of night, vanquished all folly at last. It seemed to me that a Being whom one may call Silence was brooding in solitude where living and human visitants are rare, and that in his company a harmless spirit may be at peace. Oblivious of my ungainly knife, yet keeping a firm arm on it, self seemed to be the whole scene there, and my body being so small I was perhaps less a disturber than were most intruders of that solemn repose.

Why I kept these night-walks secret, I cannot say. It was not apprehension of Mrs. Bowater. She would have questioned my discretion, but would not, I think, have attempted to dissuade me from them against my will. No. It may be that every true astronomer is a miser at heart, and keeps some Lambda or Mu or lost nebula his eternal friend, named with his name, but unrecorded on any chart. For my part I hoarded the complete north for a while.

A fright I got one night, however, kept me indoors for the better part of a week. In my going out the little house door had been carelessly left unlatched. Algol and the red planet Mars had been my quarry among the floating woolpack clouds. The wind was lightly blowing from the north-west after the calm. I drew down my veil and set off briskly and light-heartedly for home.

The sight of the dark-looking hole in the door quickly sobered me down. All was quiet, however, but on entering my room, there was a strangeness in the air, and that not due to my landlady's forlorn trumpetings from above. Through the floating vaporous light I trod across to my staircase and was soon in bed. Hardly had my eyes closed when there broke out of the gloom around me a dismal, appalling cry. I soon realized that the creeping horror this caused in me was as nothing compared with that of the poor beast, lured, no doubt, into the house by Henry, at finding itself beneath a strange roof.

'Puss, puss,' I pleaded shakenly; and again broke out that heartsick cry.

Knife in hand, I descended my staircase and edging as far as possible from the baleful globes greenly burning beneath a mahogany chair, I threw open both doors and besought my unwelcome visitor to take his departure. The night wind came fluttering; there was the blur of a scuttering, shapeless form, and in the flash of an eye I was sprawling on the floor. A good deal shaken, with a nasty scratch on my thigh, but otherwise unharmed, I waved my hand after the fugitive and returned to bed.

The blood soon ceased to flow. Not daring to send my bloodstained nightgown to the wash, I concealed it behind my dresses in the wardrobe, and the next fine morning carried it off with me and buried it as deeply as I could in a deserted rabbit-burrow in the woods. Such is an evil conscience that, first, I had the fancy that during my digging a twig had inexplicably snapped in the undergrowth; and next, for 'burnt offering', I made Mrs. Bowater the present of an oval hand-glass set in garnets (one of my grandfather's gifts). This she took down to a local jeweller's to be mounted with a pin, and wore it on Sundays in place of her usual cameo depicting the Three Graces disporting themselves under a Palm-tree beside a Fountain.

Meanwhile I had heard a little more about the 'Fanny' whom Mrs. Bowater had mentioned. My landlady was indeed a slow confider. Fanny, I gathered, had a post as mistress at a school some forty miles away. She taught the little boys 'English'. The fleeting Miss Perry returned to mind, and with a faint dismay I heard that Fanny would soon be returning home for the Christmas holidays. Mrs. Bowater's allusions to her were the more formidable for being veiled. I dreaded the invasion. Would she not come 'between us'?

Then by chance I found hidden in my star-book the photograph of an infant in arms and of a pensive, ringleted woman, who, in spite of this morsel in her lap, seemed in her gaze out of nowhere to be vaguely afraid. On the back was scrawled in pencil: 'F.: six weeks'—and an extremely cross six weeks

'F.' looked. For some inexplicable reason I pushed back this lady's photograph into the book, and said nothing about it. The suspicion had entered my mind that Fanny was only a daughter by marriage. I sank into a kind of twilight reflection at this. It seemed, in an odd fashion, to make Mrs. Bowater more admirable, her husband more formidable, and the unknown Fanny more mysterious and enigmatical. At the first opportunity I crept my way to the subject and asked my landlady if she could show me a portrait of her daughter.

The photograph she produced from upstairs had in fading almost become a caricature. It had both blackened and greyed. It depicted herself many years younger but hardly less grim in appearance in full flounced skirts, Fanny as a child of about five or six standing at her knee, and Mr. Bowater leaning with singular amenity behind her richly-carved chair, the fingers of his left hand resting disposedly on her right shoulder. I looked anxiously at the child. It was certainly crosspatch 'F.', and a far from prepossessing little creature with that fixed, level gaze. Mr. Bowater, on the other hand, had not yet adopted the wild and rigid stare which dominated the small parlour.

Mrs. Bowater surveyed the group with a lackadaisical detachment. 'Fractious!—you can see the tears on her cheeks for all what the young man could do with his woolly lamb and grimaces. It was the heyday.'

What was the heyday, I wondered. 'Was Mr. Bowater—attached to her?' seemed a less intrusive question.

'Doted,' she replied, polishing the glass with her apron. 'But not to much purpose—with an eye for every petticoat.'

This seemed a difficult conversation to maintain. 'Don't you think, Mrs. Bowater,' I returned zealously, 'there is just the faintest tinge of *Mr*. Bowater in the *chin*? I don't', I added candidly, 'see the faintest glimpse of *you*.'

Mrs. Bowater merely tightened her lips.

'And is she like that now?' I asked presently.

Mrs. Bowater re-wrapped frame and photograph in their

piece of newspaper. 'It's *looks*, miss, that are my constant anxiety: and you may be thankful for being as you might say preserved from the world. What's more, the father will out, I suppose, from now till Day of Judgment.'

How strangely her sentiments at times resembled my godmother's, and yet how different they were in effect. My thoughts after this often drifted to Mrs. Bowater's early married life. And so peculiar are the workings of the mind that her husband's star-chart, his sleek appearance as a young father, the mysterious reference to the petticoats, awoke in me an almost romantic interest in him. To such a degree that it gradually became my custom to cast his portrait a satirical bow of greeting when I emerged from my bedroom in the morning, and even to kiss my hand to his invisible stare when I retired for the night. To all of which advances he made no reply.

TENNYSON

'The good die first,' says Wordsworth in *The Excursion*,

> '*And they whose hearts are dry as summer dust*
> *Burn to the socket.*'

> '*Whom the gods love die young was said of yore,*'

sings Byron in *Don Juan*; and he himself breathed his last at
Missolonghi in his heroic thirty-sixth year. It was said of yore,
not perhaps for the first time, by Menander, who was drowned
while swimming in the harbour of Piraeus when he was fifty-
two; and it was rationalized about a century afterwards by
Plautus, who lived to be seventy: *Adolescens moritur, dum valet,
sentit, sapit*. However it may be with the generality of man, the
inference is that it is not poets in particular who are thus set
apart by the favour of the gods. Chatterton, Keats, Marlowe,
Shelley, Emily Brontë, Rupert Brooke, Wilfred Owen were
exceptional. But although sound health seldom blesses an old
body, perception, surely, need not be dulled by age, and time
may establish, ripen and enrich a natural judgment. Rogers,
Waller, Tennyson, Landor and Hardy are among the Elders
of the English poets; their average age, when they left this
world, was eighty-seven; and neither *On the Last Verses in this
Book*, nor *Crossing the Bar*, nor *The Darkling Thrush* suggests a
dusty heart, or any lack of perception and of a natural judgment. All three poems appear almost as regularly in every
new anthology of English verse as comes the cuckoo to our
English spring in the third week of April.

Tennyson (then the only outstanding Alfred among the
poets apart from the theatrical manager who was affection-
ately known to his intimates as Poet Bunn) died in 1892. The
moon that night was at the full, the Plays, open at *The Temp-*

est, lay beside him on his bed. It was an aptly romantic close to an unrivalled career. He had made poetry not merely an English but a British institution. The name of Charles Dickens became a household word; Tennyson's a drawing-room shibboleth. Gilt-edged albums by the thousand enshrined the effusions of his devotees. No other poet and artist so fastidious can have both merited and won a more abounding popularity. When, however, the drums and tramplings in Poets' Corner were stilled and the Phoenix was at rest amid her ashes, there followed a prolonged pause. Death lays an icy finger on poets as well as kings. The work of a long life was now complete; the passage of time put it in a new perspective; enthusiasm gave way to a considered judgment and a more exacting criticism.

This is the destiny of most poets of unusual repute in their own day; and on many of them oblivion by no means blindly scattereth her poppy. The records of the Public Libraries none the less suggest that the pundits are less faithful and more capricious in their affections than the common reader; and the fact that a writer is no longer written about—a heedlessness that has certainly not yet overtaken Tennyson—is not necessarily a proof that he is no longer read. Well before the close of the last century, however, his direct influence had begun to wane. A wildly bright, but in certain respects a not too particular star, Rudyard Kipling, had risen above the eastern horizon; there came the Naughty Nineties; the Yellow Book and Aubrey Beardsley broke into exotic bloom. Their activities more closely resembled a local mutiny than a lasting revolt. But 'lousy' is the last word that Victoria's poet laureate would have applied even to the most disreputable of 'ulsters', and yellow and naughty are epithets entirely alien to the author of *The Princess* and *The Idylls of the King*.

A change of far greater moment and magnitude was soon to follow. *The Dawn in Britain, The Dynasts, The Rout of the Amazons, The Sale of St. Thomas, The Everlasting Mercy*—such works as these, two at least of them of a supreme originality, were in marked contrast to a poetry typically Victorian, if, that is, we forget for the moment that Beddoes shared Tennyson's birth-year, that Emily Brontë was born when he was nine, and that Robert Browning, Swinburne and Meredith were his contemporaries. To the Georgians in general, who have little more than this convenient tag in common, he might have consented to be kind and yet reluctant to agree that he was akin. His estimate of the 'moderns', on the other hand, who reveal strikingly little kindness or kinship in respect to himself, can only be surmised. As a poet he had already declared that 'the deep moans round with many voices'; as an artist, 'some one has blundered' might have been his private summary. It is curious indeed that, while poetry itself is catholic, most poets of much account 'commence' nonconformist.

Tennysonian to the last degree Tennyson's verse certainly is. But his Juvenilia once left behind him, he seldom found himself among the rebels, and it is he himself who still remains in some degree enticingly obscure, rather than his poems. There can be few lines among his many thousands which it is a sort of exciting and perilous Blind Man's Buff to attempt to understand. There are poets who more or less resemble the recluse of Juan Fernandez; access to their inmost recesses may not be attainable. Tennyson belonged to the mainland. It is perfectly clear that he hoped and intended to communicate his thoughts and feelings, his interest and delight—to share them, that is, with every susceptible reader. At how much sacrifice of what was so individual and involved in his own mind and spirit as to be incommunicable in human language one cannot tell. Complete apprehension of the *poetry* in his poems is of course another matter.

Like most poets he had to await full recognition; but his genius was instantly detected. He was the literary Dalai Lama of his age. Third in age of three poets, born between 1807 and 1819, in a fraternity of seven sons, he embarked on an epic in his childhood. And epics (which entail even greater pains and patience to write than to read) seem to be the outcome of sheer instinct in nursery poets. In his earlier 'teens Tennyson also wrote a play which he aptly entitled *The Devil and the Lady*, since the lady is put into the care of the Devil when old Mundus, her husband, departs on his travels. This 'might easily have been the work of some young intimate of Marlowe's and Jonson's' come into the world 'two centuries late'. It may be compared with *The Bride's Tragedy*, which was published by Beddoes when he was sixteen. In certain respects it promises what was never actually fulfilled. Even more remarkable, Alfred was acclaimed by his own father. 'If that boy dies, one of our greatest poets will have gone.' When he was twenty, that 'extraordinary young man', Arthur Hallam, who, we are told, seemed to tread the earth as a spirit from some better world, described him as 'promising fair to be the greatest poet . . . perhaps of our century'. At thirty-six, he was in Wordsworth's estimation 'decidedly the first of our living poets', and a few years afterwards he was accorded the laureateship.

Poets in the past have survived the garret, neglect and semi-starvation; others must have succumbed to these incentives to live laborious days.

On the other hand, to be born in the purple may also prove to be a difficult destiny. It may encourage caution and the conventional, tend to keep the square peg in the round hole, and hinder initiative. The heart too can be ill at ease and unhappy whatever the colour of the sleeve; and Tennyson frequently told us so. He moved, even in young manhood, like a queen bee dispensing her priceless benefactions on a charmed circle of diligent and scrupulous attendants. His son's biography, the testimony of innumerable friends, so many of whom succeeded in making their mark on his generation, present the various, many-sided and yet consistent image of a closely and lovingly observed personality, although, of course, one must accept with caution tributes which are invited and intended to be more appreciative than critical. The sincere regret—'I wish I had been A.T.'s Boswell'—is almost comment enough, coming as it does from so intent a critic of humanity and literature as Edward FitzGerald, who 'saw life lazily but saw it plain'. 'He uttered by far the finest prose sayings of any man I have ever met' is a telling corroboration.

Even Thomas Carlyle, that self-indulgent expert in the acid summary, apart from a caustic jeer at the poetical dung-heap of his day, talked of Tennyson good-naturedly as 'the spoiled Lifeguardsman'. Impressive, rough-hewn, downright manliness was the outstanding feature of this humorous 'grumpy' poet, who left his hair to the chance barbering of his candle; who answered a flattering and formidable invitation to breakfast with contemporary demigods with a brusque, 'I should hate it, Duchess'; who, eager to shine his brightest, could think of nothing but beer to talk about to Robertson of Brighton; and who chanted or intoned his 'hollow oes and aes' with a 'voice like the sound of a far sea or of a pinewood' out of a cloud of tobacco smoke to any old crony that would listen to the poems scribbled down in his historical butcher's book.

There is abundant testimony to that 'magnificent voice'—like the wind in a pine forest—to those gusty bursts of Cyclopean laghter, to the simplicity and unaffectedness of this never-failing fountain of wisdom, learning, stories and chaff. No less humanizing is the information that he found it 'the height of luxury to sit in a bath and read about little birds', and soaked his straight Dublin clays in coffee, that he was pleased to be hailed by Whitman as 'the Boss', that he discovered 'a sort of tenuity' in Shelley's poetry, that he regretted he could not pass on to 'old Fritz' Jem Stephen's commentary on Wordsworth's *Heaven lies about us in our infancy*—'That is no reason why we should lie about Heaven in our old age', that he flatly refused to say 'padjent', and vowed that in all his life's wonderful work he had done nothing 'most perfect', 'only fragments of things that he could think at all so'; 'Come down, O Maid', for example, and 'Tears, idle tears'. If only that supreme delineator of humanity, John Aubrey, could have returned for but one evening from the Shades to spend a few quiet hours with so rich a quarry!

Trivial much of this may be, but it helps Tennyson to escape from the mawkish legends so helpful in making poets acceptable to those who are not in the habit of wasting time on their works. He lived in the sunshine of the world's curiosity and esteem. Devotees far and near sent him gifts of flowers, and tobacco. They begged their 'dear angel' for autographs, even for scraps of a cast-off necktie. One little Yankee boy pleaded for a cheese wherewith to tempt his mother's appetite, and an adventurous artist with a taste for the rural, begged to be endowed, at the poets' expense, with a live cow for a permanent model.

Edmund Gosse—then one of these youthful fanatics—relates how in 1871 (the poet's fifty-second year), having been hastily summoned from a 'horrible underground cage', known as the Den, in which he worked in the British Museum, he first encountered in the flesh this august and idolized frequenter of his dreams.

'Proud young spirits of the present day, for whom life opens in adulation, will find it scarcely possible to realize what such a summons meant to me. . . . The feeling of excitement was almost overwhelming: . . . Tennyson was scarcely a human being to us, he was the God of the Golden Bow. . . .

'It must, I suppose, have been one of those days on which the public was then excluded, since we found Tennyson with a single companion, alone in what was then the long First Sculpture Gallery. . . . At that time he was still one of the darkest of men, as he is familiarly seen in all his earlier portraits. But those portraits do not give . . . the singular majesty of his figure . . . in repose. . . . Bareheaded among the Roman Emperors, every inch as imperial looking as the best of them, he stood there as we approached him, very still, with slightly drooping eyelids, and made no movement, no gesture of approach. When I had been presented, and had shaken his hand, he continued to consider me in a silence which would have been deeply disconcerting if it had not, somehow, seemed kindly, and even, absurd as it sounds, rather shy. . .

'Then somebody suggested that we should examine the works of art, which, in that solitude, we could delightfully do. Tennyson led us, and we stopped at any sculpture which attracted his notice. But the only remark which my memory has retained was made before the famous black bust of Antinous. Tennyson bent forward a little, and said, in his deep, slow voice, "Ah! this is the inscrutable Bithynian!" There was a pause, and then he added, gazing into the eyes of the bust: "If we knew what he knew, we should understand the ancient world." If I live to be a hundred years old, I shall still hear his rich tones as he said this, without emphasis, without affectation, as though he were speaking to himself. And soon after, the gates of heaven were closed, and I went down three flights of stairs to my hell of rotten morocco'.

Those halcyon days are over—for the time being at least. Hero-worship is almost confined to the tabernacles of Hollywood; Apollo is now in mufti. The 'great' Victorian poets, having warmed their hands before the fire of life—excellent Wallsend, flaming and sparkling beneath the marble chimney-pieces in the very best parlour—have departed; their very role in the cast of human affairs is now obsolete. Tennyson (whatever little private reservations may have been his) not only filled that role for many years with conscious and ceremonious amplitude, he also triumphantly looked the part, and not merely dressed to it. Andrew Marvell, the young Milton and the never-elderly Byron are among his few English rivals in this respect; but he had one trifling advantage over them. He never shaved. Does this fact and the change in this particular fashion among his Georgian successors and their detractors suggest that a Delilah has insinuated herself into the company of these Muses? *Can* Jacques, when discoursing on the world that is no more than a transitory stage, have by but one consonant been misreported by the printers of the first Folio?—his soldier 'bearded like the pard'. Like him of Avon

himself, many of the famous Victorians, Browning, Longfellow, Ruskin, Carlyle, Rossetti, Morris, Swinburne as well
as Tennyson (who, it is said—'lifeguardsman' apart—was no
stranger to 'strange oaths') at least suggest that the poet in this
respect should resemble the seer. What art owes to the hair-
dresser is not indeed a purely frivolous speculation, since
Love owes even more; and no idolizer of any particular
writer, painter or musician, is unlikely to welcome beauty in
his countenance, grace in his every motion, and grandeur in
his gaze. There is only one little pitfall and danger that we
need have here in mind. No poet, not even a great poet, is
necessarily at his sweetest and his best merely because he has
donned his singing robes. It was not his mantle that conferred
the gift of prophecy upon Elisha. Springs may befall when
even 'an old man with a beard' may fail to attract so much as
the monotonous *chink-chink* of a chaffinch to its hospitality.

In direct contrast to many of the traits and oddities characteristic of Tennyson which have been referred to, are others
no less salient and more significant; his extreme sensitiveness,
for example. 'I *am* thin-skinned', he once owned frankly,
drawing up his sleeve to exhibit the two-inch ravages of a
flea-bite, as proof that it was more than a merely metaphorical
confession. His intense hunger, again, for that solitude within
solitude, introspective, brooding reverie—the temporary
Nirvana induced by sighing over and over his own name,
'Alfred, Alfred, Alfred' (and any other would have served the
same purpose); his chafing against the least show of hostility,
including even the 'pen-punctures of those parasitic animal-
cules of the Press', the reviewers, from which, none the less,
and unlike his rough-hewn rival, Robert Browning, he
deigned to accept counsel; his 'moods of misery unutterable'.
Some of the less valuable elements in such a temperament are
observable in the poems. The foursquare but highly tempera-
mental sage Samuel Johnson—another English character!—as
he is depicted by Boswell is only partially concealed in *The
Rambler*, in *Rasselas* and the *Dictionary*. He is in full eruption

in *The Lives of the Poets*. Is the Tennyson whom Edward Fitz-Gerald would have portrayed, as detectable in anything like the same degree in *his* life-work?

But poetry is the outcome and flower of circumstance and surroundings as well as of a human being. In his early days, and when under the malign influence of the 'indolent reviewer', Tennyson longed, we know, for the quiet and workaday life of a Lincolnshire yeoman, passing rich with £400 a year—just as Edward Grey pined to flee away from politics and public affairs and be at rest with William Wordsworth.

> *Be mine a philosopher's life in the quiet woodland ways,*
> *Where if I cannot be gay let a passionate peace be my lot,*
> *Far-off from the clamour of liars belied in the hubbub of lies;*
> *From the long-neck'd geese of the world that are ever hissing*
>   *dispraise. . . .*

A light fierce indeed, however flattering, came at length to beat on Farringford. Tennyson detested what must yet at last have become as natural and looked-for a diet as his daily bread—the honeyed adulation which his renown and popularity entailed. Whether an enforced obscurity, narrow means, few and humble friends, freedom from the artificial cares of the too much and the too many, and from the vexations incident to becoming a piece of public property—what effect any such seclusion would have had on his poetry, who can say? The mere profession of poet need, alas, be no irresistible invitation to the Muses. Tennyson, none the less, deliberately destined himself to become a national bard, to write for that rather nebulous norm the general reader and his appreciation. Whatever his success in this ambition may have been, and he had his ups and downs in public esteem, it is difficult to say what and how much he sacrificed in the process. What fraction of his work will eventually survive the perils and privileges of such a career and will continue to be read for its own sake only, what part of it carries the mysterious, inextinguishable lamp of genius beneath the mantle of a classic yet romantic art are questions the critics of a hundred years hence will doubtless answer without presumption, unanimously and with ease. And the critics of the following century may be of quite another mind! Our peculiar respect for posterity, indeed, may suffer a slight eclipse if we remind ourselves that *we* are Tennyson's.

If we turn, however, to the earlier and what in its kind may at last prove to be the most enduring fraction of his work—to the volumes, let us say, whose dates, 1832 and 1842, come as patly to the tongue as that which brought the Conqueror sweeping across the Channel—it is at least possible to distinguish the qualities that will probably tend to endanger and those which may at last ensure Tennyson's assured place among the English poets. Through its whole range, and in all its diversity, his poetry was singularly of a piece. The seal of his intent and individual craftsmanship (which fails of course when the imaginative material is poor or flaccid) is on all his work— from his prize poem on *The Battle of Armageddon*, immortalized as 'Timbuctoo', to that stanza written within a few years of his death, which is not only signally his own but is also one of the most gravely beautiful in English poetry:

> *But such a tide as moving seems asleep,*
> *Too full for sound and foam,*
> *When that which drew from out the boundless deep*
> *Turns again home.*

The same attachment to a definite kind of experience, the same precision of presentation, repeatedly show themselves. Every facet of the poetic art shines out in these earlier volumes and particularly in the briefer poems that unite the lyrical, the narrative and the dramatic. It was then one of his favourite devices. Nevertheless, he was not a born teller of tales, or freely endowed with that not very unusual faculty, invention. The faintest phantom of a 'story', the barest thread of a plot

were made to suffice (as indeed they have sufficed for some of
the best fiction in the world), but they were again and again
interwoven with that rather shallow and dispiriting theme,
the *mesalliance*, a game in which Mammon shuffles a well-
thumbed pack of Victorian playing-cards, long familiar to
Mrs. Grundy. Money, next to love, the main stand-by perhaps in all its machinations in prose fiction, if not in life itself,
is less likely to pay its way in poetry. He sometimes borrowed
the themes he elaborated, but in incident and treatment
seldom enriched them. Even with a promising nucleus he
may not succeed in telling his story well. His endings are often
psychologically, and in some of his lyrics are poetically, the
weakest parts of the whole.

He studied and analysed men and women, but he cannot
perfectly put them together again. Life has flown. His gaze is
intent and keen, but the strange power to divine and to become is wanting. His characters, like many of Thomas
Hardy's, are the sport of destiny rather than gifted with free
will. Unlike Hardy's they have been made, or made up, not
born. They serve their maker's purpose but it is not usually a
very profound purpose. By sheer lifegiven-ness they do not
rise into being, as do even Blake's chimney-sweeps, or Anna-
bel Lee, or the sisters in *Goblin Market*, or George Herbert in
The Collier; or stalk out of the void with an energy and a
mastery that may set a modest reader wondering if he himself
has ever really lived. Nor, on the other hand, have they the
power of hinting by subtle and cumulative innuendo that
actuality itself is nothing more than a disturbed and frag-
mentary dream.

Nearly all Tennyson's men and women are mainly pic-
torial—so many minutely observed and depicted mental and
bodily traits and features. We see with distinctness enough a
Will Waterpoof, a Farmer Allen, the fat-faced curate Edward
Bull (and apart from 'the clergyman who told' the May
Queen 'words of peace', he is not over-indulgent of the
Church), a Northern Farmer, a Grandmother, a Sir Galahad,

even a Hallam; but do these phantoms of humanity, as do Chaucer's or Wordsworth's, return to memory at the merest hint, animate and haunt us unbidden and unannounced? And how often do they evoke in us that hidden self which may seldom excite our waking attention but yet never sleeps beneath day's restless consciousness? Do we stumble on the secrets of our own hearts in theirs? Even in such a masterly piece of technique as *A Dream of Fair Women* how chill and meagre at times are the uttered words:

> *I had great beauty: ask thou not my name:*
> *No one can be more wise than destiny.*
> *Many drew swords and died. Where'er I came*
> *I brought calamity.*

How statue-like she seems to stand, how cold the agate lamp! Was *this* the face that launch'd a thousand ships, and burnt the topless towers of Ilium? In Tennyson's general treatment of women indeed there is a prevalent strain of the 'yeoman' who coldly scolded Lady Clara Vere de Vere, who appealed against her blue blood to 'the grand old gardener and his wife', and bade her go 'teach the orphan-boy to read, Or teach the orphan-girl to sew'. A suggestion of mcok modesty hangs over passages in which even modesty herself might for the time being consent to open her eyes and hold her tongue. Young women encloistered like Mariana (and how vivid and lovely is every natural detail of her stagnant moated grange!); or slowly dying, like his Queen of the May; or dead, like his Lady of Shalott, were assured of his romantic sympathy and sentiment. But he did not stoop to trace his meditations in the sand until Guinevere's accusers had silently withdrawn, and he was, as he intended he should be, to the very last things in humanity quite alone with her. Was he, indeed, ever intensely alone with any of the human creatures, reputable or otherwise, depicted in his verse?

In his private life he detested priggishness; he could speak out bluntly enough in talk; he could splash over the shallow tub of mere conventionalism, and was a man of a broad, masculine humour. And yet in his narrative poems how rare is the pinch of Rabelaisian salt—in precocious evidence in *The Devil and the Lady*—which would have added so appetizing a tang to that tantalizing niceness, that laborious simplicity. How vainly we usually listen for even the rumble of a voice against which Mrs. Grundy must dutifully stop at least one ear! 'Two notes only', wrote his friend Herbert Warren, 'are absent' from Tennyson's poetry: 'the unkind and the base'. And he adds, a trifle ambiguously, 'Those who knew him realized what he could have done had he yielded to the temptation to strike there also'. He strikes, in another sense, piercingly enough in *The Modern Timon*. Candour is not necessarily detraction, which is unfortunately by far the easiest way of winning a quick hearing; and there is nothing either base or unkind in calling a spade a spade, or meritorious in withholding the usual ha'porth of tar. These disinclinations were certainly not a family failing.[1] In so many of the longer poems there are traces of that social prudery, and of the genteel, exemplified in the opening lines of *Sea Dreams*: 'A city clerk, but gently born and bred'. His salary is referred to as 'gains'. And often when Tennyson mentions the merely

[1] Frederick Tennyson (no more than Charles, who wrote, with its exquisite finale, *Letty's Globe*) was neither as man nor poet the mere satellite of his famous brother. He referred to himself as 'a person of gloomy insignificance and unsocial monomania'. He was a keen disciple of Swedenborg, hated 'the high-jinks of the high-nosed' or 'Snookdom' and 'the frowsy diatribes of black men in white ties', settled down in 1857 in a vast hall designed by Michelangelo, engaged (it was reported) forty fiddlers to sate his love of Mozart, had four children, and that now respected resource of Mother Gamp's, 'an Umbrella'. He had little enthusiasm in general for Other People, but gladly suffered the Brownings. He remarked, however, that 'Mrs. B' was 'troubled' like other inspired ladies, with 'a chest', was inclined to agree with FitzGerald regarding her husband that

> *It once was the pastoral Cockney,*
> *And now is the Cockney profound,*

and dismissed most of his poetic performances as so much 'pure brain-work'.

ordinary it is with a rather wry effect. It shows in its context like a patch of wool in silk embroidery. But may not perhaps the quality of the silk excuse the presence of the worsted?

Walter Bagehot—a critic as original, substantive and provocative as he is exhilarating—divided poetry into three categories: the pure, the ornate, and the grotesque. He consigned Browning's to the third of these, Tennyson's to the second, and for illustration, used *Enoch Arden*. 'How simple', he comments, 'the story is in itself! A sailor who sells fish, breaks his leg, gets dismal, gives up selling fish, goes to sea, is wrecked on a desert island, stays there for some years, on his return finds his wife married to a miller, speaks to a landlady on the subject, and dies'.

There *may* be a shimmer of irony here; otherwise, perhaps, this summary is hardly fair. A prince, of Denmark, named Hamlet, having been informed by his father's ghost that he was murdered by his own brother, debates whether or not he should and shall avenge him; and finally does. As was not Euclid's way, it reduces the admirable to the absurd. Thus dissecting, are we not disposing of an animated work of art by dealing solely with its bare bones—and that far from the Valley of Jehoshaphat? What of Helen's? Is this the *skull* that launched a thousand ships? Alas, poor Yorick! With any such 'alas' still faltering on our lips we may recall that from a single bone no bigger than that found by the teeny tiny old woman in the churchyard, the great naturalist, Sir Richard Owen, reconstructed in imagination a complete prehistoric monster.

However that may be; having thus dealt with the story or plot of *Enoch Arden*, Bagehot's argument concerning it runs roughly as follows: Poetry, worthy of the name, *must* give us pleasure; 'a sailor who sells fish' cannot possibly be pleasurable company; that being so, all that concerns him in Tennyson's narrative cannot be poetry; Tennyson's description nevertheless of the castaway's island is a model of adorned art; therefore the poem is a little masterpiece of its class. In a later essay, it may be added, Bagehot has quite pleasant things to say (as had William Blake) about a chimney-sweep. But how many fascinating questions spring into view out of this presentation of his case?

Would Enoch have been more agreeable company if he had sold fish wholesale, or if he had become 'a fisher of men'? Where exactly falls the poetic sumptuary line—where sits the salt? Above or below the Ancient Mariner? How far, again, in another art, does the class or occupation of its subject affect the merit of a portrait? Is an artist with a whoreson old sexton for a sitter doomed to failure unless he includes in his canvas 'a Mr. Wilkinson, a clergyman' and the rector of the parish to retrieve the balance? Is Hogarth's Shrimp Girl, are Manet's Absinthe Drinkers, are Carpaccio's Venetian Courtesans redeemed by their pictorial setting? Apart again from the fatality of a vulgar calling, what complete ideal of human reality *can* a 'sailor who sells fish' adequately fulfil? How far short of this falls Enoch? Is any obvious deficiency the poet's responsibility; and, if so, was it intentional? And if not, and had his realization been ample enough, would it have removed this part of the poem into the category designated 'pure'?

But then, are Tennyson's characters in general, his Arthur, his Guinevere, his Knights of the Round Table, his host of the gentry, who one must assume *should* be agreeable company, more real than Enoch? If we have to admit that what is most conspicuous in them is a certain *minus* and a certain *plus* due it would seem to their being so specifically Tennysonian, how does this affect his 'ornate'—the presentation of his marvellously precise and lovely scenery, his exquisite vignettes of the observed and the divined? If these give us pleasure enough (as indeed they do) to ensure their acceptance as 'poetry', the question still remains whether or not that scenery is itself flawlessly real. Or has it too perhaps a tinge of the too idiosyncratic, of the restricted, of what is remote from human nature's daily food? Is it a thought exotic? We think of Chaucer's

Nature, of Crabbe's, of Wordsworth's, Vaughan's, and Blake's, and Hardy's, and, grateful to them one and all, may make our choice.

Tennyson himself can hardly have been fully aware that, like Enoch Arden with his 'costly funeral', his plaintive and fated 'little Alice' of *The May Queen* is not only inadequately 'three dimensional', but—if one watches her a little closely—is also unattractive; or that his Maud never really comes alive. What little 'story' there is in this poem also, so treated, as with *Aylmer's Field*, is simple to the point of insipidity; and the characterization ranges between the melodramatic and the parochial. But how exquisite at times is the *obbligato* of the voice that tells this tragic, and yet—despite its human sorrow and regret—never acutely moving tale. Again and again the natural magic and music manifest themselves, like the song of some bird of enchantment in an old folk-tale, though seldom of an Ariel or an Israfel.

> *And now 'twas like all instruments,*
> *Now like a lonely flute;*
> *And now it is an angel's song,*
> *That makes the heavens be mute.*
>
> *It ceased; yet still the sails made on*
> *A pleasant noise till noon,*
> *A noise like of a hidden brook*
> *In the leafy month of June,*
> *That to the sleeping woods all night*
> *Singeth a quiet tune.*

When indeed we think of Tennyson's lifelong and impassioned adoration of *his* Nature, far exceeding in intensity even his concern with things of the intellect, his insight into humanity, his impulse towards introspection and his keen interest in science, all such criticism seems a little graceless and niggardly, if not beside the point.

His first collection of 1830 contains a Song about 'worn Sorrow', and this is its second stanza:

> *Death standeth by;*
> *She will not die;*
> *With glazed eye*
> *She looks at her grave: she cannot sleep;*
> *Ever alone*
> *She maketh her moan:*
> *She cannot speak; she can only weep,*
> *For she will not hope.*
> *The thick snow falls on her flake by flake*
> *The dull wave mourns down the slope,*
> *The world will not change, and her heart will not break.*

In reading these lines is not one conscious of a faint sigh of relief and of renewed interest breathed from the poem itself when that 'thick snow' begins quietly to fall? And did not that dull wave 'mourning down the slope' become in Tennyson's later work a solemn reiterated and endeared refrain? The song recalls Millais' naturalistic picture of nuns digging a grave in the snow of a churchyard; and a lovely woodcut by Arthur Hughes with a similar subject. It recalls too, not Watts, but Christina Rossetti, whose imagination was also haunted by the theme of love and death. It would be quite untrue, however, to suggest that in her poem, *When I am dead, my dearest*, the cypress tree and the green grass, the shadows and the nightingale are its *in*most impulse. The very cadences of her poem deny it. Whereas in Tennyson's song we may feel just the contrary.

Is there not a subtle difference in realization between

> *In the spring a livelier iris changes on the burnished dove,*

and

> *In the spring a young man's fancy lightly turns to thoughts of*
> *love?*

This, of course, is merely to say that every poet is only most happily at home *some*where. No mind or heart can be instant tinder to every fortuitous spark; and it may be that no man, from childhood onwards, fails to reveal a pronounced if vacillating inclination to what on earth most fully satisfies for him some permanent, innate or inherited hunger, yearning and desire. A poet, any artist, however versatile, is unlikely to be exceptional in this. He may have many strings to his bow, and a full quiver, but his inward eye is apt to return repeatedly and with a renewed zest to one certain target; and all other aims are of secondary importance and value. Faithful to that, the old mill-horse may die in its tracks, but it has at least laboured to grind the corn prescribed by its secret monitor and master.

'What is Master Awlfred always a-praying for?' enquired the family cook who had heard him clanging out his verses as he paced to and fro at Somersby. Well, if it had been for the power of communicating to the world his worship of beauty, and his zeal for its perfect expression, it would have been a prayer abundantly answered. He stumbles at times simply by reason of his ardour for the last exquisite finish, the golden hair's breadth of precision. Occasionally he detachably inserts among the fresh flowers of a poem a few lines thus elaborated which he had set aside in his pocket-book for future use; occasionally he crystallizes what should be fluent and natural with too obviously chosen an epithet; and such passages ('the moan of doves in immemorial elms', for instance) are rather superficially taken as both excellent and characteristic. The verse, too, rather than unveiling its beauty, as may a morning mist the dew and flowers and loveliness of a meadow, is often as sharp and clear-cut as metal or marble. But at his best, Tennyson does not, like William Morris, portray, or, with what seems a chance word, suggest a complete scene of the imagination; he takes his reader up bodily, so to speak, and sets him there in the material midst.

> *She woke: the babble of the stream*
> *Fell, and, without, the steady glare*
> *Shrank one sick willow sere and small.*
> *The river-bed was dusty-white;*
> *And all the furnace of the light*
> *Struck up against the blinding wall.*

We shut the inward eye to escape the glare, and *breathe* that dusty-white. And he succeeds even in lines packed with 'literariness' and the pre-Raphaelite:

> *Thridding the sombre boskage of the wood,*
> *Toward the morning-star.*

It is merely a platitude to repeat that he is the master of one variety of the magic word—whether it was the blissful inspiration of the moment, or far-fetched. In what other poet is so superb, so self-evident a magic after so self-evident and eager a search?

> *Still on the tower stood the vane,*
> *A black yew gloom'd the stagnant air*
> *. . . I lingered there*
> *Till every daisy slept, and Love's white star*
> *Beam'd thro' the thicken'd cedar in the dusk.*

Who cannot at once recall or soon recover a score of such exquisitely considered touches as the rabbit's 'harmless face', the 'blue fly' singing on the pane, the 'crackling frost'? Such things as these have long ceased to be vivid images; they are now also enchanted memories. It is difficult to keep back our tears at the verbal truth and the beauty revealed, even in his best-known 'pieces':

> *When the flowers come again, mother, beneath the waning light*
> *You'll never see me more in the long grey fields at night;*
> *When from the dry dark wold the summer airs blow cool*
> *On the oat-grass and the sword-grass, and the bulrush in the pool.*

Tennyson

There is indeed scarcely a lyric of Tennyson's but has for its individual charm not a simple passionate thought, not a mystic allusiveness or a profound human emotion, but some one supremely faithful or significant fragment borrowed from a direct tryst with his Nature. His son has recorded, that however near and dear his companion, Tennyson habitually withdrew himself into a temporary solitude in order to muse upon and perhaps to record what most keenly impressed or deeply affected him in the day's journey. Out of that 'never less alone than when alone' came 'the happy harvest fields', the ship in *Tears, Idle Tears*, the shadow in *St. Agnes' Eve*, the city in *Will*, the wrinkled sea in *The Eagle*, and, again, that miraculous glimpse in the last four lines of *The Captain*. The verse blows salt on our lips, with its roar and hollow crying; and its sea-birds wheel in an abyss of air between eye and printed page. Where else, too, unless in Milton, arches such space and burns and glitters such splendour of moon and sun, of Orion and the Hyades, in a mere leash of words?

All else in his life, so far at least as this is revealed in his poetry (for his wide interests flourished in an ample field), seems to have been to him of secondary import. Beauty—but not specifically the beauty in mystery, or strangeness, or in a fantastic or sinister disguise, or in the perfectly ordinary, or in what is very seldom the concern of art—is the unfailing impulse of his genius, an island of solitude and peace amid the ocean of countless other earthly experiences. And he made, and revealed it as, his own. His interest in Science[1] was dili-

---

[1] In this he was an innovator, and he would have disdained to take much to heart, however apposite it was to his practice, Bagehot's ironical and by no means unfounded generalization:

'Some people are unfortunately born scientific. They take much interest in the objects of nature. They feel a curiosity about shells, snails, horses, butterflies. They are delighted at an ichthyosaurus, and excited at a polyp; they are learned in minerals, vegetables, animals; they have skill in fishes, and attain renown in pebbles; in the highest cases they know the great causes of grand phenomena, can indicate the courses of the stars or the current of the waves; but in every case their minds are directed not to the actions

gent and curious, but that too was in service to his love of nature. Poets there are whose vision of the world is as far removed from any accepted actuality as was the Lady of Shalott's; they weave the mirror's magic reflections into a web of fantasy: Tennyson from the windows of his eyes, 'dark, powerful, and serene', looked down direct on Camelot.

Inspiration comes and goes. Whether a man toil or tarry in patience or impatience, poetry will not be cajoled, or circumvented, or suffer compulsion; and a lifetime's patient service may be memorably recorded at last only as the outcome of a few supreme moments. Following a merely personal predilection in thought, feeling or imagination, we may set particular store on this or that above all else in our English poets —Donne's brooding intensity, Herrick's detached daintiness, Shelley's raptures, Keats's impassioned philosophy. Each is the refraction from reality of an individual experience. There remain the virgin riches of a world that would inexhaustibly suffice for theme and inspiration had every man that breathes been born to rhyme. And even from so partial a survey of Tennyson's work as that of these few pages a rare achievement stands out clearly—his intense appreciation—if with out-sight rather than with insight—of what he loved and delighted in; his supreme mastery in the recording of it; and his devotion to an ideal conception of his art to which he remained faithful to the end of his days.

The spirit within him was at peace and at home among his native dykes and wolds. Here 'Alfred's mind was moulded in silent sympathy with the everlasting forms of Nature'—a sympathy which failed to impress a fisherman who to the civil greeting of the poet whom he had encountered, sans

---

of man, but to the scenery amidst which he lives; not to the inhabitants of this world, but to the world itself; not to what most resembles themselves, but to that which is most unlike. What compels men to take an interest in what they do take an interest in, is commonly a difficult question—for the most part, indeed, it is an insoluble one; but in this case it would seem to have a negative cause—to result from the absence of an intense and vivid nature.'

hat and coat one four-o'clock-in-the-morning pacing his Lincolnshire sea-strand to the music of 'the hollow ocean-ridges roaring into cataracts', replied, 'Thou poor fool, thou doesn't knaw whether it be night or day!' Official and social obligations and privileges far from conducive to such self-communings were thrust on him, accepted, and, not without intrinsic sacrifice, triumphantly survived. With the encouragement of the wisest king that ever wore a crown, there must have been many in high places who would have agreed with the Laureate's Lincolnshire folk that to 'hev owt' to do with books is a sign of a weak intellect. Nevertheless, to these duties he devoted his great talents; his genius followed its own sweet will.

In *Timbuctoo* Arthur Hallam had seen promise of a unique greatness. The keeping of his promise was summarized by Sir Alfred Lyall; it was Tennyson's 'proud distinction', he declared, 'to have maintained the apostolic succession of our national poetry in a manner not unworthy of those famous men who went immediately before him'. That means perhaps a little less than it seems to say. It might be applied to the author of one faultless lyric. 'Greatness' is a word which, rightly or not, suggests quantity rather than quality; Longfellow rather than Poe; Dryden than Vaughan; Browning than Emily Brontë. Greatness left out of account, Tennyson, purely as a poet, may be justly compared with Coventry Patmore and Christina Rossetti. Their order of merit, which is of little importance compared with the fact that they were without question *poets*, depends on some final definition of poetry itself. But whose? 'The deep saith, It is not in me: and the sea saith, It is not with me'.

But apart from the life of the actual, of life at first hand, there are few experiences which can we so easily share and enjoy, by proxy, as that of *physical* solitude. What other theme in fiction is more deeply saturated with the romantic and the adventurous? Stories of this kind abound; and particularly in English fiction. What in general are their conditions?

First, the victim and the hero of such a fate must fight—not, as we all do, for life—but for a bare existence. And unlike many of his fellow creatures in real life he must not fight in vain. His one problem, his one craving and desire (however irrational it may be), must be merely to continue to keep alive. He must, then, have courage and enterprise. No mere dreamer, thinker or philosopher need apply.

Next, since he is to be—and for some time to remain—alone, his place of exile should be remote from the thronging haunts and highways of mankind and dangerous of access though not quite inaccessible. A naked and waterless waste from which no escape is possible would admit of but the briefest period of physical torture and a morbid activity of the mind. His resort then must offer *some* hospitality to its guest, though it should be well this side of the luxurious, since he must spend in it a quick and lively existence. And though the odds against his survival must not be overwhelming, they should at least appear to be long. He must indeed survive to tell us his tale; for of the solitude of the grave, whether in St. Innocent's churchyard or beneath the sands of Egypt, we can retrieve no direct tidings, or at best—tidings dubious, meagre and unsatisfying.

Our solitary, too—if his record is to be moving—should be more or less continually aware of his isolation. So much the better if from some point of vantage amid his wild and barbarous scenery he can keep watch on the horizon whence at length rescue will come. Finally, he may effect his own rescue. But to see him merely walk out of his trap is an eventuality not quite romantic enough. A profoundly sundering yet traversable medium must sever him, then, from his fellow-creatures.

The sands of the Sahara or of the Gobi desert would keep such a secret, or, failing these, some green and peaceful oasis in a region encircled by an unintermittent cyclone, or by a ring of subterranean fire. Jules Verne, for example, may not have completely explored the monster-haunted deeps in the centre of the earth; and the practicability of voyaging into space seems to be once more engaging the speculations not of mere visionaries only but even of the matter-of-fact.

Short of the subterranean, the submarine, and the wild vacancies of space, however, the conditions of an ideal retreat from the tumult and artificialities of man are fulfilled—solitude, danger, strangeness, the unknown, the discoverable, the eventual means of escape—if our hermitage is an island. An island volcanic or coralline, an island that out of the mists of daybreak, or in the cheating lights of evening, lifts itself from the snows of its surges, serene, strange, aloof in its forlorn beauty, dumb clock of countless ages, the haven of a few birds and roving brutes, the kindly nursery of seal and sea lion, and green with palm and tamarisk.

An island let it be, say, three or four hundred to a thousand miles or so from the nearest habitations of humanity and well out of the usual sea-trade routes, preferably uncharted, fairly commodious, say thirteen miles by four, of a climate whose extremes are not of a pitiless severity, an island which Nature's bounty has endowed with shade, fresh water, shelter and food fit for human consumption. And there—our recluse.

Every seaman, every wanderer on the deep, has hearkened to the decoy of that ideal island; and where is the landsman with soul so dead—even though his eye has been lifted over no greater expanse of salt water than can be scanned from the steps of a bathing-machine—who in his homesick moments has never caught its enchanting echo? The English in particular are as a people naturally beguiled by the thought of the smallest strip or patch of land that is surrounded by water. How could it be otherwise, since theirs is that notorious little three-cornered island of 'a natural bravery . . . with rocks unscalable and roaring waters', against whose western coasts for ever beats the prodigious Atlantic? The seas are in their blood. They have been scoffed at as a nation of shopkeepers; 'merchant adventurers' has a pleasanter sound. They have been eyed askance as a horde of money-hunting landgrabbers; freeborn crusading colonists is a pleasanter way of putting it. Again and again they have had to face the charge of insularity, but then was there ever a national shortcoming so inevitable? What wonder that, rather greedily maybe and not always with too nice a gesture, they have sucked 'of the abundance of the seas, and of treasures hid in the sand'?

Man's longed-for havens indeed are for the most part curiously simple in structure. But though the sweet, spoon-fed, simple *dolce far niente* of the South Seas may for a while allure his weary or indolent body, his true happiness must consort with desires of the mind. It is not the gemlike gates of Jerusalem but what they are the symbols of that will bring him peace in the blissful pains of Paradise, where there will be no more sea and therefore no more islands. Meanwhile he may cheat himself with the pretty illusion that if only he could secure a modest freehold of *terra firma* surrounded by water he would be at peace—not entirely perhaps with the self which it was impracticable to leave behind him, but at any rate with the world at large. Mere insularity will not however suffice. A glance at a map of the world is usually misleading or rather, seldom illuminating; but a moment's brooding over it will reveal, first, that it is but a cabalistic picture in the flat, and that the great globe is actually an enormous solid, a prodigious mass of uninviting matter, of which man knows very little apart from its skin; and next, that the seas and oceans are but puddles of salt water of various sizes occupying the hollows of its surface, many of them, the North Sea and the English Channel, for example, disillusioningly shallow. We next perceive that this habitable world of ours consists of nothing *but* islands—the whole of America since man's ingenious ditch at Panama can hardly be taken into count) being one, Europe with Asia another, and Australia, a dumpy, red, irregularly shell-shaped configuration in the right-hand corner, a third.

But an island worthy of the romantic respect is not one of this magnitude. Even the 235,000 square miles of vast and barren Baffin Island with its two great inland lakes, though it may be as rich as Croesus in coal and gold, scarcely 'invites the soul'. One pines for something a little more in proportion to one's own few inches, and it is only when we begin to examine more attentively what appear on our atlas to be specks as minute as the vagrant footprints of some tiny insect that has strayed into the cartographer's ink and then sallied out into the pale blue of the oceans, that we catch a glimpse of our actual quarry.

For these specks represent in fact a multitude of such islands, and they make a braver and more enticing show on the map, say—all to itself—of the Malay Archipelago in which that entrancing skeleton of a sea-serpent called Java and Sumatra sprawls its dusky length along from west to south. There hitherto indiscernible microscopicalities now become apparent—Flat, Spratly, Matty, and Yowl, for example; also the Moresses, the Moscos, Mandioli, Moa, Mai and all the Mes—not to mention Money for make-weight, and seed-pearls *ad infinitum*.

Nor does one need to be a globe trotter or even much of a traveller to indulge this hobby. Childhood, a millpond, a raft and a willow are enough to begin with; and shall I ever forget a certain daybreak on the edge of the Atlantic when, after only a week, of the open sea, my hungry eyes alighted on three bare, lovely lone and everlasting objects which man calls islands, and which as if out of a dream had silently revealed themselves from beneath the veils of dawn against the blue of sky and water: the Bull, the Cow, and the Calf— a mere Cockney's treasures, maybe, but still for that instant his own?

Even, too, what on the map resembles nothing more impressive than England's door-mat, the Isle of Wight, may, whether in sun or drizzle, show very dear to the eyes of an Englishman on his way home. Indeed life has few welcomes more precise, pungent, and heart-disturbing than the first glimpse of lighthouse, light-ship or beacon or winking light-buoy rocked in the cradle of the deep. Its rapid stare at you may have little speculation in it. It is not affectionate, it may even have a tinge of the ironic, yet it may stir as many memories in one's mind as the prod of a stick in an ant-heap in an English wood stirs ants. And some of these memories may be of longer continuance than even the mere number of one's birthdays would imply.

Assuredly, at any rate, of islands, and of little ones, there is no lack. Precisely *how* numerous they are, what their sum total is, as they lie scattered over the enormous wastes of the world's waters, I have not as yet been able to ascertain. Three hundred, it is said, may be counted, when clear weather stretches between sea and heaven, from the highest hummock of St. Columba's Iona alone. But then Celtic islands, unlike the common kind, may, like the Irishman's pigs, easily be counted twice. And how be sure of one's eyes in a world where so much is the creation not of men of science but of fantasy? The earlier map-makers at least attempted to be informative on this point. The Catalan map of 1375, for example, shows a prolonged semi-circular cluster of islands, in shape more or less engagingly rectangular, representing no fewer than '7,548' of them in all the *Mar de les Indes* and in the Ocean Sea washing the coasts of the empire of 'Holubeim, i.e. the Great Can', and the realms of *lo gran Senhor de GOG*

IMAGOG. Spice Islands every one, and 'naked savages' then their sole inhabitants.

That 'cosmographical dilettante' Martin Behaim (who in the green of his youth was sentenced to a week's imprisonment for dancing at a Jew's wedding in Lent), like Fra Mauro and Martellus Germanus before him, delighted in islands. In his own honour he boldly renamed Annobom *Insula Martini,* and was hospitality itself to such little oceanic paradises as the Island of the Seven Cities and the Island of St. Brandan—the pious abbot's haven at last, in A.D. 565, after his five years of voyaging over seas perpetually dark. Behaim's 'apple' or globe of the great world of 1492, now at Nuremberg, is a feast for the eye. It is adorned with no fewer than a hundred and eleven miniatures—coloured red, gold, black, blue, green umber and silver—depicting flags, banners, coats of arms, kings enthroned, saints and proselytizing missionaries, naked savages seated on pillows in tents of red and green, wild elephants roving near, and, a little aloof, tiled towers, and campaniles; ships, sea-serpents, mermaids, camels, parrots, ostriches, serpents, and various other devices, though, alas, no Eden.

But little space in Behaim's day could be spared for *Engelant* and *wildt Scotlant,* though York, huntingdon, cambridge, edmundeburgh—and lambeth—are specified. The Orkneys are referred to but not shown. Of the Western Hebrides he names *irgan, bea* and *dseds,* and he remembers *Tillf* or Thule. He gives us also Taprobana, of the Greeks, alias Serendib of the *Nights,* alias Seilan or Cylon; and Pentan (Bintang), whose coasts with a very shallow sea, says Marco Polo, are 'wild and uncultivated but the woods abound with sweet scented trees'.

Then again, the British Museum has lately acquired a probably unique copy of Giovanni Contarini's Map of the World of 1506, the first printed map, apparently, to show the naked coast (with *Terra S. Crucis,* i.e. Brazil, in the N.E. corner) of South America. Neighbouring its shores, islands

are shown, which Master Christopher Colombus, 'viceroy of
Spain and Admiral of the Ocean, discovered at the instance
of the "most serene king Ferdinand" and his Queen Isabella.'
And not far from Martin Behaim's Seilan is inserted this
record: 'Before Taprobana there are very many islands,
which are said to be 1,778 in number'.

It is that 'said to be' which is apt to prove deceptive when
objects so actual as islands are the quarry. And the *desert*
island is now unfortunately by far the most infrequent in
kind. Man, none the less, has been going to and fro in the
world and down to the sea in ships for a good many centuries,
and during these voyagings hosts of poor sailors must have
found themselves the sole survivors of shipwreck on shores
that, apart from fish and bird and insect, never showed
faintest sign of life or heed or human company. It is remarkable, then, how scanty trustworthy narratives which tell of
their experiences appear to be.

Even more remarkable, there is one island more or less
precisely after our ideal pattern that has in recorded fact
proved a sanctuary to no less than three such adventurers.
That island is Más-á-tierra. It is one of a group of three called
Juan Fernandez, the second being Má-á-fuera, i.e. 'Further-
out'. This lies a hundred miles to westward; it has nine
ravines on the eastern face of its rocky *massif*, and to each
ravine its water-course. The third, only a mile or so away, is
an islet called Santa Clara or Goat Island. Craggy and wooded
(twelve and a half miles long by three and two-thirds across
at its widest), Más-á-tierra lies under the Southern Cross, one
hundred and ten leagues from Valparaiso on the main. Its
highest hill, El Yunque, rears itself 3,005 feet above the sea.
And about the year 1570 it was chanced upon by the
Spanish navigator—Juan Fernandez—who gave the group his
name.

Más-á-tierra was then virgin soil. Fernandez landed
'Indians' on it, brought in sheep and cattle from the mainland, built thatched and timbered houses and traded in sea-

lion oil and salted fish. But his enterprise failed. He abandoned the island, and bestowed it as a gift on a friend of the same name as himself, who bequeathed it to the Jesuits. Spaniards possessed it for a while for the sake of its fish and timber and sandal-wood. Then they too deserted it, and after further vicissitudes it became towards the end of the seventeenth century a wasps' nest of buccaneers.

On 22nd March 1684, Captain William Dampier, the great English sailor, while voyaging round the world, landed on it for the second time. John Fernando, he called it. He came to seek a Mosquito Indian, one of a minute nation of Amerindians, civil, good-natured and monogamous, only a hundred men strong. A prudent people too, for when its menfolk enjoyed a carousal, the women used to hide their weapons. This Indian while engaged in hunting goats had been marooned on the island four years previously when Dampier's ship had been chased from its anchorage by Spaniards.

'Long-visaged, hard-favoured, lank-haired', his sole defence against his solitude had been a gun, a knife, and a small horn of powder. By notching his knife he had made a saw with which he sawed into pieces the barrel of his gun. Out of these he smithied harpoons, lances, fish-hooks and another long knife. He built himself a wooden hut and lined it with goat-skins. He fished with tackle of sealskin and hunted John Fernando's goats, which had long since managed to survive the Jesuits' dogs. When Spaniards landed and chased him, such were his wiles and his cunning that they began to suspect he was an apparition. When his English clothes were worn out he girded a hairy goatskin about his loins.

Having sighted Dampier's ship the day before it cast anchor, this hospitable soul killed three of his goats for his rescuer's entertainment and cooked them and served them up (English fashion) with cabbage from the 'cabbage-tree'. His English name was Will—for the Mosquito Indians were men so poor in this world's goods, they told Dampier, that they had no names of their own; and the first man to leap ashore to greet him was his fellow-countryman, Robin.

'Running to his brother Moskito man', says Dampier, 'he, Robin, threw himself flat on his face at his feet, who helping him up, and embracing him, fell flat with his face on the ground at Robin's feet, and was by him taken up also. . . . And when their Ceremonies of Civility were over, we also drew near, each of us embracing him we had found there, who was overjoyed to see so many of his old friends come hither, as he thought, purposely to fetch him'. 'Of such consequence is a Man to himself!'

These English seamen were not, we may remind ourselves, plenipotentiaries at a Peace Conference or candidates for the American Presidency. Of such we expect all the charms and graces. They were buccaneers. They pillaged, they burned, they massacred. Yet on apt occasions these were their manners; and it is 'manners makyth man', as John Silver knew well; as knew King Charles I, also, when after rising from his bed on the cold morning of 30th January 1649, he decided to put on a second and warmer shirt, with its silk knots of blue and red, in case he should be seen to shiver on the scaffold.

Twenty-five years after Will's and Robin's touching reunion, on the last day of January 1709, Captain Woodes Rogers, then commander-in-chief of two privateers of Bristol, and himself in the *Duke* (a ship of 320 tons, 30 guns and 117 men), sighted Juan Fernandez. For master of the *Duke* he had Dampier himself, who meanwhile had been marooned on the island of Nicobar, whence he escaped in a cockleshell canoe whose gunwale was only three inches above the water-line, and had also been wrecked on Ascension. Rogers had come to Juan Fernandez to water. The next evening lights were seen on shore and surmised to be those of French ships lying at anchor.

As a matter of fact, they were the watch fires of a sailor named Alexander Selcraig, of Selkirk, who on the following morning was brought off in the ship's pinnace amid a cargo of shell-fish. He was clothed in goatskins, and 'looking wilder than the first owners of them'. It is our first glimpse of one who was destined to become the prince and prototype of all castaways.

Like Hans Andersen and so many folk-tale heroes, he was the son—and the seventh son—of a cobbler. He was born at Largo, a sea-village in Fife. There to-day stands his effigy in stone, gazing—like Martin Behaim's at Nuremberg and Drake's at Plymouth—(and a little ironically, one might suppose) on the haunts of his youth. When he was nineteen he was cited for misbehaviour in kirk and ran away to sea. Six years afterwards he came home again, but quarrelled with his brothers, once more decamped, and in the spring of 1703 shipped with Captain William Dampier as sailing master of the galley, the *Cinque Ports*, Dampier himself being in command of the *St. George*. Having arrived, in a leaky ship, at Juan Fernandez, after a bitter altercation with his commander, and at his own suggestion—of which he speedily repented— Selkirk was marooned on Más-á-tierra in September 1704.

He landed there a man much richer in this world's goods than the Mosquito Indian. He had a sea chest, clothes, bedding, a firelock, a pound of gunpowder, a bag of bullets, flint and steel, some tobacco, a hatchet, a knife, a kettle, a Bible, mathematical instruments and some books of devotion. Yet in spite of these luxuries, after four years and four months' solitude, Selkirk told Rogers his story in a Scots English so broken and rusty for want of use as to be hardly intelligible. 'We could scarce understand him . . . he seemed to speak his words by halves'.

So too Marco Polo when, with his father and uncle, he returned from the splendours of Kublai Khan to Venice in 1295. It is recorded that when these three famous travellers reached home in their shabby Tartar clothes after four and twenty years' absence they had not only almost lost the use of their native tongue, but their relatives failed to recognize them. When, however, on ripping up the seams of their clouts they disclosed a secret store of precious stones, all doubts were set at rest. For precious stones, like fennel, have a secret and singular 'propertie to mundifie our sight and take away the filme or web that overruleth and dimmeth our eyes'.

For eight long months Selkirk had lived in melancholy and horror, 'scarce able to refrain from doing himself violence'. Day after day he had sat in watch, his face towards the sea, until his eyes and the light failed him and he could watch no more. By night he had lain shivering with terror at the howlings of sea-monsters on the shore, and the first show of dawn lighting up his great prison-house had roused him only to a sharper consciousness of his forlorn and miserable state. He spent his time for weeks together roaming aimlessly about his island, staring, listening, weeping, talking to himself.

As time went on, however, Selkirk's spirits began to revive, as human spirits, please Heaven, are apt to revive even in the most adverse of circumstances. He vanquished his blues, he set to work, kept tally of his days, and, like Orlando, cut his name in the trees. He fed plentifully on turtle until he could no more stomach it except in jellies. He built himself two huts, thatched them with grass and lined them with goatskins; the one for a kitchen, the other wherein to sleep, to read, to sing Scots psalms and to pray. Thus he became, he confessed, a better Christian than he had ever been before, or was likely to be again.

For warmth, cheer, and candle he burned the fragrant all-spice wood, but had squandered nearly all his gunpowder before he got fire by rubbing two sticks together. He had no grain, physic, salt, ink, paper, or even rum. He fed on craw-fish, goats' flesh, broiled or boiled, turnips—sown by Dampier—and a small black plum, difficult of access on the island's rocky heights. Of living things, apart from goats, he had the company only of seals, which in November came ashore to 'whelp and engender', their bleating and howling so loud that the noise of them could be heard inland a mile from the shore. Another creature strange to Selkirk was the sea lion, the hair of whose whiskers is 'stiff enough to make toothpickers'. Of birds there was only a sort of blackbird with a red breast, and the many-coloured humming-bird, 'no bigger than a large humble bee'.

So life went on. When his ammunition failed him, he came to run, barefoot, with such celerity that he had chased down and killed, he said, no less than 500 goats. After ear-marking and laming their young kids, he had set free as many more—beasts which Lord Anson was thus able to identify over thirty years afterwards. When his clothes fell off his back, Selkirk took to himself hairy breeches, and, unravelling the worsted of his worn-out stockings, hemmed himself shirts out of his scanty stock of linen, by means of a shred of goat sinew threaded through a nail. When his knife was worn to the back, he made substitutes out of hoop-iron, beaten thin and ground on the rocks.

Twice he narrowly escaped death, the first time from a fall of a hundred feet—he lay unconscious for three days and nights, a period which he afterwards computed by the appearance of the moon; and the second time from voyaging Spaniards, who, sighting his fire at sea, landed and pursued him. He hid himself in a tree-top and listened to them talking beneath. But rats were his worst enemy; they gnawed his calloused feet and his clothes, until he had bred up cats to teach them manners. These would 'lie about him in hundreds'. Thus best we picture him, praying aloud, singing and dancing with his kids and cats in the flames and smoke of his allspice wood, and the whole world's moon taunting and enchanting him in her seasons.

His feet restored to shoes, and his tongue to its original English, Alexander Selkirk sailed away as mate of the *Duke*. She was crammed with booty in the shape of wine and brandy taken from a Spanish prize; and a mutiny broke out which her commander ingeniously suppressed by making one ringleader flog the other. Selkirk came home safe but weary to England in October 1711, and after the publication of Captain Woodes Rogers' book, *A Cruising Voyage Round the World*, in the following year, seems to have enjoyed, or at any rate to have endured, a passing notoriety. He was interviewed by Prue's wayward and enchanting husband Richard Steele, and was made the subject of a paper in the *Englishman*, from which most that we know about him is derived.

Better still, but less certainly, Selkirk is said to have actually met in Bristol at the house of a Mrs. Damaris Daniel (seductive name) yet another and a more notorious journalist, a man—as his enemies described him when about twenty years previously he had been 'wanted', and at £50 reward—'a man middle sized and spare . . . of a brown complexion, and dark-brown-coloured hair, but wears a wig; a hooked nose, a sharp chin, grey eyes, and a large mole near his mouth'. This man, though in the well-known portrait his chin is almost femininely rounded and the mole appears to be missing, was Daniel Defoe. And rather more than two centuries ago— on 25th April, 1719—Defoe being then about sixty years of age —forty-eight years older, that is, than a boy of twelve!— Samuel Johnson ten, the first George five years on the throne, and the South Sea Bubble on the eve of bursting, appeared *The Life and Strange Surprising Adventures of Robinson Crusoe, of York, Mariner. . . . Written by Himself.*

A PORTRAIT

Old: yet unchanged;—still pottering in his thoughts;
Still eagerly enslaved by books and print;
Less plagued, perhaps, by rigid musts and oughts,
But not less frantic in vain argument;

Still happy as a child, with its small toys,
Over his inkpot and his bits and pieces,—
Life's arduous, fragile and ingenuous joys,
Whose charm failed never—nay, it even increases!

Ev'n happier in watch of bird or flower,
Rainbow in heaven, or bud on thorny spray,
A star-strewn nightfall, and that heart-break hour
Of sleep-drowsed senses between dawn and day;

Loving the light—laved eyes in those wild hues!—
And dryad twilight, and the thronging dark;
A Crusoe ravished by mere solitude—
And silence—edged with music's faintest *Hark!*

And any chance-seen face whose loveliness
Hovers, a mystery, between dream and real;
Things usual yet miraculous that bless
And overwell a heart that still can feel;

Haunted by questions no man answered yet;
Pining to leap from A clean on to Z;
Absorbed by problems which the wise forget;
Avid for fantasy—yet how staid a head!

Senses at daggers with his intellect;
Quick, stupid; vain, retiring; ardent, cold;
Faithful and fickle; rash and circumspect;
And never yet at rest in any fold;

Punctual at meals; a spendthrift, close as Scot;
Rebellious, tractable, childish—long gone grey!
Impatient, volatile, tongue wearying not—
Loose, too: which, yet, thank heaven, was taught to pray;

'Childish' indeed!—a waif on shingle shelf
Fronting the rippled sands, the sun, the sea;
And nought but his marooned precarious self
For questing consciousness and will-to-be;

A feeble venturer—in a world so wide!
So rich in action, daring, cunning, strife!—
You'd think, poor soul, he had taken Sloth for bride,—
Unless the imagined is the breath of life;

Unless to speculate bring virgin gold,
And *Let's-pretend* can range the seven seas,
And dreams are not mere tales by idiot told,
And tongueless truth may hide in fantasies;

Unless the alone may their own company find,
And churchyards harbour phantoms 'mid their bones,
And even a daisy may suffice a mind
Whose bindweed can redeem a heap of stones;

Too frail a basket for so many eggs—
Loose-woven: Gosling? cygnet? Laugh or weep?
Or is the cup at richest in its dregs?
The actual realest on the verge of sleep?

One yet how often the prey of doubt and fear,
Of bleak despondence, stark anxiety;
Ardent for what is neither now nor here,
An Orpheus fainting for Eurydice;

Not yet inert, but with a tortured breast
At hint of that bleak gulf—his last farewell;
Pining for peace, assurance, pause and rest,
Yet slave to what he loves past words to tell;

A foolish, fond old man, his bed-time nigh,
Who still at western window stays to win
A transient respite from the latening sky,
And scarce can bear it when the Sun goes in.

ENGLAND

No lovelier hills than thine have laid
    My tired thoughts to rest:
No peace of lovelier valleys made
    Like peace within my breast.

Thine are the woods whereto my soul,
    Out of the noontide beam,
Flees for a refuge green and cool
    And tranquil as a dream.

Thy breaking seas like trumpets peal;
    Thy clouds—how oft have I
Watched their bright towers of silence steal
    Into infinity!

My heart within me faints to roam
    In thought even far from thee:
Thine be the grave whereto I come,
    And thine my darkness be.

THE OLD MEN

Old and alone, sit we,
  Caged, riddle-rid men;
Lost to Earth's 'Listen!' and 'See!'
  Thought's 'Wherefore?' and 'When?'

Only far memories stray
  Of a past once lovely, but now
Wasted and faded away,
  Like green leaves from the bough.

Vast broods the silence of night,
  The ruinous moon
Lifts on our faces her light,
  Whence all dreaming is gone.

We speak not; trembles each head;
  In their sockets our eyes are still;
Desire as cold as the dead;
  Without wonder or will.

And One, with a lanthorn, draws near,
  At clash with the moon in our eyes:
'Where art thou?' he asks: 'I am here,'
  One by one we arise.

And none lifts a hand to withhold
  A friend from the touch of that foe:
Heart cries unto heart, 'Thou art old!'
  Yet, reluctant, we go.

JACKDAWS

This dry old dotard lived but to amass
Old prints, books, pictures, porcelain, and glass—
As some hoard Wealth, Fame, Knowledge. Such he was.
There pottered in Another, and peered round:
But he his treasures buries underground.

SLIM CUNNING HANDS

Slim cunning hands at rest, and cozening eyes—
Under this stone one loved too wildly lies;
How false she was, no granite could declare;
　　　Nor all earth's flowers, how fair.

I AM

I am the World . . . Unveil this face:
Of brass it is; cold—ice-cold hard;
It broods on the splendour of my disgrace—
Remorseless and unmarred.

I am the Flesh . . . With drooping lid
My eyes like sea-flowers drowse and shine
Unfathomably far. I bid
The lost all hope resign.

I am the Devil . . . *H'sst*, stoop close!
The hatred in my vulture stare
Thy doubting, fainting soul will dose
With cordials rich and rare.

I am the World . . . Come, enter, feast!
Look not too nearly—gilt, or gold?
Nor heed the wailing of man and beast,
The clamour of bought and sold!

I am the Flesh . . . Enormous, dim,
Dream doth invite thee, thick with fumes,
Of burning gums. Faint visions gleam,
Sea's phosphor the vague illumes.

I am the Devil . . . Head askew,
And dwelling eye. See, how earth's straight
Distorted-crooked crocks. And through
Time's bars grins gibbering Fate.

ARROGANCE

I saw bleak Arrogance, with brows of brass,
Clad nape to sole in shimmering foil of lead,
Stark down his nose he stared; a crown of glass
Aping the rainbow, on his tilted head.

His very presence drained the vital air;
He sate erect—stone-cold, self-crucified;
On either side of him an empty chair;
And sawdust trickled from his wounded side.

AN OLD CANNON

Come, patient rust;
Come, spider with thy loom,
Make of this enginery,
War's dateless tomb!

Frail bindweed, clamber, and cling,
And clog this motionless wheel;
Upon its once hot throat
Hoar-frost, congeal!

O, may its thunder have won
A last surcease,
And its dark mouth of woe
Ever yet hollower grow
In praise of peace!

NAPOLEON

'What is the world, O soldiers?
  It is I:
I, this incessant snow,
 This northern sky;
Soldiers, this solitude
 Through which we go
   Is I.'

THE FIELD

Yes, there was once a battle here:
There, where the grass takes on a shade
Of paradisal green, sun-clear—
 There the last stand was made.

THE HOUSE

'Mother, it's such a lonely house,'
The child cried; and the wind sighed.
'A narrow but a lovely house,'
The mother replied.

'Child, it is such a narrow house.'
The ghost cried; and the wind sighed.
'A narrow and a lonely house,'
The withering grass replied.

ECHO

'Who called?' I said, and the words
  Through the whispering glades,
Hither, thither, baffled the birds—
  'Who called? Who called?'

The leafy boughs on high
  Hissed in the sun;
The dark air carried my cry
  Faintingly on:

Eyes in the green, in the shade,
  In the motionless brake,
Voices that said what I said,
  For mockery's sake:

'Who cares?' I bawled through my tears;
  The wind fell low:
In the silence, 'Who cares? Who cares?'
  Wailed to and fro.

TO A CANDLE

Burn stilly, thou; and come with me.
I'll screen thy rays. Now . . . Look, and see,
Where, like a flower furled,
Sealed from this busy world,
Tranquil brow, and lid, and lip,
One I love lies here asleep.

Low upon her pillow is
A head of such strange loveliness—
Gilded-brown, unwoven hair—
That dread springs up to see it there:
Lest so profound a trance should be
Death's momentary alchemy.

Venture closer, then. Thy light
Be little day to this small night!
Fretting through her lids it makes
The lashes stir on those pure cheeks;
The scarcely-parted lips, it seems,
Pine, but in vain, to tell her dreams.

Every curve and hollow shows
In faintest shadow—mouth and nose;
Pulsing beneath the silken skin
The milk-blue blood rills out and in:
A bird's might be that slender bone,
Magic itself to ponder on.

Time hath spread its nets in vain;
The child she was is home again;
Veiled with Sleep's seraphic grace.
How innocent yet how wise a face!
Mutely entreating, it seems to sigh,—
'Love made me. It is only I.

153

'Love made this house wherein there dwells
A thing divine, and homeless else.
Not mine the need to ponder why
In this sweet prison I exult and sigh.
Not mine to bid you hence. God knows
It was for joy he shaped the rose.'

See, she stirs. A hand at rest
Slips from above that gentle breast,
White as winter-mounded snows,
Summer-sweet as that wild rose . . .
Thou lovely thing! Ah, welladay!
Candle, I dream. Come, come away!

TARBURY STEEP

The moon in her gold over Tarbury Steep
    Wheeled full, in the hush of the night,
To rabbit and hare she gave her chill beams
    And to me on that silvery height.

From the dusk of its glens thrilled the nightjar's strange cry,
    A peewit wailed over the wheat,
Else still was the air, though the stars in the sky
    Seemed with music in beauty to beat.

O many a mortal has sat there before,
    Since its chalk lay in shells in the sea,
And the ghosts that looked out of the eyes of them all
    Shared Tarbury's moonlight with me.

And many, as transient, when I have gone down,
    To the shades and the silence of sleep,
Will gaze, lost in dream, on the loveliness seen
    In the moonshine of Tarbury Steep.

CLAVICHORD

Hearken! Tiny, clear, discrete:
The listener within deems solely his,
     A music so remote and sweet
    It all but lovely as silence is.

THE GALLIASS

    'Tell me, tell me,
     Unknown stranger,
  When shall I sight me
      That tall ship
On whose flower-wreathed counter is gilded,
   Sleep?'

    'Landsman, landsman,
     Lynx nor kestrel
  Ne'er shall descry from
      Ocean steep
That midnight-stealing, high-pooped galliass,
   Sleep.'

    'Promise me, Stranger,
     Though I mark not
  When cold night-tide's
      Shadows creep,
Thou wilt keep unwavering watch for *Sleep.*'

    'Myriad the lights are,
     Wayworn landsman,
  Rocking the dark through
      On the deep:
She alone burns none to prove her *Sleep.*'

NOD

Softly along the road of evening,
  In a twilight dim with rose,
Wrinkled with age, and drenched with dew
  Old Nod, the shepherd, goes.

His drowsy flock streams on before him,
  Their fleeces charged with gold,
To where the sun's last beam leans low
  On Nod the shepherd's fold.

The hedge is quick and green with brier,
  From their sand the conies creep;
And all the birds that fly in heaven
  Flock singing home to sleep.

His lambs outnumber a noon's roses,
  Yet, when night's shadows fall,
His blind old sheep-dog, Slumber-soon,
  Misses not one of all.

His are the quiet steeps of dreamland,
  The waters of no-more-pain,
His ram's bell rings beneath an arch of stars,
  'Rest, rest, and rest again.'

THE SLEEPING CHILD

Like night-shut flower is this slumbering face,
  Lamplight, for moon, upon its darkness spying;
That wheat-stook hair, the gold-fringed lids, the grace
  Of body entranced, and without motion lying.

Passive as fruit the rounded cheek; bright lip;
  The zigzag turquoise of that artery straying;
Thridding the chartless labyrinths of sleep,
  River of life in fount perpetual playing.

Magical light! though we are leagues apart,
  My stealthiest whisper would at once awake thee!
Not I, thou angel thing! At peace thou art.
  And childhood's dreams, at least, need not forsake thee.

THE SLEEPER

The Lovely, sleeping, lay in bed,
  Her limbs, from quiet foot to chin,
Still as the dust of one that's dead
Whose spirit waits the entering-in.

Yet her young cheek with life's faint dye
Was mantled o'er; her gentle breast
Like sea at peace with starry sky,
  Moved with a heart at rest.

Fair country of a thousand springs,
  Calm hill and vale! Those hidden eyes
And tongue that daylong talks and sings,
  Wait only for the sun to rise.

Let but a bird call in that ear,
  Let beam of day that window wan,
This hidden one will, wakening, hear,
  And deathlike slumber-swoon be gone:

Her ardent eyes once more will shine,
  She will uplift her hair-crowned head;
At lip, miraculous, life's wine,
  At hand, its wondrous bread.

THE OWL

Apart, thank Heaven, from all to do
To keep alive the long day through;
To imagine; think; watch; listen to;
There still remains—the heart to bless,
Exquisite pregnant Idleness.

Why, we might let all else go by
To seek its Essence till we die . . .

Hark, now—that Owl, 'a-snoring in his tree,
'Till it grow dark enough for him to see'.

ULLADARE

Down by thy waters, Ulladare,
  A cedar gloomy and profound
Bids the north wind awaken there
  How sad a sound!

No exile's harp-strings could entice
  Sorrow so heedfully as this
To wake with music memories
  Of bygone bliss.

Then what far peace, to me unknown,
  Seems by that gently lipping wave,
That shrouded tree, to brood upon,
  Unless the grave?

From WINGED CHARIOT

Were moments seeds, we then therein might say
What hidden kind, hue, value, beauty lay,
Virtue and quality. But, these away,

Theirs only quantity, mere measurement,
Sans substance, pattern, form, shape, taste and scent—
Flimsier than bubble, and more transient.

Should, then, a Stranger from another Sphere
Enquire, '*This time, of which so much I hear?*
Light—dark; heat—cold; void—solid; these are clear;
But TIME? What is it? Show *me some, Monsieur!*'

What should we choose for semblance? A flake of snow?
A beach-brine bubble? A tiny shell or two?
Poised in the sun, pure diamond of dew?
Or whisper, '*Look! a* clock! *Now watch Time flow;*
It's a Machine, *you see. It makes it go.*'

Bland face; sly jerking hands: staring he'd stay,
Dumbly astonished. And then turn, and say,
Closer to Nothingness could nothing stray!
And now, pray, make Time flow the other *way!*'

Nimbused in his own song at dawn of day,
From earth's cold clods the skylark wings his way,
Into the sun-gilt crest of heaven to stray.

Housed in the dark of sleepy farms below,
At their own hour the cocks craned up to crow,
Their harems hearkening in obsequious row.

But wheel and barrel, ratchet, pawl, and spring?
Dear heart alive, how dull and dead a thing,
Compared with any creature on the wing,
Wherewith to measure even a glimpse of Spring.

Or, 'splitting seconds', to attempt to mete
The thrill with which a firefly's pinions beat.
Yes, or the languor, lingering and sweet,

When, lulled in the embraces of the sun,
The rose exults that her brief course is run
And heat-drowsed honey-bee has come; is gone.

Last night, at window idling, what saw I
Against the dusky summer greenery?—
Midges, a myriad, that up and down did fly,
Obedient to the breezes eddying by—
Sylphs scarcely of Time but of mere transiency:

An ovoid of intricate *winged* things, beautiful;
As on some sea-breeze morning, sunned and cool,
One may peer down upon a wavering shoal—
Like eddying weed in ebb-tide's lap and lull—
Of tiniest fish-fry in a rock-bound pool . . .

WINTER EVENING

Over the wintry fields the snow drifts; falling, falling;
    Its frozen burden filling each hollow. And hark;
    Out of the naked woods a wild bird calling,
        On the starless verge of the dark!

Verse Selections

From THE TRAVELLER

In this oblivion he dreamed a dream:—
He dreamed the transitory host of men,
Debased by pride, lust, greed and self-esteem,
Had gone their way; that Earth was freed again.

Their minds had brewed a poison in the blood;
The sap of their own nature had decayed.
They had chosen evil, had resigned the good;
False, faithless, pitiless, and of naught afraid.

Nature, released from this vile incubus,
Had wooed into being creatures of other kind,
Resembling those long since deemed fabulous,
As exquisite in aspect as in mind.

Beings, too, once adored for beauty and grace,
Who had left but echoes in the mirroring air,
Had sought again their bygone dwelling-place;
As happy birds in springtime homeward fare.

And he?—the sport of contraries in sleep!—
To childhood had returned; gone grief and woe;
That Eden of the heart, and fellowship
With innocence, that only children know;

And in a garden played, serene, alone;
Bird, flower, water, shining in his eyes;
And magic hidd'n in even the tiniest stone . . .
When, suddenly, a Trumpet rent the skies:

To Judgement had been called the Sons of Light,
The stellar host, the Sun and all his brood:
Rank beyond rank, height above heavenly height,
Within the eternal peace of God they stood,

Hymning his glory. And, alas, he knew
That, chosen envoy of the Earth, he had come,
Garbed in her beauty, and enraptured too;
But, though he had yearned for joy, his soul was dumb.

And by unuttered edict exiled thence,
He had fallen, as Satan fell, in leaden dismay,
And thus had wakened to the rock-land whence
His spirit, in fantasy, had winged away. . . .

On high a dwindling, sun-bedazzled moon
Paled in the homeless solitudes of space,
Casting gaunt shadow here—his vision gone—
For void companionship in this bitter place.

He, Envoy of the Earth!—that mothering breast;
Those Suns and Sons, what meaning could he find?—
A cold satanic irony at best,
Or scoff of that mocking-bird in sleep, his mind.

Oh, that he had but one bright candle here
To pierce the double-dark of body and soul!
Could but a strain of music reach his ear
To ease this heartsick wretchedness and dole!

From lifted brow his leaden-lidded eyes
Searched the vast furrows of unanswering stone
To where the cedar-arc'd abyss must rise
Whence he had journeyed to this end, alone.

Gazing, he mused, beset by mystery,
Mere Sentience in the silence of the night;
Could Earth itself a living creature be,
And he its transitory parasite?—

A frosted incubus, by the cold congealed,
Doubting his senses, vacantly aware
Of what already instinct had revealed—
His deadliest danger now was blank despair.

Like an old zany, he seemed, who, year by year,
The slave has been of an Excelsior,
Its goal Eureka; and when that draws near
Hears fleshless knuckles on his chamber-door!

Or like a doting lover who at last
By one whose source had seemed of heavenly grace
Forsaken is, in outer darkness cast,
Her cheating blandishment a Lamia's face.

Meagre his saddlebag as camel's hump
When, sand-marooned, she staggers to her doom.
As shrunken too, his Arab's ribs and rump
Showed taut as vellum stretched upon a drum.

He strove in vain to reason, numbed with sleep,
But conscious that at first faint token of dawn,
Wraiths at whose beauty even the blind might weep,
Wooed to his solitude, had come, and gone—

Wraiths all but lost to memory, whose love
Had burned in hearts that never more would beat;
Of whose compassion sense could bring no proof,
Though solace 'twas beyond all telling sweet—

Like flowers that a child brings home; to fade.
Alas, alas, no longing could restore
Life to the faithful by neglect betrayed!
Too late for ransom; they'd return no more—

Had left him, like a castaway adrift,
Lashed to a raft upon a chartless sea,
His only motion the huge roller's lift,
Its depths his only hope at peace to be.

'Sea'! when this waste of stone in which he lay
Like night-blue porcelain was, untinged with red.
But when his cracked lips stirred, as if to pray,
He caught but leaf-dry whisper of what they said.

So tense was this his solitude—the sky
Its mute and viewless canopy—that when
His grieved 'O God!' was followed by a sigh,
It seemed eternity had breathed amen.

THE VISION

O starry face, bound in grave strands of hair,
Aloof, remote, past speech or thought to bless—
Life's haunting mystery and the soul's long care,
Music unheard, heart's utter silentness,
Beauty no mortal life could e'er fulfil,
Yet garnered loveliness of all I see,
Which in this transient pilgrimage is still
Steadfast desire of that soul's loyalty;

Death's haunting harp-string, sleep's mandragora,
Mockery of waking and the dark's despair,
Life's changeless vision that fades not away—
O starry face, bound in grave strands of hair!
Hands faintly sweet with flowers from fields unseen,
Breasts cold as mountain snow and far waves' foam,
Eyes changeless and immortal and serene—
Spent is this wanderer, and you call him home!

THE TRUTH OF THINGS

'You might have told me the truth of things!'—
  ' *"The truth of things"*, *my dear?*'
'How softly the wind, as if in ruth,
    Breathes in the willows here. . . .
    It may be a comfort at last to dream
    Where the dead their mole-mounds rear.'

'You might have told me the facts of life!'—
  ' *"The facts of life"*, *my dear?*'
    'How blazingly looked that stranger's wife
    With love. Why did he leer
And writhe from her clutching hand as if
    From a tainted shape on a bier?'

'You might have told me what's never told.'—
  ' *"What's never told"*, *my dear?*'
'Those queer little gleams that were darkly rolled
    From mother's eyes, ere the day drew near
When they took her away for ever and aye. . . .
    Are mine as strangely clear?'

ONE IN THE PUBLIC GALLERY

The Seraph scanned the murderer in the dock—
The motionless Judge, beneath the court-room clock,
The listening jury, warders, counsel, Clerk;
Ay, one and all who shared that deepening dark:
    And then, as I shunned to see,
He turned his burning eyes and looked at me.

PEEPING TOM

I was there—by the curtains
When someone brought a box:
And one at the house of
    Miss Emily knocks:

A low *rat-tat-tat*.
The door opened—and then,
Slowly mounting the steps, stooped
    In the strange men.

Then the door darkly shut,
And I saw their legs pass,
Like an insect's, Miss Emily's
    Window-glass—

Though why all her blinds
Have been hanging so low
These dumb foggy days,
    I don't know.

Yes, only last week
I watched her for hours,
Potting out for the winter her
    Balcony flowers.

And this very Sunday
She mused there a space,
Gazing into the street, with
    The vacantest face:

Then turned her long nose
And looked up at the skies—
One you would not have thought
    Weather-wise!

Yet . . . well, out stepped the men—
One ferrety-fair—
With gentlemen's hats, and
    Whiskers and hair;

And paused in the porch.
Then smooth, solemn, grey,
They climbed to their places,
    And all drove away

In their square varnished carriage,
The horse full of pride,
With a tail like a charger's:
    They all sate outside.

Then the road became quiet:
Her house stiff and staid—
Like a Stage—while you wait
    For the Harlequinade . . .

But what can Miss Emily
Want with a box
So long, narrow, shallow,
    And without any locks?

THE PENNY OWING

Poor blind Tam, the beggar man,
I'll give a penny to as soon as I can.
Where he stood at the corner in his rags, and cried,
The sun without shadow does now abide.

Safe be my penny till I come some day
To where Tam's waiting. And then I'll say,
'Here is my ghost, Tam, from the fire and dew,
And the penny I grudged kept safe for you.'

OFF THE GROUND

Three jolly Farmers
Once bet a pound
Each dance the others would
Off the ground.
Out of their coats
They slipped right soon,
And neat and nicesome,
Put each his shoon.

One—Two—Three!—
And away they go,
Not too fast,
And not too slow;
Out from the elm-tree's
Noonday shadow,
Into the sun
And across the meadow.
Past the schoolroom,
With knees well bent
Fingers a-flicking,
They dancing went.
Up sides and over,
And round and round,
They crossed click-clacking,
The Parish bound.
By Tupman's meadow
They did their mile,
Tee-to-tum
On a three-barred stile.
Then straight through Whipham,
Downhill to Week,
Footing it lightsome,
But not too quick,

Up fields to Watchet,
And on through Wye,
Till seven fine churches
They'd seen skip by—
Seven fine churches
And five old mills,
Farms in the valley,
And sheep on the hills;
Old Man's Acre
And Dead Man's Pool
All left behind,
As they danced through Wool.

And Wool gone by,
Like tops that seem
To spin in sleep
They danced in dream:
Withy—Wellover—
Wassop—Wo—
Like an old clock
Their heels did go.
A league and a league
And a league they went,
And not one weary,
And not one spent.
And lo, and behold!
Past Willow-cum-Leigh
Stretched with its waters
The great green sea.

Says Farmer Bates,
'I puffs and I blows,
What's under the water,
Why, no man knows!'
Says Farmer Giles,
'My wind comes weak,

And a good man drownded
Is far to seek.'
But Farmer Turvey,
On twirling toes
Up's with his gaiters,
And in he goes:
Down where the mermaids
Pluck and play
On their twangling harps
In a sea-green day;
Down where the mermaids,
Finned and fair,
Sleek with their combs
Their yellow hair. . . .

Bates and Giles—
On the shingle sat,
Gazing at Turvey's
Floating hat.
But never a ripple
Nor bubble told
Where he was supping
Off plates of gold.
Never an echo
Rilled through the sea
Of the feasting and dancing
And minstrelsy.
They called—called—called:
Came no reply:
Naught but the ripples'
Sandy sigh.
Then glum and silent
They sat instead,
Vacantly brooding
On home and bed,
Till both together

Stood up and said:—
'Us knows not, dreams not,
Where you be,
Turvey, unless
In the deep blue sea;
But axcusing silver—
And it comes most willing—
Here's us two paying
Our forty shilling;
For it's sartin sure, Turvey,
Safe and sound,
You danced us square, Turvey;
Off the ground!'

'DRY AUGUST BURNED'

Dry August burned. A harvest hare
Limp on the kitchen table lay,
Its fur blood-blubbered, eyes astare,
While a small child that stood near by
Wept out her heart to see it there.

Sharp came the *clop* of hoofs, the clang
Of dangling chain, voices that rang.
Out like a leveret she ran,
To feast her glistening bird-clear eyes
On a team of field artillery,
Gay, to manœuvres, thudding by.
Spur and gun and limber plate
Flashed in the sun. Alert, elate,
Noble horses, foam at lip,
Harness, stirrup, holster, whip,
She watched the sun-tanned soldiery,
Till dust-white hedge had hidden away—

Its din into a rumour thinned—
The laughing, jolting, wild array:
And then—the wonder and tumult gone—
Stood nibbling a green leaf, alone,
Her dark eyes, dreaming. . . . She turned, and ran,
Elf-like, in to the house again.
The hare had vanished. . . . 'Mother,' she said,
Her tear-stained cheek now flushed with red,
'Please, may I go and see it skinned?'

STILL LIFE

Bottle, coarse tumbler, loaf of bread,
Cheap paper, a lean long kitchen knife:
No moral, no problem, sermon, or text,
No hint of a Why, Whence, Whither, or If;
Mere workaday objects put into paint—
Bottle and tumbler, loaf and knife. . . .
And engrossed, round-spectacled Chardin's
        Passion for life.

HERE I SIT

Here I sit, and glad am I
So to sit contentedly,
While with never-hastening feet
Time pursues the Infinite;
And a silence centuries-deep
Swathes my mind as if in sleep.
Passive hand, and inward eyes
Press on their transient enterprise;

As, across my paper's white,
Creeps the ink from left to right,
Wooing from a soundless brain
The formless into words again:
So I sit, and glad am I
So to sit contentedly.

SEEN AND HEARD

Lovely things these eyes have seen—
Dangling cherries in leaves dark-green;
Ducks as white as winter snow,
Which quacked as they webbed on a-row;
The wren that, with her needle note,
Through blackthorn's foam will flit and float,
      And sun will sheen.

Lovely music my ears have heard—
Catkined twigs in April stirred
By the same air that carries true
Two notes from Africa, *Cuck-oo*;
And then, when night has darkened again,
The lone wail of the willow-wren,
And cricket rasping on, 'Goode'n—goode'n',
      Shriller than mouse or bird.

Ay, and all praise would I, please God, dispose
For but one faint-hued cowslip, one wild rose.

THE LITTLE CREATURE

Twinkum, twankum, twirlum and twitch—
My great grandam—She was a Witch.
Mouse in wainscot, Saint in niche—
My great grandam—She was a Witch;
Deadly nightshade flowers in a ditch—
My great grandam—She was a Witch;
Long through the shroud, it grows stitch by stitch—
My great grandam—She was a Witch;
Wean your weakling before your breech—
My great grandam—She was a Witch;
The fattest pig's but a double flitch—
My great grandam—She was a Witch;
Nightjars rattle, owls scritch—
My great grandam—She was a Witch.

   Pretty and small,
   A mere nothing at all,
   Pinned up sharp in the ghost of a shawl,
   She'd straddle her down to the kirkyard wall,
   And mutter and whisper and call,
   And call. . . .

Red blood out and black blood in,
My Nannie says I'm a child of sin.
How did I choose me my witchcraft kin?
Know I as soon as dark's dreams begin
Snared is my heart in a nightmare's gin;
Never from terror I out may win;
So dawn and dusk I pine, peak, thin,
Scarcely knowing t'other from which—
My great grandam—She was a Witch.

TOM'S ANGEL

No one was in the fields
But me and Polly Flint,
When, like a giant across the grass,
The flaming angel went.

It was budding time in May,
And green as green could be,
And all in his height he went along
Past Polly Flint and me.

We'd been playing in the woods,
And Polly up, and ran,
And hid her face, and said,
'Tom! Tom! The Man! The Man!'

And I up-turned; and there,
Like flames across the sky,
With wings all bristling, came
The Angel striding by.

And a chaffinch overhead
Kept whistling in the tree
While the Angel, blue as fire, came on
Past Polly Flint and me.

And I saw his hair, and all
The ruffling of his hem,
As over the clovers his bare feet
Trod without stirring them.

Polly—she cried; and, oh!
We ran, until the lane
Turned by the miller's roaring wheel,
And we were safe again.

175

SALLIE'S MUSICAL BOX

Once it made music, tiny, frail, yet sweet—
Bead-note of bird where earth and elfland meet.
Now its thin tinkling stirs no more, since she
Whose toy it was, has gone; and taken the key.

NICHOLAS NYE

Thistle and darnel and dock grew there,
   And a bush, in the corner, of may,
On the orchard wall I used to sprawl
   In the blazing heat of the day;
Half asleep and half awake,
   While the birds went twittering by,
And nobody there my lone to share
    But Nicholas Nye.

Nicholas Nye was lean and grey,
   Lame of a leg and old,
More than a score of donkey's years
   He had seen since he was foaled;
He munched the thistles, purple and spiked,
   Would sometimes stoop and sigh,
And turn his head, as if he said,
    'Poor Nicholas Nye!'

Alone with his shadow he'd drowse in the meadow,
   Lazily swinging his tail,
At break of day he used to bray,—
   Not much too hearty and hale;
But a wonderful gumption was under his skin,
   And a clear calm light in his eye,
And once in a while: he'd smile ...
    Would Nicholas Nye.

Seem to be smiling at me, he would,
   From his bush in the corner, of may,—
Bony and ownerless, widowed and worn,
   Knobble-kneed, lonely and grey;
And over the grass would seem to pass
   'Neath the deep dark blue of the sky,
Something much better than words between me
     And Nicholas Nye.

But dusk would come in the apple boughs,
   The green of the glow-worm shine,
The birds in nest would crouch to rest,
   And home I'd trudge to mine;
And there, in the moonlight, dark with dew,
   Asking not wherefore nor why,
Would brood like a ghost, and as still as a post.
     Old Nicholas Nye.

OLD SHELLOVER

'Come!' said Old Shellover.
'What?' says Creep.
'The horny old Gardener's fast asleep;
The fat cock Thrush
To his nest has gone;
And the dew shines bright
In the rising Moon;
Old Sallie Worm from her hole doth peep:
Come!' said Old Shellover.
'Ay!' said Creep.

THOMAS HARDY

Mingled the moonlight with daylight—the last in the nar-
  rowing west;
Silence of nightfall lay over the shallowing valleys at rest
          In the Earth's green breast:
Yet a small multitudinous singing, a lully of voices of birds,
Unseen in the vague shelving hollows, welled up with my
  questioning words:
All Dorsetshire's larks for connivance of sweetness seemed
  trysting to greet
Him in whose song the bodings of raven and nightingale
  meet.

Stooping and smiling, he questioned, 'No birdnotes myself
  do I hear?
Perhaps 'twas the talk of chance farers, abroad in the hush
  with us here—
          In the dusk-light clear?'
And there peered from his eyes, as I listened, a concourse of
  women and men,
Whom his words had made living, long-suffering—they
  flocked to remembrance again;
'O Master,' I cried in my heart, 'lorn thy tidings, grievous thy
  song;
Yet thine, too, this solacing music, as we earthfolk stumble
  along.'

THE OLD AUTHOR

The End, he scrawled, and blotted it. Then eyed
Through darkened glass night's cryptic runes o'erhead.
'My last, and longest book.' He frowned; then sighed:
          'And everything left unsaid!'

'HERE SLEEPS'

Here sleeps, past earth's awakening,
A woman, true and pretty,
Who was herself in everything—
Tender, and grave, and witty.
Her smallest turn of foot, hand, head,
Was way of wind with water;
So with her thoughts and all she said—
It seemed her heart had taught her.
O thou most dear and loving soul
Think not I shall forget thee;
Nor take amiss what here is writ
For those who never met thee!

ROSE

Three centuries now are gone
Since Thomas Campion
Left men his airs, his verse, his heedful prose.
Few other memories
Have we of him, or his,
And, of his sister, none, but that her name was Rose

Woodruff, far moschatel
May the more fragrant smell
When into brittle dust their blossoming goes.
His, too, a garden sweet,
Where rarest beauties meet,
And, as a child, he shared them with this Rose.

Faded, past changing, now,
Cheek, mouth, and childish brow.
Where, too, her phantom wanders no man knows.
Yet, when in undertone
That eager lute pines on,
Pleading of things he loved, it sings of Rose.

THE MOTH

Isled in the midnight air,
Musked with the dark's faint bloom,
Out into glooming and secret haunts
The flame cries, 'Come!'

Lovely in dye and fan,
A-tremble in shimmering grace,
A moth from her winter swoon
Uplifts her face:

Stares from her glamorous eyes;
Wafts her on plumes like mist;
In ecstasy swirls and sways
To her strange tryst.

BLOW, NORTHERN WIND

Blow, northern wind; fall snow;
And thou—my loved and dear,
See, in this waste of burthened cloud
How Spring is near!

See, in those labouring boughs,
Buds stir in their dark sleep;
How in the frost-becrumbling ruts
    The green fires creep.

The dreamless earth has heard
Beneath snow's whispering flakes
A faint shrill childlike voice, a call—
    Sighs, ere she wakes . . .

What Spring have we? Turn back!—
Though this be winter's end,
Still may far-memoried snowdrops bloom
    For us, my friend.

THE ROUND

I watched, upon a vase's rim,
An earwig—strayed from honeyed cell—
Circling a track once strange to him,
    But now known far too well.

With vexed antennae, searching space,
And giddy grope to left and right,
On—and still on—he pressed apace,
    Out of, and into, sight.

In circumambulation drear,
He neither wavered, paused nor stayed;
But now kind Providence drew near—
    A slip of wood I laid

Across his track. He scaled its edge:
And soon was safely restored to where
A sappy, dew-bright, flowering hedge
    Of dahlias greened the air.

Ay, and as apt may be my fate! . . .
Smiling, I turned to work again:
But shivered, where in shade I sate,
    And idle did remain.

AN EPITAPH

Last, Stone, a little yet;
And then this dust forget.
But thou, fair Rose, bloom on.
For she who is gone
Was lovely too; nor would she grieve to be
Sharing in solitude her dreams with thee.

THE OLD SUMMERHOUSE

This blue-washed, old, thatched summerhouse—
Paint scaling, and fading from its walls—
How often from its hingeless door
I have watched—dead leaf, like the ghost of a mouse,
Rasping the worn brick floor—
The snows of the weir descending below,
And their thunderous waterfall.

Fall—fall: dark, garrulous rumour,
Until I could listen no more.
Could listen no more—for beauty with sorrow
Is a burden hard to be borne:
The evening light on the foam, and the swans, there;
That music, remote, forlorn.

MUSIC

When music sounds, gone is the earth I know,
And all her lovely things even lovelier grow;
Her flowers in vision flame, her forest trees
Lift burdened branches, stilled with ecstasies.

When music sounds, out of the water rise
Naiads whose beauty dims my waking eyes,
Rapt in strange dreams burns each enchanted face,
With solemn echoing stirs their dwelling-place.

When music sounds, all that I was I am
Ere to this haunt of brooding dust I came;
While from Time's woods break into distant song
The swift-winged hours, as I hasten along.

AFRAID

Here lies, but seven years old, our little maid,
Once of the darkness Oh, so sore afraid!
Light of the World—remember that small fear,
And when nor moon nor stars do shine, draw near!

THE CHART

That grave small face, but twelve hours here,
Maps secrets stranger than the seas',
In hieroglyphics more austere,
And older far than Rameses'.

MAERCHEN

Soundless the moth-flit, crisp the death-watch tick;
Crazed in her shaken arbour bird did sing;
Slow wreathed the grease adown from soot-clogged wick:
    The Cat looked long and softly at the King.

Mouse frisked and scampered, leapt, gnawed, squeaked;
Small at the window looped cowled bat a-wing;
The dim-lit rafters with the night-mist reeked:
    The Cat looked long and softly at the King.

O wondrous robe enstarred, in night dyed deep:
O air scarce-stirred with the Court's far junketing:
O stagnant Royalty—A-swoon? Asleep?
    The Cat looked long and softly at the King.

'AS I WENT TO THE WELL-HEAD'

    As I went to the well-head
    I heard a bird sing:
    'Lie yonder, lie yonder
    The Islands of Ling.

    'Leagues o'er the water
    Their shores are away,
    In a darkness of stars,
    And a foaming of spray.'

PROSE SELECTIONS

THE TRUMPET

'For Brutus, as you know, was Caesar's angel . . .'
'And he said . . . Am I my brother's keeper?'

The minute church, obscurely lit by a full moon that had not yet found window-glass through which her direct beams could pierce into its gloaming, was deserted and silent. Not a sound, within or without, disturbed its stony quiet—except only the insect-like rapid ticking of a clock in the vestry, and the low pulsating thump of a revolving cogwheel in the tower above the roof. Here and there a polished stone gleamed coldly in the vague luminous haze—a marble head, a wing-tip, a pointing finger, the claws and beak of the eagle on the brazen lectern, the two silvergilt candlesticks flanking the colourless waxen flowers upon the altar. So secret and secluded seemed the church within its nocturnal walls that living creature might never have been here at all—or creatures only so insignificant and transitory as to have left no perceptible trace behind them.

Like a cataleptic's countenance it hinted moreover at no inward activity of its own. And yet, if—fantastic notion—some unseen watcher through the bygone centuries had kept it perpetually within gaze, he might at last have concluded that it possessed a *sort* of stagnant life or animation, at least in its passive obedience to the influences of time, change, decay, and the laws of gravitation. Now it revealed not the faintest symptom of it. If, on the other hand, any immaterial sentinel were still, as ever, on guard within it, he made no sign of his presence here.

Unhasteningly, like water dripping from a fateful urn, the thump-recorded moments ebbed away; and it was approaching midnight and first cockcrow when from beyond the thick stone chancel walls there came the sound of a stealthy footfall, crunching the rain-soaked gravel. An owl squawked, the footsteps ceased; and after a brief pause, began again. The groping rattle of a key in the wards of a lock followed, and presently— with a motion so slow that it was barely perceptible—the heavy curtain that hung over the entrance to the vestry began as if with an extreme caution to be drawn aside; and the slender cone-shaped rays from the thick glass of a small bull's-eye lantern—its radiance thinning into the dusk of the moonlight as it expanded in area—to funnel inquisitively to and fro.

The lantern-bearer himself now appeared—a small boy. His thick fair hair was tousled over a pale forehead, his mouth was ajar and his lips were drawn back a little above his teeth, his eyes gleamed as they moved. The collar of his dark greatcoat had been turned up about his ears, but nevertheless disclosed in the crevice between its lapels the stripes of his pyjama's jacket which had been tucked into a pair of old flannel breeches. Stockinged ankles and damp mud-stained rubber shoes showed beneath the greatcoat. His cheeks at this moment were so pale as scarcely to be tinged with red, and since the pupils of his blue eyes were dilated to their full extent they appeared to be all but jet-black. He was shivering, in part by reason of the cold, in part because of certain inward qualms and forebodings. Only by an effort was he preventing his teeth from beginning to chatter. Still acutely cautious and intent, his head thrust forward, his eyes searching the darker recesses of the building around him as they followed the direction of his tiny searchlight, he stole a pace or two forward, the border of the heavy curtain furtively swinging-to behind him. In spite of the door-key safe in his pocket, he appeared to be divided in mind between hope and dread that he might prove to be not the sole occupant of the church.

Where there is space enough for the human cranium to pass, the shoulders, it is said, can follow; and particularly if they all three belong to a child. One small diamond-paned window in the vestry he had already observed was open. Images, too, less substantial in appearance than those of human beings were occupying his mind's eye. When then a little owl in the dark of the yew tree over the south gate in the moonlit churchyard again suddenly screeched, he started as if at an electric shock. And twice his mouth opened before he managed to call low and hoarsely, 'Are you there, Dick? . . . Dick, are you there?'

Not a stony eyelid in the heads around him had so much as flickered at this timid challenge. The stooping eagle—a large shut Bible on its outstretched wings—had stirred not a feather; the pulpit remained cavernously empty. But a few high-panelled pews, relics of the past, were within view, and even moonlight and lantern-light combined were powerless to reveal anything or anybody that might be hiding behind them. The trespasser appeared to be on the point of retiring as secretly as he had come, when a jangling gurgle, as of some monster muttering in its sleep, began to sound above his head, and the clock chimes rang out the second quarter of the hour. The vibrant metal ceased to hum; and, as if reassured by this interruption, he drew out of his pocket a large stone— a flint such as his remote ancestors would have coveted— roughly dumb-bell in shape, and now waisted with a thick and knotted length of old blindcord. This primitive weapon, long treasured for any emergency, he gently deposited on the shelf behind him, and then followed it into the pew.

Lantern still in hand, he seated himself on the flat faded red cushion that lay along the seat. It was that of one of the mighty, the rector's warden. Even in this half-light, as easily as a cat in the dark, he could spy out all about him now, organ recess to gallery; but he opened his brand-new lantern none the less and trimmed as best he could with his finger nail its charred and oily wick. The fume and stench of the hot metal made him sneeze, whereupon he clicked-to the glass, covered it with his hand, and began listening again. 'Sneak,' he muttered, then suddenly plumped down on the hassock at his feet, rapidly repeated a prayer, with a glance over his shoulder half-covertly crossed himself, then as promptly sat up again; glancing as he did so at the pulpit over his head which he was accustomed to find comfortably brimmed with his father's portly presence.

Fortified by his prayer and by his wrath with the friend who it seemed at the last moment had abandoned their enterprise, he was now comparatively at ease. Tortoise-fashion he snuggled down in his greatcoat in the corner of the pew, having discovered that by craning his neck a little he could fix his vacant eyes on the brilliant disc of the still-ascending moon.

She was the Hunter's moon, and her beams had now begun to silver a clear-glassed square-headed window high up in the south wall of the chancel. He watched her intently, lost in astonishment that at this very moment she should be keeping tryst with him here. But before she had edged far enough above the sill to greet the gilded figure of an angel that surmounted an ornate tomb opposite her peephole, a faint thief-like shuffle from the direction of the vestry door caught his ear. He instantly dropped out of sight into the shelter of his pew. The shuffling ceased, the door creaked. He crouched low; a smile at once apprehensive and malicious creasing his still-childish face. He would give his friend Dick a taste of his own physic.

In the hush, an anguished *Oh, oh, oh, oh!*—like the wailing of a lost soul—fountained up from his lips into the dusk of the roof. *Oh, oh, oh!* Then silence—and silence. And still there came no response. The smile faded out of his face; he had begun to shiver again. He was positively certain that this must be the friend whom he was expecting. And yet—suppose it was not! He leapt up, flashing at the same instant his toy lantern full into the glittering eyes of a dwarfish and motion-less shape which were fixed on him through the sockets of a pitch-black battered mask—a relic of the last Fifth of November.

He had realized what trick was being played on him almost before he had time to be afraid. Nevertheless, for a few moments, his mouth wide-open, he had failed to breathe; and stood shuddering with rage as well as terror. His friend Dick, however, having emerged from his lair in the folds of the curtain, was now plunging about half doubled-up and almost helpless with laughter.

'You silly fool!' he fumed at him in a whisper, 'what did you want to do that for? Shut up! Shut *up*, I tell you! You think it's funny, I suppose. Well, I don't. You're hours late already, and I'm going home. Stop it, do you hear? Can't you remember you're in a *church*?'

From beneath its mask a small sharp-nosed and utterly sober face now showed itself—all laughter gone. 'Who began it, then?' Dick expostulated, dejectedly squeezing his pasteboard mask into his pocket. 'You tried it first on me, with your Oh-oh-oh-ing. And now just because . . . You didn't think of "church" then.'

'Well, I do now. Besides, it's near the time, and I might have broken my neck for all you cared, getting out of the window. What made you so late?'

Dick had been eyeing his friend as might a sorrowful mouse a slice of plum cake a few inches out of its reach. 'I'm sorry, Philip,' he said. 'I didn't mean any harm; honest, I didn't. It was only a lark.' He turned penitently away, and the next instant, as if all troubles were over and all discord pacified, began peeping about him with the movements and anglings of some little night-creature on unexpectedly finding itself in an utterly strange place.

'I say, Philip,' he whispered, 'doesn't it look creepy, just— the moon shining in? I had a dream, and then I woke. But I couldn't have come before. My father was downstairs with a lamp, reading. Besides I was waiting for you *out*side, under the trees. Why did you come *in*? It's by the gate you see them. That's what my mother heard *your* mother say. Oh, I'm glad I came; aren't you?'

The sentences were sprayed out in minute beads of words like the hasty cadenzas of a bird. The neat black head, the small bright eyes, the shallow wall of close-cropped hair, the sloping shoulders—every line, movement and quick darting variation of postures gave him a resemblance to a bird—including the alert, quick, shy yet fearless spirit within that neat skull's brittle walls.

Philip, who had been intently watching him meanwhile, had now recovered his equanimity, his pulse had sobered down, but he was still only partially placated, and querulous.

'Of course I came in. What was the good of loafing out there where *any*body might see us? It's cold and mouldy enough in here. You don't seem to remember I mustn't go out at night, because of my chest. I've been waiting until my feet are like stones. Did you hear that owl just now—or something?'

Dick having at last ventured in from the other end of the pew, had now seated himself beside his friend on the flat crimson cushion.

'Golly!' he exclaimed, his sharp eyes now fixed on the flint, 'what's that for? I shouldn't care to have a crump over the head with that!' He peered up winningly into his companion's fair face. 'I didn't really expect you would come, Philip. But', he sighed, 'I'm glad.'

'Didn't I *say* I would come?' retorted Philip in a small condescending voice. 'That's nothing.' He nodded at his stone. 'I always carry that at night. How was I to know. . . .? *Didn't I*?'

The neat small head nodded violently. 'M'm.'

'Then why didn't you expect me to?'

'Oh, well, I didn't.' A thin ingratiating little smile passed over Dick's face and as quickly vanished. 'It wasn't so easy for you as it was for me. That's why.'

'That stone', said Philip incisively, 'keeps any harm from happening to me. It's got magic in it.'

'Has it, Philip? . . . What did *that*?' He was eyeing the patch of dried blood on the hand that clutched the bent wire handle of the lantern.

'Oh, that?' was the lofty reply. 'That's nothing; that was only the rope. It burned like billy-ho, and I fell half-way from my bedroom window-sill on to the lawn. An awful crack. But nobody heard me, even though the other windows were wide open round the corner. You could see them against the sky. My mother always sleeps with her windows open—all the year round. A doctor in London told her it would be good for her. I don't believe that about your father reading, though. When everybody is in bed and asleep! I didn't even know your father *could* read.'

'Well, he was, or I wouldn't have said so. He was reading the Bible. How could I tell that if he wasn't reading at all?'

'Anyhow, I bet it wasn't the Bible. Even my father wouldn't do that—not after evening prayers. Would he whack you much if he caught you?'

Dick shook his head. 'No fear. My mother won't have *him* punishing me, whatever happens. He preaches at me no end; and says I'll never be good for anything. Once,' he added pensively, as if scarcely able to believe his own ears, 'once he said I was a little imp of hell. Then my mother flared up. But he wouldn't beat me; oh no, he wouldn't beat me. Yesterday my mother came back with a big bundle of old clothes. There was a black silk jacket, and some stockings and hats and feathers and things, an *enormous* bundle. And this—look!'

He undid a button of his jacket and pulled out from underneath it a pinch of an old green silk dressing-gown.

'Why, that's mine!' said Philip. 'I've had it for ages.' He stared at it censoriously, as if dubious whether or not to ask for it back. 'But I don't think I want it now, because it's miles too small for me. My grandmother gave it me for a Christmas present donkey's years ago. She's so rich she doesn't mind *what* things cost—when she gives me anything. That's real Spitalfields silk, that is; you can't get it anywhere now. You'll crumple it up and spoil it if you wear it stuffed in like that.' He peered closer. 'What have you got on underneath it! You're all puffed out like a turkey-cock.'

Dick promptly edged back from the investigating finger, a sly look of confusion passing swiftly over his face. 'That's my other clothes,' he explained.

'What *I* say,' said Philip, still eyeing his companion as if only a constant vigilance could hope to detect what he might not be up to next, 'what *I* say is, your mother's jolly lucky to get expensive things given to her—good things, even if they *are* left-offs. Most of our old stuff goes to the Jumble Sales. I bet,' he suddenly broke off, 'I bet if your *real* father found you skulking here, he'd whack you hot and strong.'

The alert and supple body beside his own had suddenly stiffened, and the dangling spindle legs beneath the pew ceased to swing.

'No, he wouldn't,' Dick hardly more than whispered.

'Why not?'

'For one thing he just wouldn't. He knows he's nothing to do with me; not now; and leaves me alone. For all that, I went out rabbiting with him one night last summer. And nobody knew. It was warm and still and pitch-black—not like this; and when the moon began to come up over the woods, he sent me home. I know *he* wouldn't either. Besides,' he drew in his chin a little as if the words were refusing to come out of his throat, 'he's dead.'

'Dead! Oh, I say! I like that! Oh no, he isn't; *that's* not true. *He* isn't dead. Why, I heard them reading out about him in the newspapers only a few weeks ago. That's what you *say*. I know what has become of him; and I bet your tongue is burning. What's more, if your other father hadn't been Chapel you would never have had *any* father—not to show, I mean. Your mother would have been just like any other woman, though I don't suppose she could have gone on living in the village. But as he *is* Chapel, and, according to what you say, sits up as late as this reading in the Bible, I can't understand why he lets you sing in our choir. I call *that* a hypocrite. I'd like to see my father letting *me* go to Chapel. He must be just a hypocrite, Bible or not.'

Dick made no attempt whatever to examine this delicate moral question. 'Oh, no, he isn't,' he retorted hotly. 'He's as good as yours any day. He goes by what my mother says: if you are Chapel, keep Chapel. *She's* not a hypocrite. And you'd better not say so, either.'

'I didn't say it. I didn't say that your mother was a hypocrite; not a *hypocrite*. I like your mother. And nobody's going to prevent me from going with you either, if I want to. Not if I want to. Your mother's been jolly decent to me—often. Mrs. Fuller sneaks: *she* doesn't.'

'So is your mother to me—when you aren't there. At least she talks to me sometimes then. And I'm glad you're my friend, Philip. The other day she gave me a hunch of cake, and she made me share a sip of wine from my mother's glass. Because it was her birthday. Some day I'm going to be a sailor, and going to sea. She had been crying, because her eyes were red; and *your* mother said that crying was no use at all—because I'm growing up more and more like her every day, and shall be a comfort to her when I'm a man. And so I will; you *see!*'

' "Wine"! Did she just? But that was only because she's always kind to people—to everybody. She doesn't mind *who* it is. That's why she likes being liked by everybody. But after what my father read out in the newspaper, he said he entreated her to be more careful. She must think of *him*, my father said. He didn't want to have the village people talking. He tapped his eyeglasses on the paper and said it was a standing scandal. That's what he said. He was purple in the face.' His voice rather suddenly fell silent, as if, like a dog, he had scented indiscretions. 'But I say: *if* your real father is just dead, he would be the very person according to you to be coming here to-night. *Then* you'd look mighty funny, I should think.'

Dick's legs, like opposed pendulums, had begun very sluggishly to swing again. 'Oh no, I wouldn't, because that's just what doesn't happen; and I told you so. It's the people who are going to die soon—next year—who come: *their* ghosts. Wouldn't they look white and awful, Philip, coming in under the yew tree. . . . I expect its roots go down all among the coffins. Shall we go out now and watch? It's as bright as day; you could see a bird hopping about.'

' "Ghosts"!' was the derisive reply. 'I like that! *You* can. I'm not. How can they be ghosts, silly, if they're still alive? Besides, even if there are such things, and even if what your mother told you is really true, you said yourself that they would come *into* the church. So if any *should* come and we keep here and hide and peep over the edge, they can't possibly see us—if ghosts do see. And then we shall be near the door in there. They would be surprised to find that one open, I should think. But even if they were, and ghosts don't mind doors, they wouldn't come in at a potty little door like that.'

He paused as if to listen, and continued more boldly. 'Not mind you, that I believe a single word of anything you've said —all that stuff. Not really. I came . . .' he faltered, turning his head away, 'only just for a game, and because you dared me to. Why you asked me to come *really* is because you were frightened of being here alone. You wait and see, I'll dare *you* in a minute. Besides, how do you know anybody *is* going to die in the village next year—except old Mrs. Harrison? And she's been dying ever since I can remember. She takes snuff, but she can't stir a foot out of her bed. I bet she hasn't any ghost left. *She* wouldn't come.' The sentence suddenly concluded in a prodigious shuddering yawn. It reminded him that he was cold and that the fatal moment was rapidly nearing. 'Did you say, before, or after, the clock strikes?'

Dick paused a moment before replying, and then piped up confidently: 'It's the very second while the last clump of the bell is sounding. That's when they get to the church. Because it's midnight. And all the ghosts begin to walk then. Some come up out of their graves. But'—he sighed, as if saddened at the poverty of his expectations—'only very seldom. The people who go to heaven wouldn't want to, and the Devil wouldn't let the others out. At least that's what I think.'

'What *you* think! And yet', retorted Philip indignantly, 'you talk all that stuff about ghosts; and believe it too. I'd just like to see your ghost. That'd be a skinny one if you like —like a starved bird. Would *you* come back?'

Dick leant his body forward; he was sitting on his hands; and at this his black, close-cropped head nodded far more vigorously than a china Mandarin's. 'I don't *know*,' he said; 'but I like being out at night. I like—oh, everything. . . . If ghosts can smell,' he began again in small matter-of-fact tones, 'they'd soon snuff *us* out. Look at it smoking.'

The two boys sat mute for a while, watching the tiny slender thread of sooty smoke from the lantern wreathing up in the luminous air; and in the silence—which, after their tongues had ceased chattering, immediately flooded the church fathoms deep—they stayed, listening; their senses avid for the faintest whisper. But the night was windless, and the earth coldly still in the deathly radiance of the moon. And if the Saints in their splendour were themselves assembled in the heavens to celebrate their earthly festival, no sound of their rejoicings reached these small pricked-up human ears.

'If,' at last Dick exploded, gazing up into the vaporous glooms of the roof above his head, 'if any more light comes in, the walls will burst. I love the moon; I love the light. . . . *I*'m going to have a peep.'

With a galvanic wriggle he had snatched his arm free from Philip's grasp, had nimbly whipped out of the pew, and vanished behind the curtain that concealed the vestry door.

Philip shuffled uneasily in his seat, hesitating whether or not to follow him. But from a native indolence and for other motives, and in spite of his incredulity, he decided to stay where he was. It seemed safer than the churchyard. From a few loose jujubes in his greatcoat pocket he chose the cleanest, and sat quietly sucking, his eyes fixed on the monument that not only dominated but dwarfed the small but lovely chancel. The figure of its angel was now bathed with the silver of the moon. With long-toed feet at once clasping and spurning the orb beneath them, it stood erect, on high. Chin out-thrust, its steadfast sightless eyes were fixed upon the faded blue and geranium red of the panelled roof. Its braided locks drawn back from a serene and impassive visage, its left hand lay flat upon its breast, and with the right it clasped a tapering, up-lifted, bell-mouthed, gilded trumpet, held firmly not against but at a little distance from its lips.

Unlike Dick, Philip was not a chorister. He was none the less his father's son, and as soon as he had learned to behave himself, to put his penny in the plate and to refrain from babbling aloud, he had been taken to church every Sunday morning. This had been as natural an accompaniment of the Sabbath as clean underclothes, Etons, and hot sausages for breakfast. Thus he had heard hundreds of his father's sermons —sermons usually as simple as they were short. If only he had listened to them he might by now have become well-founded in dogma, a plain but four-square theologian. Instead of listening, however, he would usually sit 'thinking'. Side by side with his mother, his cheek all but brushing her silks, with their delicate odours, his fingers—rather clammy fingers when the weather was hot—lightly clasping hers while he counted over and over the sharp-stoned rings on her dainty fingers, he had been wont to follow his fancies.

Morning service had been the general rule. During the last few years however his mother had become the victim of periodical sick headaches, of lassitude and palpitations, and had been given strict injunctions not to overdo things, to rest. Occasionally too she had worldly-minded visitors, including a highly unorthodox sister, whom it would be tactless even to attempt to persuade to spend her Sundays as, usually, she felt dutifully impelled to spend her own. All this she would confide to Philip. She must on no account, she repeatedly admonished him, be alarmed or worried, distressed or disturbed. As for his stout and rubicund father, who was at least ten years her senior, he adored every bone in her body. But though by nature placable and easy-going, he was also subject to outbursts of temper and fits of moroseness as periodical as her attacks of migraine. It was therefore prudent, if only for her sake, to avoid anything in the nature of a scene. 'So Philip,' she would cajole him, 'you will *promise* me to be a good boy, and you'll go to church this evening, won't you—instead of now? And you won't make any fuss about it? You know your father wishes it.'

Philip might demur, and, if it was practicable, bargain with her; but at heart he much preferred this arrangement. It meant that on these particular Sundays he was safe from interference, and could spend the whole morning as he pleased. It was too the darkening evenings about the time of the equinox, when it was not yet necessary to light the brass oil-lamps that hung in the nave, and two solitary candlesticks alone gleamed spangling in the pulpit—it was these he loved best. Only the village and farm people came to evening service, and not many even of them. Philip would sit in his pew, and, absorbed in his secret cogitations, enjoy the whole hour. The church changed then its very being. It welled over with mystery. Even in the joy of a Harvest Festival, when he could admire the flowers and vegetables and the gigantic loaf of bread under the lectern, the bloom of grapes and apples, the minute sheaves of wheat and barley gently nodding their heads to the more impulsive strains of the organ, there was still a faint tinge of sadness. And the unheeded sermon drowsed his senses like an incantation. His father's honeyed pulpit voice rose and fell like that of some dulcet Old Man of the Sea; and he himself, though not, like Dick, sporting and whispering noiselessly with his surpliced choir-mates out of sight of the preacher, was at any rate beyond any direct scrutiny. Meanwhile the bulky family cook, his mother's usual proxy on these occasions, would settle down beside him into a state of apathy so complete, her cotton-gloved hands convulsively clasped over her diaphragm, that it was only by an occasional sniff he could tell that she was perhaps leading as active an internal life as he was, and was neither asleep nor dead.

Now and then he had himself been wafted away in sleep into regions of the most exorbitant scenery, events and vagaries; to be aroused suddenly by, 'And now to God, the Father . . .', blear-eyed, lost, and with so violent a start that it had all but dislocated his neck. The most beguiling and habitual of these reveries had been concerned with the angel. How and when his speculations on it had originated, what random bird had dropped his extravagant seed of a hundred daydreams into his mind, was beyond discovery now. But it was to the cook that he had confided his first direct questions concerning it.

One low thundery evening, during their brief solitary journey through the churchyard into the hedged-in narrow lane by the coach-house and stables, and so through the garden and back to the rectory, he had managed to blurt out, 'Mrs. Sullivan, why did they make the angel so as she can't *blow* the trumpet?' And this although his mind had been busied over the wholly different and more advanced problem— What exactly would happen if for any reason she ever did?

Until this moment Mrs. Sullivan had been unaware of the angel's perpetual predicament, and her attitude was cautious and tentative.

'I *expect*', she said, 'it was because they couldn't help themselves. Besides, Master Philip, what you are talking about isn't a real angel, no more than what her trumpet is a real trumpet. And who's to say if even a real angel could blow a trumpet that isn't real. I wouldn't care to go so far as that myself. Besides who's to know as she is a she?'

Here, in this darker quiet, under the thick-leaved ilexes,

Philip always drew a little nearer to his stout and panting companion; and sometimes for reassurance slipped a hand under her elbow. Free again, and the stars visible in the autumn sky, he had ventured to protest.

'But *why* couldn't they? And of course it's a she. Besides it was *I* who said she can't. *I* told *you*. It's three inches at least from her mouth. Like this. I've measured it heaps and heaps of times.'

' "*Measured* it", Master Philip! Well, that's a nice thing to be getting up to! All I can say is if that's the kind of mischief you are after I don't know what your father wouldn't say.'

'I didn't mean *really*,' was the impatient reply. 'How could I? I meant by looking, of course. How *could* I mean "really"?' There was scorn in his voice, even though his question had fallen like a hint from heaven into the quiet of his mind.

'If it's just guessing,' Mrs. Sullivan had complacently decided, 'I wouldn't suppose it could be *three*. And, though *your* young eyes may be better than mine, it might be no more than just a shadow. . . . It looks as if it had been raining, according to all these puddles.'

Philip had paid no attention to the puddles, except that he had continued to enjoy quietly walking through them. 'But you said just now,' he persisted, 'that you'd never even seen the angel. So how can you possibly tell? Anyhow, it *is* three, it's more than three, it's more likely four or five. You don't seem to remember how far she is up under the roof. Why, the end of her trumpet nearly touches the ceiling. *I* think that was silly. *Why* didn't they?'

They were drifting back to his original riddle again. But Mrs. Sullivan, reminded of another kind of trumpet, was meditating vaguely at this moment on a deaf bedridden sister who lived in the Midlands. 'I never knew a boy with so many questions,' she answered him ruminatively, almost as if she were explaining the situation to a third party. 'I suppose it's because the Last Day hasn't risen on us as yet. That at least is what it was meant to mean for the gentleman that's laid in the tomb beneath it—and for all of us for that matter. God send it never may!'

'You mean *you* think *she* is waiting for the Last Day? I don't know what you mean by "never". There must be *a* Last Day, and that would be *the* Last Day. And if she's waiting for that, what will happen then—*after* the last?'

'Well, Master Philip, if you are the son of your own father, which I take you to be, you should best be able to answer that question for yourself. I don't hold with such pryings. It's far from ready *I'm* likely to be.'

'Why not?'

'Because', said Mrs. Sullivan, 'I'm getting old, and time is not what it was. When I was a young girl I nearly brooded all the blood out of my body thinking of things like that; though you might not suppose so now. Not that the young should or need be doing so, though I'm not saying there's no need even for *them* not to mind their p's and q's. There is.'

'What are p's and q's?'

But this tepid and lifeless inquiry might have been borne on the winds of Arabia, it seemed so far away.

'Goodness gracious, you've got a tongue like an empty money-box. I see your mamma has gone to bed. Let's hope her sick headache is no worse. And here comes the Rector.'

Philip had accepted Mrs. Sullivan's complex solution of his difficulty with reservations, and had pondered continually on parts of it. After that, apart perhaps from a stray dog or bird, or a strange human face, nothing in church, or in the scriptures, not even Jezebel or the Scarlet Woman, or Gideon, or Og, or Samson's foxes in the wheat, or golden Absalom hanging in the oak tree, or hairy Esau with his mess of pottage, or Elisha and the widow's cruse—nothing had so instantly galvanized him into a rapt attention as the least word he heard uttered about an angel or a trumpet. He had even taken to searching the Bible on his own account to satisfy his craving.

To-night, none the less, was the first time he had ever been alone with his angel—wholly alone. And he had risked a good deal for her sake—a caning from his father; a break-neck fall from his bedroom window if the clothes-line had proved as rotten as it looked; a scurry, heart in mouth, through the fusty dark of the shrubbery; and the possibility, far more affrighting than he had confessed, of strange meetings at the lych gate. Besides there was the humiliation of having been beguiled into this crazy expedition by a friend who was frowned at if not forbidden, and who was not only one of the 'village boys' but clouded and compromised at that.

It was a companionship that fretted Philip at times almost beyond bearing, but from which he could not contrive to break free. Scrubbed and polished Dick might be, but he never *looked* clean. He could be stupider than an owl, and yet was as sharp and quick as a pygmy sparrow-hawk, and feared nothing and nobody. Sometimes even the mere sight of his intent, small-nosed face, and its dark eyes, now darting with life and eagerness, now laden with an inscrutable melancholy; of his very hands, even—small and quick—and his tiny pointed ears filled Philip with an acute distaste. Yet there was a curious and continual fascination in his company.

He was like a mysterious and unintelligible little animal, past caging or taming, and possessed of a spirit of whose secret presence he himself was completely unaware. Contrari-wise, he could be as demure, submissive and affectionate as a little girl, and it was past all hope to discover where his small mind was ranging; Philip admired, despised, was jealous of, and sometimes bitterly hated him.

Why, he wondered, did his father always become so flus-tered and unreasonable at the mere mention of his name; or why his mother either, for that matter? If an unexpected tradesman's bill from London or the county town accom-panied his *Morning Post*, why was the heated discussion of this particular topic almost bound sooner or later to follow? First 'words'—and these of a steadily densening drift; a desultory wrangle; but at last his mother, flaming with anger, in tears, would flare up like a loose heap of gunpowder, and his father would subside into a sulky and cowed acquiescence.

Even if Dick was *not* the son of the sober and crusted old wheelwright at the other end of the village, what did that matter? And if Dick's mother *was* so close a confidante of his own mother, what did that? Wasn't there every reason why she should be? Only a few years before this, she had been parlourmaid at the Rectory, a quiet, fair, meditative creature. And then all of a sudden she had left and got married. But she was still the best 'help' in the house imaginable. No one could wait at table so deftly and sedately as she could; and not even Philip's indolent and elegant mother was such a marvel with her needle. And yet she was so quiet and so far-away that when suddenly spoken to she would start and flush as if she had but just come out of some secret hiding-place.

It was only the spiteful new cook, Mrs. Sullivan's successor, who had steadily refused to be won over; and Philip hated *her* anyhow. His father, on the other hand, took no more notice of Dick when he passed him by in the Rectory garden than if he had been a toadstool.

It was a mystery. If ever on any rare feast or festival, there was a solo to be sung in the minute village choir, it was Dick who sang it—'As pants the hart', 'With verdure clad'—and as roundly and sweetly and passionlessly as the strains of some small woodland flute. His voice at any rate would need no angelic tuition—even in a better world. Nevertheless, although the Rector had been known to boast of the prowess of his choir, Philip could not recall a single word of commendation from his father after the service was over, not even so much as a pompous little pat on the head. So far as *he* was concerned, Dick might have been a deaf-mute.

Yet if nuts, or peppermints, or marbles, or a grasshopper, or a glow-worm in a matchbox were brought into church for furtive display, and Dick was discovered to be the culprit, very little happened. Other boys when they were caught were given a good lecture in the Rector's study, and one runagate far less enterprising than Dick had been expelled from the choir.

However closely he listened, Philip could never unravel the secret of this mystery. Even when he most enjoyed Dick's company, he could never for a moment conceal his own sense of superiority. At one moment he might be green with envy of Dick's silly, dare-devil, scatter-brained ways; at the next utterly despise him. There was a perpetual conflict in his mind between affection, jealousy and contempt. And Dick would detect these secret feelings, as they were expressed solely in his face and actions, as neatly and quickly as a robin pecks up crumbs. Yet he never referred to them, or for more than a minute or two together seemed to resent a single one.

Just now, however, his protective stone and the increasing stench of his lantern unheeded, Philip had all but forgotten what had brought him into his present extraordinary situation. Like the restless imp he always was, Dick had taken himself off. Let him stay away, then! Meanwhile he had himself sat stolidly on, lost in contemplation, the prey of the most fantastic and ridiculous hopes and forebodings.

The church was brimmed so full of limpid moonlight that at any moment, it seemed, the stone walls, the pulpit, the roof itself might vanish away like the fabric of a dream. Its contents appeared to have no more reality than the reflection in a glass. Every crevice in the mouldings of the arches, every sunken flower and leaf in the mullions of the windows, even the knot in the wood of the pew beneath his nose stood out as if it had been blacked in with Indian ink. Every jut and angle, corbel and finial, marble nose and toe and finger seemed to have been dipped in quicksilver. And Philip, his eyes fixed on the faintly golden, winged, ecstatic figure—mutely 'shaking her gilded tresses in the air'—whose gaze he pined and yet feared even in imagination to meet, was lost for the time being to the world of the actual. He failed even to notice urgent reminders that one of his legs from knee to foot had gone numb, and that he was stone-cold.

The premonitory whirring rumble of the clock over his

head and the chimes of midnight roused him at last from this lethargy. He 'came to', and listened starkly to the muffled, sullen booming of the bell, as if he had suddenly escaped from the mazes of a dream. '. . . Eleven . . . Twelve'. The sonorous vibrations ebbed into inaudibility, and a dead and empty silence again prevailed. He had steadily assured himself, from the moment the project had been decided on, that nothing would happen. Nothing *had* happened. He felt spiritless and vacant, and now realized miserably that in spite of this radiance and beauty, he was further away from his angel than he had ever been before. It was she who had withdrawn herself from him, and with that withdrawal a faltering speechless faith and belief in her had almost faded out of his heart.

And as he crouched there, chilled and sick, there rose suddenly into the night beyond the chancel windows a restrained yet fiendish screech, compared with which his own *Oh, oh, oh,* had been sweet as the lamentations of a mermaid. Even though he had instantly guessed its origin, he sat appalled. His eyes fixed on the heavy folds of the curtain that had softly swayed forward as if in a waft of the wind through the open door, he had in his horror almost ceased to breathe. What if he were mistaken? What ghoulish wraith might *not* be skulking there! All but indetectably the curtain was edging apart to disclose at length a lean faceless shape draped as if with a shroud from its flat-topped shapeless and featureless head downwards. Even in his consternation he marvelled at the delicate play of the moonlight in the folds of the cambric. With pointing sooty finger, this ridiculous scarecrow had now begun noiselessly edging towards his pew. The effort to prevent a yell of terror from escaping his throat had brought the taste of blood to Philip's lip; and he at once fell into a violent passion.

'You're nothing but a damn silly little fathead,' he bawled, as it were, under his breath, 'and it would serve you jolly well right if I gave you a good licking. Stop that rot! Stop it! Come *out*! I say!'

The Trumpet

The spectre, notwithstanding had fallen into a solemn yet nimble negro shuffle and a voice out of its middle began to intone:

> Dearly beloved brethren, is it not a sin
> To eat raw potatoes and throw away the skin?
> The skin feeds the pigs and the pigs feed you;
> Dearly beloved brethren, is—it—not—TRUE?

Pat with the last word, and having flung off the Rector's surplice and discarded the semi-hairless broom of the old church charwoman, Dick edged out of his disguise, looking smaller and skinnier than ever. Then it was as if his high spirits, having learned that the same jest is seldom successful twice, had been crushed out of him for good by this last rebuke. He stood dumbly staring at Philip, like a stricken and downcast little monkey that has been chastised by its master.

'Keep your silly wig on,' he expostulated at last. 'That's what you always do. You can't take any joke unless you've made it yourself. I'm tired of being here. There's nothing coming—and there never was. Perhaps if you had been alone. . . .' Unstable as water, his mood began to revive again. '*I* know! Let's go down to the mill-pond, Philip, and look at the fish. The moon's like glass. You could catch 'em with your hands with that lantern. Let's try. Come on.'

'Oh no, you don't,' retorted Philip morosely. 'You needn't suppose you're going to wriggle out like that. You dared me to come, and I dare *you* to stay. Anyhow, you shan't put your nose ever into our house again or into the garden, either, I can promise you, if you're nothing but a sneak—and afraid. I know something that will soon put a stop to that.'

Dick stood irresolute, eyeing him sharply; his high cheekbones a bright red, his eyes shining, his mouth ajar.

'I'm not a sneak. And who'—a doleful quaver jarred his thin clear treble voice—'who *wants* to come into your silly old garden. If my mother. . . . Besides, you *know* I'm not afraid!'

'Oh, do I!' A crafty stealthy designing look had crept into

Philip's fair face, and a slight haze into his blue eyes. A faint ambiguous smile faded out of his angel features. He glanced covertly about him. 'What's more likely is you only want to show off,' he sneered. 'Wheedle.' He half yawned. 'You know perfectly well that I shouldn't be here now except for some silly story you told me and couldn't have understood. Dare for yourself! Why, you haven't even the pluck to climb up into the belfry and give the least tiny ding on one of the bells. Not all alone.'

'Oh, wouldn't I! Yes, I would. Where's the key? There's an old owl's nest in the belfry. . . . *"One!"*—why, even if anybody in the village woke and heard it, they'd think it was nothing but the wind.'

'Well, *three* dings, then. Anybody can make excuses. And you knew I haven't the key! What's more, you wouldn't take a single flower, not even a scrap of a green leaf, from one of those vases up there.'

Dick's gaze angled swiftly over the silver candlesticks upon the altar, the snow-white linen, the rich silk embroidered frontal, with its design in gold thread—I.H.S., the flat hueless shields of hothouse flowers. 'Yes, I would, if I can reach them.'

'Oh, would you! And there you are again—*"if!"*. But you shan't—not while *I'm* here. That would be worse than stealing even, because this is a church, and that's the altar. And that's holy. This is not one of your mouldy old chapels.' Once again he glanced about him. 'I bet this, then. You wouldn't go up into the gallery and scratch out the eye in *that*—not even if I lent you my knife to do it with. Why, you'd be scared even of falling off the chair!'

The 'that' he was referring to was an ancient painted lozenge-shaped hatchment, fastened by tenpenny nails in its clumsy black frame to the lime-washed western wall. It was blazoned with a coat of arms, and above the coat was a crest—the turbaned head of a Saracen in profile; and beneath the coat, in bold Gothic lettering, the one word, *Resurgam*.

The Trumpet

Dick gazed motionlessly at its darkened green and vermilion and at the tilted head. 'Yes, I would,' he muttered. 'What does *Resurgam* mean?'

'It's Latin,' replied Philip, as if he were a little mollified by the modesty of the inquiry. 'And it means, *I shall rise up again.* But it *might* be the subjunctive. It's what's called a motto, and the head's the crest, and the body's down in the vault. I expect he was a crusader. Anyhow, *any*body could do that; because you know very well it mightn't be noticed for ages. Never, p'raps. Besides, what's the use? . . . I'll give you a last chance. I'll tell you what you *wouldn't* do, not if you stayed here for a month of Sundays, and not a single soul came into the church to see you!'

His cheek had crimsoned. He nodded his head violently. 'You wouldn't climb up that, and—and blow that trumpet.'

Dick wheeled about, lifting his dark squirrel-bright eyes as he did so towards the Angel, and looked. He continued to look: the angel at this moment of its nightly vigil, though already the hand that clasped the trumpet had lost its silver, seemed with an ineffable yearning as if about to leap into a cataract of moonlight, like a siren erecting her green-haired head and shoulders out of a rippleless sea to scan the shore.

'You *said*, what would be the use?' he protested at last in a small, scarcely audible voice, and without turning his head. 'Even if I did, no one would hear. . . . Why do you *want* me to?'

'*Who* "wants" you to!' came the mocking challenge. 'You asked me to give you a dare. And now—what did I say! Shouldn't *I* hear? I don't believe you've ever even looked at it, not even *seen* it before!'

'Oh, haven't I!' Dick faltered. 'You say that only because on Sundays I don't sit on your side. And what's the use? Staring up gives you a crick in the neck. But it's not because I am afraid. . . . Besides, she's only made of stone.' In spite of this disparagement he continued to gaze at the angel.

'*Is* she then! Stone! That's all you know about it. She's

made of wood, silly. How could she be that colour if it were marble or even *any* stone? Anybody could see that! And even if she *is* only wood, there are people all over the world who worship idols and—and images. I don't mean just savages either. If she'—for an instant his eyes shut and revolved beneath their pale rounded lids—'if she or anybody else was to blow through that trumpet, it would be the Last Day. I say it, and I *know*. Even if your father has ever heard of angels, I bet he doesn't believe in them. I'm *sure* he doesn't. My father does believe in them, though. And if you had ever really listened to what he reads out about them in the Lessons you'd know too. *I—have*.'

He sat for a moment, torpid as a spider engaged in digesting or contemplating a visitor to its nets. Dick's small, alert, yet guileless face was still turned away from him, upwards and sidelong. As one may put one's ear to a minute device in clockwork and listen to the wheels within going round, the very thoughts in his cropped, compact head seemed audible. And then, as if after a sudden decision to dismiss the subject from his mind, Philip casually picked up his bull's-eye lantern, idly twisted its penthouse top, and directed first a greenish, then a thin red beam of light towards the lustrous monument. But the moon made mock of this trivial rivalry.

'What,' was Dick's husky inquiry at last, 'what *does* the Bible say about angels? It must be a lovely place where they are, Philip.'

Philip ignored the sentimental comment. 'Oh, heaps of things. I couldn't tell you; not half of them, not a quarter.' A mild, absent-minded, almost hypnotic expression now veiled his pale cold features. He began again as though he were repeating a lesson, in tones low yet so confident that the whole church could easily play eavesdropper to his every word. Nevertheless the sentences followed one another tardily and piecemeal, as if, like a writer of books, he could not wholly trust his faculties, as though words and ideas were stubborn things to set in order and be made even so much as to hint at what was pent up in his mind.

'Well, first there was St. Paul; he went to a man's house who had *seen* an angel. Then there was the angel who came to tell his mother about Samuel, when she was sitting alone sewing in her bedroom. . . . And there was the angel that spoke to a man called Lot before he came out of a place called Sodom that was burned in the desert and his wife was turned into a pillar of salt. Because she turned back. Oh, heaps! *You* seem to suppose that because people can't see them now, there never were angels. What about the sea-serpent, then; and what about witches? And what about the stars millions and billions of miles out in space, and mites and germs and all that, so teeny-tiny *no*body ever saw them until microscopes and telescopes were invented? I've looked through a microscope, so I know.'

Dick nodded vacantly. 'If people can *see* them,' he admitted, 'there must be sea-serpents. And I *have* seen a witch. There's one lives in Colney Bottom, and everybody says she's a witch. She's humpty-backed, with straggly grey hair all over her shoulders. I crept in through the trees once and she was in her garden digging potatoes. At least I *think* it was potatoes. She was talking; but there was nobody there and it wasn't to *me*. But you were telling me about the angels, Philip. Won't you go on?'

' "Go on"!' echoed Philip in derision, and began again fumbling with his lantern. 'Good heavens, you don't expect me to tell you half the Bible, do you? Why don't you listen? I don't believe you've any more brains than a parrot. "Go on"! Why, *everybody* has heard of the angel that when Moses was with his sheep called to him out of the middle of the burning bramble bush on the mountains. Its leaves and branches were all crackling with flames. That's another. And when Elijah was once lying asleep in the desert under a juniper tree an angel came in the morning and touched him to wake him because he had brought him some cake, and

o   209

some fresh water to drink. That,' he pondered a moment or two, 'that was before the ravens. And I suppose you've never even heard of Joshua either? He was a captain of Israel. And when he was standing dressed in his armour on the sand, with his naked sword in his hand, and looking at the enormous walls of Jericho, he saw an angel there beside him, in armour too, just as you might see a man in a wood at night. They stood there together looking at the *enormous* walls of Jericho. But you couldn't see them very plainly because it was getting dark, and there weren't any lamps or lights in the houses. So nobody inside knew that they were there, not even the woman who had talked to the two spies who had stolen the bunches of grapes.'

Philip, unperceived, had quickly and suddenly glanced at his friend, who, his face wholly at peace, had meanwhile been emptily watching the coloured lights succeeding one another in the round, glass, owl-like eye of the toy lantern.

'I should like to see an angel,' he said.

'Oh, would you? Then that's all you know about it. There are thousands upon thousands of them, most of them miles taller than any giant there ever was and others no bigger than —than ordinary. Not all of them have only two wings either; some of them have six—here, and here, and here; with two they fly and with two they cover their faces when they are asleep. And they have names too; else God wouldn't be able to call them. But don't you go and think they are like *us*; because they aren't. They are more like demons or ghosts— real ghosts, I mean, not the kind *you* were talking about. And I don't believe either that just because anything is made of wood or stone, it hasn't any life at all—not at *all*. Even savages couldn't be as stupid as all that. You only *think* you could touch angels. But you couldn't. And some angels, though I don't know even myself if they are most like women or men' —his voice ebbed away almost into a whisper, like that of a child murmuring in its sleep, as if he were not only nearing the end of his resources, but was losing himself in the rapture of some ineffable vision in his mind—'some angels are far far more beautiful to look at than any woman, even the most beautiful woman there ever was. And even than—*that!*'

Yet again Dick lifted his intense small eyes towards the image. It had, it seemed, as if in an instant, returned to an appearance of mute immobility; but only in the nick of time, to elude his silent questioning.

'I shouldn't mind any angel,' he said, 'if it were only like that. Not *mind*, I mean. If she *looked* at me, perhaps I might. She's like Rebecca, the girl that lives up at the farm. My mother taught me a hymn once to say when I am in bed. I can't remember the beginning now, but some of it I can:

> *Four corners to my bed;*
> *Four angels round my head:*
> *One to bless, and one to pray,*
> *And one to bear my soul away. . . .*

If you are not afraid, she says, not anywhere, ever, *nothing* can do anything against you.'

'Oh, they can't, can't they! That just shows all *you* know about it. Besides, what you've been saying is only a rhyme for children. It's only a rhyme. My nurse told me that ages ago. Those angels are only one kind. Why, there are angels so enormously strong that if one of them no more than touched even the roof of this church with the tip of his finger it would crumble away into dust. Like that'—he firmly placed his own small forefinger on the dried-up corpse of a tiny money-spider that had long since expired in the corner of the pew—'absolutely into dust. And their voices are as loud as thunder, so that when one speaks to another, the sound of their shouting sweeps clean across the sky. And some fly up out of the sea, out of the East, when the sun rises; and some come up out of a huge frightful pit. And some come up out of the water, deep dangerous lakes and great rivers, and they stand on the water, and can *fly*—straight across, as if it was lightning, from one edge of the world to the other—like tremendous birds. I should jolly well like to see what a pilot of an aeroplane would do at the edge of the night if he met one. They can'—he bent forward a little, his pale face now faintly greened with his own lantern—'they can see without looking; and they stay still, like great carved stones, in a light—why, this moon wouldn't be even a candle to it!

'And some day they will pour awful things out of vials down on the earth and reap with gigantic sickles not just ordinary corn, but men and women. Men and women. And besides the sea,' his rather colourless eyes had brightened, his cheeks had taken on a gentle flush, his nervous fingers were clasping and unclasping themselves over the warm metal of his lantern, 'and besides the sea, they can stand and live exulting in the sun. But on the earth here they are invisible, at least *now*, except when they come in dreams. Besides, everybody has two angels; though they never get married, and so there are never any children angels. They are called cherubs. And I know this too—you can tell they are there even when you cannot see them. You can hear them listening. If *they* have charge of you, nothing can hurt you, not the rocks—nor the ice—not even of the highest mountains. And that was why the angel spoke to Balaam's donkey when they were on the mountain pass, because he wished not to frighten him; and the donkey answered. But if you were cursed by one for wickedness, then you would wither up and die like a gnat, or have awful pains, and everything inside of you would melt away like water. And don't forget either that the devil has crowds of angels under his command who were thrown out of heaven millions of years ago, long before Adam and Eve. They are as proud as he is, and they live in hell. . . . They are awful.'

It was doubtful if Dick had been really attending to this prolonged, halting, almost monotoned harangue; his face at any rate suggested that his thoughts had journeyed off on a remote and marvelling errand of their own.

'Well,' he ventured at last, with a profound half-stifled sigh,

'I *would* climb it anyway. And not because you dared me to, either. Even *you* couldn't say what I might not see up there.'

He tiptoed a pace or two nearer the shallow altar steps and again fixed his eyes on his quarry. 'What about the trumpet?' he suddenly inquired, with a ring of triumph in his voice, as if he had at last managed to corner his learned friend. 'The trumpet? You didn't say a single word about the trumpet.'

'Well, what if I didn't?' was the flat acrimonious answer. 'I can't say two things at once, can I? You don't know *anything*. And that is simply because you never pay any attention. You're just like a fly buzzing about among the plates seeing what you can pick up. I don't suppose, if I asked you even now, you could tell me a single word of *all* that I've been saying!'

Dick turned, glancing a little sadly and wistfully at his friend. 'I could, Philip. At least, I think I could. Besides flies do settle sometimes; I suppose then they are asleep.'

'Oh, well, anyhow,' replied Philip coldly, 'I don't think I want to. But I could if I had the time.' He sighed. 'You don't even seem to understand there are so many *kinds* of trumpets. You don't seem ever to have heard even of Gideon's trumpets. Some are made of brass and some are silver and some are great shells and some are made out of sheep's horns, rams'. And in the old days, ages ago, war-horses loved the sound of trumpets—I don't mean just men going hunting. It made them laugh and prance, with all their teeth showing. "*Ha-ha!*"—like that. Simply maddened to go into battle. And besides, clergymen, priest they were called in those days, used to have trumpets, but that was ages before Henry VIII. And they used to blow them, like that one, up there, when there was a new moon; and when,' he glanced sidelong, his eyelids drooping a little furtively over his full eyes, and his voice fell to a mumble, 'and when there was a *full* moon too. And at the end there will be incense, and dreadful hail, and fire, and scorpions with claws like huge poisonous spiders. And there's a Star called Wormwood; and there will be thousands and thousands of men riding on horses with heads like lions. . . .' He fell silent and sat fumbling for a few moments. 'But I wasn't really going to talk about all that. It's only because *I* have listened. And it's just what I've said already, and I know the very words too.' He nodded slowly as if he were bent on imparting a deathless and invaluable secret: ' "The trumpet shall sound and the dead shall be raised." Those are the very words. And *I* see what they mean.'

Dick had meanwhile become perfectly still, as if some inward self were lost in a strange land. He appeared to be profoundly pondering these matters. 'And supposing,' he muttered at length, as though like the prophet he had swallowed Philip's little book and it were sweet as honey, 'supposing *nothing* happens, Philip? If I do? Perhaps *that* trumpet is only solid wood all through. Then it wouldn't make *any* sound. Then you would only burst your cheeks, trying. Wouldn't it be funny—if I burst my cheeks, trying!'

'That,' replied Philip, disdaining the suggestion, 'that would only mean that it isn't really a trumpet. But you wouldn't even be *thinking* of that if you weren't too frightened to try. You're only talking.'

'*You* wouldn't.'

'I like that!' cried Philip, as if in a brief ecstasy. 'Oh, I like that! Who *thought* of the angel, may I ask? Who *asked* to be dared? Besides, as I have said again and again, this is my father's church; and chapel people don't believe in angels. They don't believe in anything that really matters.'

'You can say what you like about chapel people,' said Dick stubbornly, his eyes shining like some dangerous little animal's that has been caught in a snare. 'But I'm *not* afeared even if you won't go yourself.'

'Oh, well'—a cold and unforeseen fit of anxiety had stolen into Philip's mind as he sat staring at his friend. 'I don't care. Come on, let's clear out of this, I say. You can *try* if you want to, but I'm not going to *watch*. So don't get blaming anything on to me. It's nothing to do with me. That's just what you

214

always do. You're a silly little weathercock. First, yes; then, no.'

Cramped and spiritless, he had got down from his pew and, as if absent-mindedly, had pushed his magic dumb-bell flint into his greatcoat pocket and shut off the light of his lantern. The moonlight, which a few moments before, from pavement to arching roof, had suffused the small church through and through, had begun to thin away into a delicate dusk again; and at the withdrawal even of the tiny coloured lights of the lantern, its pallor on the zigzag-fretted walls and squat thick stone shafts of the piers had become colder. Moreover the quietude around them had at once immeasurably deepened again now that the two boys' idle chirruping voices were stilled.

Philip took up the lantern, and looked at his friend. A curious, crooked, scornful alarm showed on his own delicate features. But it was the scorn in it that his ardent, undersized and peeping devotee had detected most clearly. His intensely dark eyes were searching Philip's face with an astonishing rapidity.

'You said, "blaming",' he half entreated. 'And did I ever? I—I. . . . Haven't I always shown that we—I. . . ! It's only because I didn't think anything might happen. But I'm not afeared, whatever you may think. Besides, you asked me, Philip. And anything—*anything* you asked me. . . . So it couldn't be *only* a dare.'

Like a cork on a shallow stream that has come momentarily to rest in the midst of rippling and conflicting currents, Philip stood motionless, his pondering eyes intent on the young adventurer whom he had at last decoyed into action. A faintly apprehensive, faintly melancholy expression had now crept into his features. The cold detaining fingers he had thrust out of his coat-sleeve fell slackly to his side again. For Dick had already straddled over the thick red plaited cord that dangled between nave and chancel, disclosing as he did so a frayed gaping hole in the canvas of one of his shoes. Their rubber soles made not the faintest sound as he trod lightly over the thick Persian rug and the stone slabs towards the great monument in the further corner, only a few paces from the altar.

It was a monument constructed of many ornate marbles, and these supplied cold couch and canopy for the effigy in alabaster of a worthy knight who, as its inscription declared, had long ago surrendered the joys and sorrows of this world. He reposed, rather uneasily, on his left elbow; his attire, ruff and hose, not less decorative and rococo than the wreathings and carvings, the cherubs and pilasters of his tomb. But like an Oriental bed in a small English bedroom, the tomb was a size or two too large for the church.

Until this moment Philip had not fully realized its loftiness, and how angularly its pinnacles soared up under the roof. Dark and dwarfed against the whiteness of its marble, Dick had now begun to climb. But he had mounted only a few feet from the ground when Philip noticed that the moon had now abandoned the carved ringlets, the rounded cheeks, the up-turned sightless face of his angel. Though her pinions and feet were still chequered with its silvering beams, her trump now lifted its mouth into a cold and sullen gloom. An unendurable misgiving had begun to stir in him.

'The moon's gone, Dick,' he whispered across. 'What's the good? Come down!'

'I say,' came the muffled but elated answer, 'the ledges are simply thick with dust, and don't they just cut into the soles of your feet. I can't hear what you're saying.'

'I said,' repeated Philip, still patiently, 'come down!' But he might as well have been pleading with the angel itself. There came no response. 'Dick, Dick,' he reiterated, 'I said, Come down! Oh, I'm going.' In a sudden fever he pushed his way under the curtain into the vestry and vanished. But it was only a ruse. He came flying back in a few moments as if in utter confusion.

'Quick, Dick; quick, I say!' he all but shouted. 'Come

down! There's someone, something *coming*. It isn't a man and
it isn't a woman. Quick! It won't be a minute before it's in
the church. Oh you silly, silly fool! I tell you there's someone
coming!' His voice broke away into a sob of bewilderment,
rage, apprehension and despair. 'My God,' he called, 'I'll tell
my father of this! You see if I don't.'

But the snail-slow groping figure, still radiantly lit with the
moon's downcast beams as it continued to scale the monument, was far too much engrossed in its mission to pay any
attention to him now, and hardly paused until with a small,
black, broken-nailed hand it had securely clasped the angel's
foot. 'I'm nearly up, Philip,' he called down at last. 'Look!
Look where I am! I'm even with the gallery now, and can
hardly see because of the dazzle. It's cold and still and awful,
but oh, *peaceful*; and I can see into the moon. The angel's
lovely too, close to, but much, much bigger. Supposing I
blow with all my might and the trumpet doesn't sound? It
won't be my fault, will it? And we will still keep friends, always, won't we, Philip?'

'Oh, you fool, you idiot crock fool,' called Philip hoarsely.
'Didn't I *tell* you, didn't I tell you, what might come to *everybody*? . . . And you believed it! Oh, it was all a story, a lie,
a story. Dick, I will give you anything in the world if you will
only come down.'

'I don't want anything in the world,' was the dull, stubborn
retort. Even as he spoke, the lower dust-dried hand had crept
cautiously up to join its fellow, and in a few moments, himself
half in and half out of the moonlight, his fingers were clutching the acorn tassels of the cord that bound its convoluted
hood to the angel's head. Philip was now all but past motion
or speech. He was shivering from head to foot, and praying
inarticulately in his terror, 'Oh God, make him come down!
Oh God, make him come down!'

'I believe', a calm but rapturous voice was declaring, 'it *is*
hollow, and I *think* she knows I'm here. You won't say I was
afraid now! Philip, I'd do anything in the world for you.'

The Trumpet

But at this moment, it seemed, the ancient guardians of the sanctity of the edifice had deemed it discreet to intervene. A cock crowed from its perch in the hen-roost at the farm where Rebecca now lay fast asleep. A vast solemn gust of wind evoked from nowhere out of space had swept across the churchyard and in at the open vestry door, powerful enough in its gust to belly out the dark green felt curtain and to add its edge of terror to Philip's appalled state of mind. 'Look! Quick! It's coming. Didn't I *say* it was all. . . .'

And this time the small human creature clinging to its goal, a lean skinny arm outstretched above his head, had heard the warning cry. 'Who? What's coming?' he called, faint and far. 'Oh, it's lovely up here. I'm alone. I can't stop now. I'm nearly there.'

'I say, you are *not* to, you are *not* to.' Philip was all but dancing in helpless fear and fury. 'It's wicked! It's *my* angel, it's *my* trumpet! I hate you! Listen!—I tell you! I *command* you to come down!'

But his adjurations had become as meaningless as is now the song the Sirens sang.

A rending snap, abrupt as that of a pistol shot, had echoed through the church. The tapering wooden trumpet, never since its first fashioning visited by any other living creature than capricious fly and prowling spider, had splintered off clean from the angel's grasp. And without a cry, a syllable, either of triumph or despair, Dick had fallen vertically on to the flag-stones beneath, the thud of his small body, and the minute crack as of some exquisitely delicate and brittle vessel exposed to too extreme a tension being followed by a silence soft, and thick, and deep as deep and heavy snow.

The stolid pendulum had resumed its imperturbable thumping again, the fussy vestry clock its protest against such indifference. By any miracle of mercy, *could* this be only yet another of this intrepid restless little Yorick's infinite jests? The sharp-nosed crusader continued alabaster-wise to stare into his future. The disgraced angel, breast to lock-crowned head, stood now in shadow as if to hide her shame. Her mute wooden trumpet remained clutched in a lifeless hand. . . . No.

'Dick! Dick!' an anguished stuttering voice at last contrived to whisper. 'I didn't mean it. On my oath I didn't mean it. Don't let me down . . . Dick, are you dead?'

But since no answer was volunteered, and all courage and enterprise had ebbed into nausea and vertigo, the speaker found himself incapable of venturing nearer, and presently, as thievishly as he had entered it, crept away out into the openness of the churchyard, and so home.

From HENRY BROCKEN

If I see all, ye're mine to ane!—OLD BALLAD

I was awakened by a sustained sound as of an orator speaking in an unknown tongue, and found myself in a sunny-shadowy loft, whither I suppose I must have been carried in my sleep. In a delicious languor between sleeping and waking I listened with imperturbable curiosity awhile to that voice of the unknown. Indeed, I was dozing again when a different sound, enormous, protracted, abruptly aroused me. I got up hot and trembling, not yet quite my own master, to discover its cause.

Through a narrow slit between the timbers I could view the country beneath me, far and wide. I saw near at hand the cumbrous gate of the stockade ajar, and at a little distance on the farther side Mr. Gulliver and his half-human servant standing. In front of them was an empty space—a narrow semicircle of which Gulliver was the centre. And beyond— wild-eyed, dishevelled, stretching their necks as if to see, inclining their heads as if to hearken, ranging in multitude almost to the sky's verge stood assembled, it seemed to me, all the horses of the universe.

Even in my first sensation of fear admiration irresistibly stirred. The superb freedom of their unbridled heads, the sun-nurtured arrogance of their eyes, the tumultuous sea-like tossing of crest and tail, their keenness and ardour and might, and also in simple truth their numbers—how could one marvel if this solitary fanatic dreamed they heard him and understood?

Unarmed, bareheaded, he faced the brutal discontent of his people. Words I could not distinguish; but there was little chance of misapprehending the haughty anguish with which he threatened, pleaded, cajoled. Clear and unfaltering his voice rose and fell. He dealt out fearlessly, foolishly, to that long-snouted, little-brained, wild-eyed multitude, reason beyond their instinct, persuasion beyond their savagery, love beyond their heed.

But even while I listened, one thing I knew those sleek malcontents heard too—the Spirit of Man in that small voice of his—perplexed, perhaps, and perverted, and out of tether; but none the less unconquerable and sublime.

What less, thought I, than power unearthly could long maintain that stern, impassable barrier of green vacancy between their hoofs and him? And I suppose for the very reason that these were animals of a long-sharpened sagacity, wild-hearted, rebellious, yet not the slaves of impulse, he yet kept himself their king who was, in fact, their captive.

'Houyhnynms?' I heard him cry: 'pah—Yahoos!' His voice fell; he stood confronting in silence that vast circumference of restless beauty. And again broke out inhuman, inarticulate, immeasurable revolt. Far across over the tossing host, rearing, leaping, craning dishevelled heads, went pealing and eddying that hostile, brutal voice.

Gulliver lifted his hand, and a tempestuous silence fell once more. 'Yahoos! Yahoos!' he bawled again. Then he turned, and passed back into his hideous garden. The gate was barred and bolted behind him.

Thus loosed and unrestrained, surged as if the wind drove them, that concourse upon the stockade. Heavy though its timbers were, they seemed to stoop at the impact. A kind of fury rose in me. I lusted to go down and face the mutiny of the brutes; bit, and saddle, and scourge into obedience man's serfs of the centuries. I watched, on fire, the flame of the declining sun upon those sleek, vehement creatures of the dust. And then, I know not by what subtle irony, my zeal turned back—turned back and faded away into simple longing for my lost friend, my peaceful beast-of-evening, Rosinante. I sat down again in the litter of my bed and earnestly wished myself home; wished, indeed, if I must confess it, for the familiar face of my Aunt Sophia, my books, my bed. If these were this land's horses, I thought, what men might here be met! The unsavouriness, the solitude, the neighing and tumult and prancing induced in me nothing but dullness at last and disgust.

But at length, dismissing all such folly, at least from my face, I lifted the trap-door and descended the steep ladder into the room beneath.

Mr. Gulliver sat where I had left him. Defeat stared from his eyes. Lines of insane thought disfigured his face. Yet he sat, stubborn and upright, heedless of the uproar, heedless even that the late beams of the sun had found him out in his last desolation. So I too sat down without speech, and waited till he should come up out of his gloom, and find a friend in a stranger.

But day waned; the sunlight went out of the great wooden room; the tumult diminished; and finally silence and evening shadow descended on the beleaguered house. And I was looking out of the darkened window at a star that had risen and stood shining in the sky, when I was startled by a voice so low and so different from any I had yet heard that I turned to convince myself it was indeed Mr. Gulliver's.

'And the people of the Yahoos, Traveller,' he said, 'do they still lie, and flatter, and bribe, and spill blood, and lust, and covet? Are there yet in the country whence you come the breadless bellies, the sores and rags and lamentations of the poor? Ay, Yahoo, and do vicious men rule, and attain riches; and impious women pomp and flattery—? hypocrites, panders, envious, treacherous, proud?' He stared with desolate sorrows and wrath into my eyes.

Words in disorder flocked to my tongue. I grew hot and eager, yet by some instinct held my peace. The fluttering of the dying flames, the starry darkness, silence itself; what were we who sat together? Transient shadows both, phantoms, unfathomable and mysterious as these.

I fancied he might speak again. Once he started, raised his

arm, and cried out as if acting again in dream some frenzy of the past. And once he wheeled on me extraordinary eyes, as if he half-recognized some idol of the irrevocable in my face. These flashes were momentary, however. Gloom returned to his forehead, vacancy to his eyes.

I heard the outer gate flung open, and a light, strange foot-fall. So for a while we seated ourselves, all three, round the smouldering fire. Mr. Gulliver's servant scarcely took his eyes from my face. And, a little to my confusion, his first astonish-ment of me had now passed away, and in its stead had fallen such a gentleness and humour as I should not have supposed possible in his wild countenance. He busied himself over his strips of skin, but if he caught my eye upon his own he would smile out broadly, and nod his great, hairy head at me, till I fancied myself a child again and he some ungainly sweetheart of my nurse.

When we had supped (sitting together in the great room), I climbed the ladder into the loft and was soon fast asleep. But from dreams distracted with confusion I awoke at the first shafts of dawn. I stood beside the narrow window in the wall of the loft and watched the distant river change to silver, the bright green of the grass appear.

This seemed a place of few and timorous birds, and of fewer trees. But all across the dews of the grasses lay a tinge of pow-dered gold, as if yellow flowers were blooming in abundance there. I saw no horses, no sign of life; heard no sound but the cadent wail of the ash-grey birds in their flights. And when I turned my eyes nearer home, and compared the distant beauty of the forests and their radiant clouds with the nakedness and desolation here, I gave up looking from the window with a determination to be gone as soon as possible from a country so uncongenial.

Moreover, Mr. Gulliver, it appeared, had returned during the night to his first mistrust of my company. He made no sign he saw me, and left his uncouth servant to attend on me. For him, indeed, I began to feel a kind of affection springing up; he seemed so eager to befriend me. And whose is the heart quite hardened against a simple admiration? I rose very gladly when, after having stuffed a wallet with food, he signed to me to follow him. I turned to Mr. Gulliver and held out my hand.

'I wish, sir, I might induce you to accompany me,' I said. 'Some day we would win our way back to the country we have abandoned. I have known and loved your name, sir, since first I browsed on pictures. Being measured for your first coat in Lilliput by the little tailors; Straddling the pinnacled city. Ay, sir, and when the farmers picked you up 'twixt finger and thumb from among their cornstalks. . . .'

I had talked on in hope to see his face relax; but he made no sign he saw or heard me. I very speedily dropped my hand and went out. But when my guide and I had advanced about thirty yards from the stockade, I cast a glance over my shoulder towards the house that had given me shelter. It rose, sadcoloured and solitary, between the green and blue. But, if it was not fancy, Mr. Gulliver stood looking down on me from the very window whence I had looked down on him. And there I do not doubt he stayed till his fellow-yahoo had passed across his inhospitable lands out of his sight for ever.

I was glad to be gone, and did not, at first, realize that the least danger lay before us. But soon, observing the extraordinary vigilance and caution my companion showed, I began to watch and listen, too. Evidently our departure had not passed unseen. Far away to left and to right of us I descried at whiles now a few, now many, swift-moving shapes. But whether they were advancing with us, or gathering behind us, in hope to catch their tyrant alone and unaware, I could not properly distinguish.

Once, for a cause not apparent to me, my guide raised himself to his full height, and, thrusting back his head, uttered a most piercing cry. After that, however, we saw no more for a while of the beasts that haunted our journey.

All that morning, till the sun was high, and the air athrob

with heat and stretched like a great fiddle-string to a continuous, shrill vibration, we went steadily forward. And when at last I was faint with heat and thirst, my companion lifted me up like a child on to his back and set off again at his great, easy stride. It was useless to protest. I merely buried my hands in his yellow hair to keep my balance in such a camel-like motion.

A little after noon we stayed to rest by a shallow brook, beneath a cluster of trees scented, though not in blossom, like an English hawthorn. There we ate our meal, or rather I ate and my companion watched, running out ever and again for a wider survey, and returning to me like a faithful dog, to shout snatches of his inconceivable language at me.

Sometimes I seemed to catch his meaning, bidding me take courage, have no fear, he would protect me. And once he shaded his eyes and pointed afar with extreme perturbation, whining or murmuring while he stared.

Again we set off from beneath the sweet-scented shade, and now no doubt remained that I was the object of very hostile evolutions. Sometimes these smooth-hoofed battalions would advance, cloudlike, to within fifty yards of us, and, snorting, ruffle their manes and wheel swiftly away; only once more in turn to advance, and stand, with heads exalted, gazing wildly on us till we were passed on a little. But my guide gave them very little heed. Did they pause a moment too long in our path, or gallop down on us but a stretch or two beyond the limit his instinct had set for my safety, he whirled his thong above his head, and his yell resounded, and like a shadow upon wheat the furious companies melted away.

Evidently these were not the foes he looked for, but a subtler, a more indomitable. It was at last, I conjectured, at scent, or sight, or rumour of these that he suddenly swept me on to his shoulders again, and with a great sneeze or bellow leapt off at a speed he had, as yet, given me no hint of.

Looking back as best I could, I began to discern somewhat to the left of us a numerous herd in pursuit, sorrel in colour, and of a more magnificent aspect than those forming the other bands. It was obvious, too, despite their plunging and rearing, that they were gaining on us—drew, indeed, so near at last that I could count the foremost of them, and mark (not quite callously) their power and fleetness and symmetry, even the sun's gold upon their reddish skins.

Then in a flash my captor set me down, toppled me over (in plain words) into the thick herbage, and, turning, rushed bellowing, undeviating, towards their leaders, till it seemed he must inevitably be borne down beneath their brute weight, and so—farewell to summer. But almost at the impact, the baffled creatures reared, neighing fearfully in consort, and at the gibberish hurled back on them by their flame-eyed master, broke in rout, and fled.

Whereupon, unpausing, he ran back to me, only just in time to rescue me from the nearer thunder yet of those who had seized the very acme of their opportunity to beat out my brains.

It was a long and arduous and unequal contest. I wished very heartily I could bear a rather less passive part. But this fearless creature scarcely heeded me; used me like a helpless child, half tenderly, half roughly, displaying ever and again over his shoulder only a fleeting glance of the shallow glories of his eyes, as if to reassure me of his power and my safety.

But the latter, those distant savannahs will bear witness, seemed forlorn enough. My eyes swam with weariness of these crested, earth-disdaining battalions. I sickened of the heat of the sun, the incessant sidelong jolting, the amazing green. But on we went, fleet and stubborn, into ever-thickening danger. How feeble a quarry amid so many hunters.

Two things grew clear to me each instant. First, that every movement and feint of our pursuers was of design. Not a beast that wheeled but wheeled to purpose; while the main body never swerved, thundered superbly on toward the inevitable end. And next I perceived with even keener assurance that my guide knew his country and his enemy and his own power and aim as perfectly and consummately; knew, too—this was the end.

Far distant in front of us there appeared to be a break in the level green, a fringe of bushes, rougher ground. For this refuge he was making, and from this our mutinous Houyhnynms meant to keep us.

There was no pausing now, not a glance behind. His every effort was bent on speed. Speed indeed it was. The wind roared in my ears. Yet above its surge I heard the neighing and squealing, the ever-approaching shudder of hoofs. My eyes distorted all they looked on. I seemed now floating twenty feet in air; now skimming within touch of ground. Now the sorrel squadron behind me swelled and nodded; now dwindled to an extreme minuteness of motion.

Then, of a sudden, a last shrill pæan rose high; the hosts of our pursuers paused, billow-like, reared, and scattered—my poor Yahoo leapt clear.

For an instant once again in this wild journey I was poised, as it were, in space, then fell with a crash, still clutched, sure and whole, to the broad shoulders of my rescuer.

When my first confusion had passed away, I found that I was lying in a dense green glen at the foot of a cliff. For some moments I could think of nothing but my extraordinary escape from destruction. Within reach of my hand lay the creature who had carried me, huddled and motionless; and to left and to right of me, and one a little nearer the base of the cliff, five of the sorrel horses that had been our chief pursuers. One only of them was alive, and he, also, broken and unable to rise—unable to do else than watch with fierce, untamed, glazing eyes (a bloody froth at his muzzle) every movement and sign of life I made.

I myself, though bruised and bleeding, had received no serious injury. But my Yahoo would rise no more. His master was left alone amidst his people. I stooped over him and bathed his brow and cheeks with the water that trickled from the cliffs close at hand. I pushed back the thick strands of matted yellow hair from his eyes. He made no sign. Even while I watched him, the life of the poor beast near at hand welled away: he whinnied softly, and dropped his head upon the bracken. I was alone in the unbroken silence.

It seemed a graceless thing to leave the carcasses of these brave creatures uncovered there. So I stripped off branches of the trees, and gathered bundles of fern and bracken, with which to conceal awhile their bones from wolf and fowl. And him whom I had begun to love I covered last, desiring he might but return, if only for a moment, to bid me his strange farewell.

This done, I pushed through the undergrowth from the foot of the sunny cliffs, and after wandering in the woods, came late in the afternoon, tired out, to a ruinous hut. Here I rested, refreshing myself with the unripe berries that grew near by.

I remained quite still in this mouldering hut looking out on the glens where fell the sunlight. Some homely bird warbled endlessly on in her retreat, lifted her small voice till every hollow resounded with her rapture. Silvery butterflies wavered across the sun's pale beams, sipped, and flew in wreaths away. The infinite hordes of the dust raised their universal voice till, listening, it seemed to me that their tiny Babel was after all my own old, far-off English, sweet of the husk.

Fate leads a man through danger to his delight. Me she had led among woods. Nameless though many of the cups and stars and odours of the flowers were to me, unfamiliar the little shapes that gambolled in fur and feather before my face, here dwelt, mummy of all earth's summers, some old ghost of me, sipper of sap, coucher in moss, quieter than the dust.

So sitting, so rhapsodizing, I began to hear presently another sound—the rich, juicy munch-munch of jaws, a little blunted maybe, which yet, it seemed, could never cry Enough! to these sweet, succulent grasses. I made no sign, waited with eyes towards the sound, and pulses beating as if for a sweetheart. And soon, placid, unsurprised, at her extreme ease, loomed into sight who but my ox-headed Rosinante in these dells, cropping her delightful way along in search of her drowned master.

I could but whistle and receive the slow, soft scrutiny of her familiar eyes. I fancied even her bland face smiled, as might elderliness on youth. She climbed near with bridle broken and trailing, thrust out her nose to me, and so was mine again.

Sunlight left the woods. Wind passed through the upper branches. So, with rain in the air, I went forward once more; not quite so headily, perhaps, yet, I hope, with undiminished courage, like all earth's travellers before me, who have deemed truth potent as modesty, and themselves worth scanning print after.

NATURALISTS

'I am going a long journey,' said Frank Buckland on his death-bed, 'a long journey where I think I shall see a great many curious animals. That journey I must go alone'; and he set out on it in the belief that God who is 'so very good to the little fishes would not let their inspector suffer shipwreck at last'. It is a more modest, substantive claim than many of Life's sea-farers could establish—except perhaps the stowaways, even if to the orthodox it may hover between the sentimental and the profane. The hymn asks mercy for us worms on earth (and little in my youth did I relish repeating it), but animals, however 'curious', familiar, strange or beautiful, would for most aspiring souls be a saddening substitute for the paradisal harps and the society of the angels. Even if we bear in mind Montaigne's wry admonition that every traveller, whatever his destination, will have himself for company, and an ideal self is not an easy conception, the heavenly Jerusalem is seldom associated with the beasts that perish. A horse, a 'faithful' dog, how welcome the responsive bark or whinny, but even a house-cat edging cautiously on her way through the gates of pearl looks a little odd. And if there shall be no more sea, where then the inspector's fish? He must have hied off to some obscure and peaceful creek, having borrowed one of Charon's old discarded boats.

> . . . *And in that heaven of all their wish*
> *There shall be no more land, say fish.*

Buckland's notion of the Better Land, and few of us would find it easy to be more specific, was an intensification of the happiest and possibly also the busiest of his hours on earth, of a renewed earth, that is, securely possessed of *all* loved, lovely and living things. The man in the street, and there are a great many of him, seldom nowadays even sees a horse. He may visit the Zoo, but that is chiefly for his children's sake; and a bag of buns or nuts is his simple tribute. Humanitarians we may profess to be, even *vis-à-vis* a leg of mutton; but a robin in a cage is more likely to excite our superstition than our rage; and fine feathers are not yet a disgrace to fine ladies.

True naturalists, patient, ardent, imaginative devotees of that perpetual miracle we so easily dismiss as 'Nature', are rare. The term is more frequently applied to collectors of facts, statistics and carcases. Man, none too happy even among his own kind, kith and kin, has wantonly and to a lamentable degree estranged himself from the fellow-beings who rejoice and share in that Nature; symbols of energy, freedom and strangeness whose only language (and that as yet not confined in any human dictionary) is sweet or raucous noise, or silence. Unlike Selkirk on his island he is flattered rather than shocked by the tameness of the creatures he has '*domesticated*'—a condition not easily distinguishable from a helpless servility. He enters a wood, and instantly a hostile and vigilant hush intensifies its stillness, such as would fall on our modern Gomorrahs at the first windings of the Last Trump.

He is an excellent and sedulous utilitarian, but to his own ends. By unnatural selection he has contorted, dwarfed, fantasticated, or doubled earth's flowers, fruits, animals; has squandered its life in riotous hunting, and has made something of a guy of his original image. Yet he is fairly complacent in his tower of Babel and can still say *bo* to a goose.

'There is no doubt that men are very ignorant about Nature. . . . We are not *in* Nature; we are out of her, having made our own conditions; and our conditions have reacted upon and made us what we are—artificial creatures. Nature is now something pretty to go and look at occasionally, but not too often nor for too long a time.'

It is W. H. Hudson speaking. And even the primordial spirit in our house-cat, which of all animals profits most self-securely from our artificialities, if given a tongue (though not of the 'Saki' variety), might echo the words which he put into the mouth of Sir Walter Raleigh, having imagined him come back to earth to inspect our 'modern conveniences':

'Oh, but you have now gone too far in that direction! Your rooms, your tables, all the thousand appointments of your establishment, your own appearance, your hard-scraped skins, your conversation suffocates me. Let me out—let me go back to the place I came from!'

When Hudson confesses himself to be a rank sentimentalist, it is merely to take the words out of his critics' mouths. His heart is hard enough for all honest purposes. He does not tell us to peel off our clothes and go nudist (and protective colouration is usually more congenial and decorative); or to eat nothing but nuts, or to sleep in the snow, or to lead the simpleton's life. In the presence of the vegetarian he muses on the seduction of roast pig. The usual Englishman's idol is a dog. Hudson (and A. C. Bradley seems to have taken some little pleasure in proving that a highly unusual and much-admired Englishman, William Shakespeare, was of the same opinion) flatly refused to bend the knee to this carrion creature. His affection and admiration were for what he deemed finer, cleaner and more intelligent company—'the fairy' marmoset, that 'night wood-ghost' the lemur, the Patagonian dilochotis, the red-gold agouti and that small mountain troglodyte (beloved perhaps of the Incas), the chinchilla. Like Buckland, he too was an absorbed inspector, but of all creatures great and small. His own chosen paradise, we can take it for 'granted (or grunted)', harbours that very sagacious animal the pig; welcomes the serpent; is enjewelled by the toad. No 'Philistine fly-fisher' with his greed for trout will be found therein; but heron and otter, martin and swallow in all abundance; the raven, and the dove.

How is it, then, that even mere literary parasites, denizens by comparison of only a paper ghost-land, who don't know a hawk from a handsaw, call a cockroach a beetle, would cry

Profiteer! on the poulterer that asked a ha'-penny for three sparrows, and who cannot free themselves from a visiting horsefly by an instinctive appeal to their 'twitching' muscles, how is it that they do not find Hudson's naturalism

> *pathetically rustical*
> *Too pointless for the city?*

Well, as Burton puts it, the mocker at country life 'may say "Pish!" and frown, and yet read on'. The rest unfalteringly include him in the company, of those natural divines and diviners, White—to all eternity 'of Selborne'—and Izaac Walton. With what ingenuous delight we at once renounce the city's 'several gymnics and exercises' for these country 'recreations': when they are shared in an armchair. In Hudson's company we are *'veré Saturnus'*. 'No man ever took more delight in springs, woods, groves, gardens, wells, fishponds, rivers, etc.,' than, with him for philosopher and friend, do we. By some charm, such a charm as he cannot express even in his chapter 'Advice to Adder-Seekers', he captivates even readers who are scarcely even novices in his themes, utter dunces in his school. And what we win from him is priceless.

Just so, when the white electric glare of a railway carriage fails for a while and out of our small upholstered cage we may see suddenly loom up beyond its smudged oblong of window-glass a wonderland of reality—tree and meadow, hill and water, spectral, lovely, dreamlike in wash of star and moon-light in the deep, spacious night; so any one of his treasured books transitorily illumines and revivifies for us a world to which we are habitually strangers. We all but recover a fore-gone and secret understanding. Nature is no longer 'something outside ourselves and interesting only to men of curious minds'.

Is it the child in us, the lost or the forsaken youth of the imagination, that Hudson addresses? Such a child as Words-worth once was, and Traherne and as another referred to in

Naturalists

The Sayings of the Children, who declared to his mother: 'I can
see lots of things with my heart. . . . I've got green trees and a
lot of flowers in my heart'; who spoke of a flower as of 'a for-
giving blue', and in pacification of his own question, 'Where
was I before I came to you?' replied, 'I was a ram upon the
hills, and you came and gave me a roseleaf, and I ate it, and
became me. . . . I was an eagle, because I've got big thumbs.'
Milk for babes; meat for grown men. None the less, is it still
perhaps that wraith of the child left in us which in Mr. Hudson's company reinherits the world?

'In his nearness to or oneness with Nature, resulting from
his mythical faculty, and in the quick response of the organism
to every outward change, he is like the animals. . . . Whatever
is rare or strange, or outside of Nature's usual order, and opposed to his experience, affects him powerfully and excites the
sense of mystery.'

It is, at any rate, this child who never fled from or abandoned him—or whom he won back. He tells how, after killing an adder in the New Forest, a change came over his mental attitude towards living things. Although his chief happiness had until then always been in 'observing their ways', his
feeling was suddenly changed for a while to that of the sports-
man and collector, intent on killing and corpse-keeping. His
mind in this condition could still delight in 'the power, beauty
and grace of the wild creatures', in the imagination of their
unceasing adjustment to an ever-changing environment, and
of the age-long inheritance through conflict and mutation
manifest in the individual of each diverse species. But a rarer
sense was forgotten and for the time being lost:

'The main thing had been the wonderfulness and eternal
mystery of life itself; this formative, informing energy—this
flame that burns in and shines through the case, the habit,
which in lighting another dies, and albeit dying yet endures
for ever; and the sense, too, that this flame of life was one, and
of my kinship with it in all its appearances, in all organic
shapes, however different from the human. Nay, the very fact

that the forms were unhuman but served to heighten the interest—the roe-deer, the leopard and wild horse, the swallow
cleaving the air, the butterfly toying with a flower, and the
dragon-fly dreaming on the river; the monster whale, the
silver flying fish, and the nautilus, with rose and purple-tinted
sails spread to the wind.'

Although, as Hudson says himself, 'what one reads does not
inform the mind much, unless one observes and thinks for
oneself at the same time', and although, as William James
declares, a generous impulse towards life that is not put into
action is a waste of energy and a step towards the formation
of a bad habit, and although also even the best of Hudson's
books may be only a glass wherein we discern the vividly
seen, it none the less enables us to share something of its
writer's peace and happiness, his hours of solitary transport.
A flower, no less than bird, roe-deer, leopard, nautilus, or
'big-game', can confer this rare transitory sense of being *in*
nature' and freed from the conditions which have made us
creatures of, if not in positive servitude to artifice and convention. He tells us how, when seeking shelter one morning
from the furious Atlantic winds at Zennor (once in Francis
Kilvert's words desolate, solitary, bare, dreary . . . a sort of
place that might have been quite lately discovered and where
'fragments of forgotten peoples might dwell', but which also
resembles a drop-scene between the actual and a further
reality), he suddenly chanced on a slope of smooth turf at the
foot of the rocks, powdered with the grey-blue of vernal
squills—close-clustering, as if in faint reflection of the sky,
and almond-scented in the cold April sunshine. That was one
such moment. It reminds me of a calm, brilliant Sunday of
many years ago when, the dazzling dark blue sea beneath us,
the gulls like snow against the blue above, I was sitting with a
beloved friend on another Cornish cliff, also powdered with
the grey-blue of vernal squills, and having happened to glance
landward, we saw one after another the white blinds being
drawn over the windows of a large grey neighbouring farm-

house. Another such ecstatic moment for Hudson was when he chanced suddenly on myriads and myriads of daisies, a band of white, like snow, carpeting the disused Roman road on the downs at Dorchester; and, yet again, the serpentine green of a mile-long British earthwork in Wiltshire crested with the shining yellow of bird's-foot trefoil; and yet again, one of the rarest of English wild flowers, with their serpent-like hieroglyphics, the fritillaries, the chequered daffodils—darkening the earth over an area of about three acres. 'It was a marvellous sight, and a pleasure indescribable to walk about among them'.

Naturalists in general are far less intent on conveying mere feelings. But it is not by accident that there are so many *d*'s in an ironical reference to 'our exceedingly industrious lepi-dopterists'. The term is as much the halter of a bad name as when he breathes 'canophilist' at the serfs, say, of the parasitic Pekineses, 'weak in their intellectuals'. It is the imagination in such writers as Richard Jefferies and Edward Thomas and Walton, and Traherne, that weaves enchantment into, tinges with magic, the common things which they have seen and describe. The simple and precise prose of the scholarly, con-templative, 'curious' Gilbert White thrills with a perceptible exaltation when he recounts the ravages of the 'rugged Si-berian weather' in Selborne during the great frost of January 1766, and of December 1784:

'Many of the narrow roads were now filled above the tops of the hedges; through which the snow was driven into most romantic and grotesque shapes, so striking to the imagination as not to be seen without wonder and pleasure. The poultry dared not to stir out of their roosting places; for cocks and hens are so dazzled and confounded by the glare of snow that they would soon perish without assistance. The hares also lay sullenly in their seats, and would not move till compelled by hunger.'

The eye as it reads these words is itself dazzled hardly less than were the cocks and hens; the wintry silence and whiteness become all but an hallucination, as they do also in Robert Bridges' 'London Snow'. And what is that 'wonder' but the inarticulate realization of Hudson's 'eternal mystery of life itself'? Poor Robin Herrick exiled from the wits and taverns of the metropolis, objurgated (and languished in) the rusticalities of his 'living' in barbarous Devon. Contrariwise, what a mercy, then, it is for those to whom *Selborne* is an unfailing source of ease and pleasure, that its author was never banished to some eighteenth-century equivalent of our London slums, or buttoned into gaiters and made a dean. His parochial duties can never have been onerous—another blessing; his incumbency of Norton Pinkney was a sinecure.

He had begun his *Garden Kalendar* when he was just over thirty; and he spent the last forty-one years of his seventy-three in the peace and quiet of the place where he was born. Few suns can have risen for him a wink too soon. 'I love all beauteous things, I seek and adore them' might have been his own matter-of-fact summary of his life on earth. Indeed, this faithful old bachelor had only one Platonic mistress, Nature herself. Not the hardy and austere matron which the term usually brings to mind, but a lovely thing—young, 'natural' and a trifle demure. We dip into him, again and again, always pacified, always revived in so doing, and all but solely for the delight he and his chosen company, chiefly 'singing birds sweet', bestow on us. Only incidentally for his facts and information—stiff and starchy terms indeed for his own variety of them.

None the less he felt that his devotion needed a defence and vindication. For one thing, he had the 'gentleman of fortune' in mind; and even in his tryst with Echo of a still clear dewy evening, he had to assure himself that the gravest man need not be ashamed to appear taken with 'such a phenomenon, since it may become the subject of philosophical or mathematical inquiries'. The mere 'nature-lover' whose 'country' is little more than a houseless adjunct of London, whose rustics are 'yokels' and who is himself a kind of week-end migrant, may wilt a little at this reminder. And yet it is the quiet-hearted and the solitary man rather than the light and gay and facetious who more easily 'returns' to nature. A casual observer, however ardent, who habitually wears his heart on his sleeve, or at the faintest note of a decoy flits off into fantasy and rapture, is less likely to add much to our store of knowledge or of accurate observation. Yet an inquirer bereft of imagination, and without that peculiar sense of the 'fantasy' of the God who made the world, is blind in his best eye.

To be specific, there are three W. H. Hudsons present and active in his books, and they may be clumsily denominated as the field naturalist pure and simple, the human naturalist and the super naturalist. As the first of these—like the Gilbert White of the tortoise, the bee-boy, and the goat-sucker (or croon-owl or night-jar) that shook with its rattle the straw 'hermitage' in which he and his friends one summer evening sate drinking tea—Hudson watches, scrutinizes, plays 'I spy', and collects. He classifies and experiments. He is a child in the wilds of Nature, and by no means a dreamy child, taking notes. But whether it is the precision of his senses, of eye, ear, nose, hand, and tongue; or the ease with which he places, and bathes, so to speak, the object observed and examined, in its time, space and atmosphere; or the intimate companionableness of his solitude, that makes the reading of him, as compared with most writers of 'nature books' so peculiar a pleasure, it is impossible to say. These qualities are all of them in some degree necessary to any good book of this kind. Rather than any particular one of them being the leaven then, it is an elixir distilled from them all that is his own secret. And this is as difficult to analyse as the sheen of a starling's wing, or the dream of spring upon the 'smiling face' of winter.

When he speaks of the crystalline sparkle of a perfectly cooked potato; of the pale enamelled turquoise of an adder's belly, such as would have filled with joy and despair the heart

of an old Chinese master-potter; or when he plucks rich clusters of elderberries to gratify his friend the pig; or refers
casually to the grey of a jackdaw's eye, or to the cries of a
heron; or retrieves the tragic fable of a squirrel from his
earliest memories and adds to it a gloss out of mature experience; or as placidly and ripplingly as Coleridge's quiet-tuned
brook gossips meanderingly on and on of worms and moles
and wasps and sheep and foxes and moths and of the disreputable John-go-to-bed-at-noon—well, conjured up by his influence, there steals a spirit into our sophisticated mind that
drinks it all in naïvely and wonderingly, and all but makes an
'actual' memory of it. It is then, in a momentary exaltation,
that we are tempted to claim to be among the elect who (if
not with the microscopical intensity of a Henri Fabre) are
'accustomed to watch insects closely and note their little acts',
and who therefore must be possessed of some small share of
'ladies' brains', seeing that they are 'of a finer quality than
men's'.

Children, chameleonic in attention though they may be,
are often thus engrossed. Our medicine-man may survey us
occasionally with some little attention; the novelist keeps a
wary, divining, analytic eye on his fellows; the poet, like Patmore, focuses his gaze perhaps some few inches *beyond* the re-
garded face; the psychologist is an expert in reactions; the
priest is a student of the soul. But how rarely is *any* such student of *humanity* even comparable to a Fabre; how rarely is
even the confirmed and incorrigible introvert a Hudson!
'Ladies' brains' are notoriously in close connivance with their
owners—according, that is, to man. Their surroundings,
physical, social and mental are dyed with themselves. And
'woman of science' is still a novelty in phrases. So in part then
must it be with Hudson and his fellow-devotees. The worms
he dug up out of his friend's weedkiller-poisoned lawn are, as
with Charles Darwin, red-hot poker in hand, or bassoon at
lip, in an odd fashion *his* worms only. The toad, clearly of the
same lineage as Gilbert White's, which he watched one day

come shambling and panting down the hot stony dusty lane towards the peace, perfect peace, of the pool at its foot, is a toad unique and unprecedented. When he tells us of a pet lamb on the far-away and long-ago farm of his childhood that was wont to sleep and hunt and roister with its eight dogs, or of that adult sheep, also of Patagonia, that would devour tobacco and even books with a gusto shared only by the anatomist of melancholy and the historian of decadent Rome, even although his lamb be of the species beloved of 'Mary', and his sheep as precisely similar to any other specimen of its species now abroad on the outskirts of Kensington Gardens as trotter is to trotter, yet both of them are as exclusively Hudson's sheep and Hudson's lamb as Alice's sage old bespectacled ewe with her knitting needles in the all-sorts shop was Lewis Carroll's. Even as eventual mutton their flavour, we fancy, would still have been his own. The objects and experiences, that is, which were common in his workaday life as a field naturalist, however ordinary they may be in themselves (and any lucky anybody's for the asking), are almost always touched with the idiosyncratic. When these experiences, while still of the detective order, are strange and *un*common, he not only conveys them with an easy exactitude, he also dramatizes them. We are in his mind as we read, just as we are in the mind of Jessica sighing her love-reverie, 'In such a night. . . .'

In what follows, his tiny dazzling humming bird lives for us as if we ourselves had thridded its native thickets, or as if we had discovered it at liberty in the cage of a poem. Moreover, we survey Hudson's face through *its* eyes:

'I have had one dart at me, invisible owing to the extreme swiftness of its flight, to become visible—to materialize, as it were—only when it suddenly arrested its flight within a few inches of my face, to remain there suspended motionless like a hover-fly on misty wings that produced a loud humming sound; and when thus suspended, it has turned its body to the right, then to the left, then completely round as if to exhibit its beauty—its brilliant scale-like feathers changing their colours in the sunlight as it turned. Then, in a few seconds, its curiosity gratified, it has darted away, barely visible as a faint dark line in the air, and vanished perhaps into the intricate branches of some tree, a black acacia perhaps, bristling with long needle-sharp thorns.'

Again and again he repeats this achievement. As when, in describing the marvellous sixth sense of the bat, he stands, check cap on head, in a sunken lane at evening whirling his light cane around and above his head, while to and fro the flittermice veer and waver, and, in their hawking swoop into and *through* its scarcely visible rotations, untouched, unscathed, unstartled! Or, again, as when the wife of 'a gentleman in a southern county', with a 'taste for adders and death's-head moths', emptied over him out of her cardboard box 'such as milliners and dressmakers use . . . a shower of living, shivering, fluttering, squeaking or creaking death's-head moths'. 'In a moment,' he says, 'they were all over me, from my head right down to my feet . . . so that I had a bath and feast of them.' Here again, for an instant, we seem to have pierced behind the veil of an alien life; the mere words momentarily illumine it, as may the flame of a singularly clear candle the objects in a dark and beautiful room.

The biographer of Charles Waterton, one of the most original and lovable of our host of English 'characters',[1]

---

[1] 'On the top floor of the house, in the opposite direction to the organ gallery, was the chapel, and a small room which was at once Waterton's study, bird-stuffing workshop, and bed-room, if bed-room it could be called even when there was not any bed. The Wanderer always slept on the boards, wrapped up in a blanket. His pillow was a block of oak, which had been originally rough, and in course of years had become almost polished by use. The entire room revealed at a glance the simple tastes of its occupant. Some prints on the walls, some shelves contained his favourite books, his jug and basin stood on a chair, and he had a little round looking-glass and a table. Over the mantelpiece was an old map of Guiana, a record to him of living scenes and loving memories. For mere ornament's sake, there was nothing. To the sleeping eye all rooms are equally blank. . . .

speaks of 'the light which sparkles on his pages'. Light, as a matter of fact, is the sovereign grace of every book which has a human imagination in its keeping. It could not be otherwise. The imagination lives on light, as, in the old belief, the bird-of-paradise lived on air and dew. Since light alone not only reveals colour but is an essential element in life itself (and even bodily sleep in a chinkless darkness is frequently *lit* by dreams), no disciple of life can keep its influence out of the words he uses. There are radiant, luminous, scintilating; twilit, gloomy and dark books. Some are of a Stygian darkness, having emanated from darkened minds. A few are written as if in the fabulous gloaming of a moon in her eclipse, and some shed the phosphorescence of decay.

So lucid, lucent, clear and wasteless, so wholly in the service of what it joys in and conveys, is the finer style of such writers as Hudson, Gilbert White, Charles Waterton, Izaak Walton, Edward Thomas (and particularly in his poems), that we may fail to recognize it as a style at all. It partakes not only of the

'His way of life (and he lived to be 83) was primitive. He got up at three, lit his fire, and lay down upon the floor again for half an hour, which he called a half hour of luxury. He had shaved and dressed by four, and from four to five he was upon his knees in the chapel. On his return to his room, he read a chapter in a Spanish life of Saint Francis Xavier, which concluded his early devotions, and he began the secular work of the day with a chapter of Don Quixote in the original. He next wrote letters, or carried on bird-stuffing, till Sir Thomas More's clock struck eight, when, punctual to the moment, the household at Walton sat down to breakfast. His was frugal, and usually consisted of dry toast, watercress, and a cup of weak tea. Breakfast ended, he went out till noon, superintending his farm, mending fences, or clipping hedges. If the weather was cold he would light a fire in the fields. From noon to dinner, which was at half-past one, he would sit indoors and read or think. Dryden, *Chevy Chase*, Dyer's *Grongar Hill*, *Tristram Shandy*, *The Sentimental Journey*, Goldsmith, White's *Natural History of Selborne*, and Washington Irving, were his favourite English literature, and what he liked, he read many times over. After dinner he walked in the park, and came in a little before six to tea. He retired early to bed, but if the conversation was interesting he would stay till near ten. He rose at midnight to spend a few minutes in the chapel, and then went back to his wooden bed, and oaken pillow.'

writer himself but of the very objects whose qualities and whose beauties have been transfigured in his mind. It appears as little like a slowly attained acquisition as the pigments of a chaffinch or a sun-beetle or the grace with which a harebell grows. It is then no particular faculty of the intellect that is called upon in reading them—however unusual and acute an intellect may have aided in their making—but our purest senses and a self-escape for the while from the network of human and social circumstances. The highbrow may smile at one's childish enthusiasm for such books; it is one of his few chances to smile at all. The earnest raise inquisitory eyebrows, and the sophisticated scoff. There are more important and edifying things; more gregarious, social, sociable, civilized, profitable, genteel, smart, witty doings in our personal affairs, both temporal and eternal, than quietly sharing the company of a moth, a robin, a long-tailed tit, an ant, a tortoise, or a toad, even if they are being divined only through words.

But even although our fellow humans possess souls, not always conspicuous, and minds, not invariably attractive, and tongues, at times tedious, they too are only dressed-up mammalia; their habits are familiar. And there is a first nature in us that is not only invoked by the presence of a mountain, but also, it may be, by that of a harvest mouse.

On opening any such book, it is as if out of the heat and dust and noise and shallow fluster of everyday life we had entered into the coolness and quiet of some solitary building, of an age so extreme that it has acquired a natural and living state and beauty; for here every coloured creature, bird, beast, butterfly, leaf and flower and creeping thing in the painted windows, in the capitals, in arch and mullion, niche and corbel, although it be only representative, is alive. The sun streams in; we are alone; but alone in a marvellous small paradise as was the First Man before Eve was taken out of his side. Nor, when we are in serene contemplation of any object, animate or inanimate, are we in that company only. Nor, however simple and common a thing it may be, are its effects and influences on mind and being necessarily rudimentary. That depends on the mind and the being. Monsieur Paul Valéry concludes a profound and fascinating essay entitled 'L'Homme et la Coquille' in *Les Merveilles de la Mer* with these words:

'Je vais rejeter ma trouvaille, comme on rejette une cigarette consumée. Cette coquille m'a *servi*, excitant tour à tour ce que je suis, ce que je sais, ce que j'ignore. . . . Comme Hamlet ramassant dans la terre grasse un crâne, et l'approchant de sa face vivante, se mire affreusement en quelque manière, et entre dans une méditation sans issue que borne de toutes parts un cercle de stupeur, ainsi, sous le regard humain, ce petit corps calcaire creux et spiral appelle autour de soi quantité de pensées, dont aucune ne s'achève. . . .'

As with Hudson's moths and birds and adders, so with his fine fawn odd-coloured-eyed horse, Cristiano. This horse was haunted by memories of the wild, and at wail of a plover would start, snort, and stand at gaze, as if mocked by an illusion. His neigh echoingly evokes some remote vestige of ancient memories darkly interred within ourselves, although only Cunninghame Graham, of all our literary acquaintance, could have bitted and mounted him as to the manner born. Cristiano, that is, is tinged not only with the human but with the praeter-human.

So, as if to square the account, Hudson, as *human*-naturalist, touches the people he meets and talks to with his Nature. In the same degree as Cristiano seems to be a somewhat more than normal horse, his human-kind appear to be different from normal humanity; his own father, for instance—master of the potato; the dignified little native girl who, unaccustomed to fine manners and that tuber, put it into her tea; the wife of the old friend already referred to who decanted the death's-head moths; the sisters who cooked the heron; the blind man in Kensington Gardens; and last, Mr. Redburn, the retired bank manager, who took twelve months to discover that his caged thrush—an inimitable mimic—would preen itself the sprucer if cosseted with a daily worm or two, and thereupon became a rook observer, and whose jackdaw, being given its freedom, found a mate, only to perish with her in their tree-top by a celestial stroke of lightning. Of all the English poets perhaps, and Hudson was a poet who merely preferred to express himself in prose, Mr. W. H. Davies is likeliest to confer on those worthy of him a similar fascination. He dyes his objects with himself:

> . . . *It seemed as though I had surprised*
> *And trespassed in a golden world*
> *That should have passed while men still slept!*
> *The joyful birds, the ship of gold,*
> *The horses, kine and sheep did seem*
> *As they would vanish for a dream.*

And, nearer the margin yet:

> . . . *This man had seen the wind blow up a mermaid's hair*
> *Which, like a golden serpent reared and stretched*
> *To feel the air away beyond her head* . . .

There is nothing, it may be, peculiar about Mr. Redburn except his extraordinary ordinariness; and yet, somehow, he seems to be the heaven-sent nucleus for a detective story by G. K. Chesterton. Hudson confesses, indeed, 'to a De Quincey-like craving to know everything about the life of every person I meet from its birth onwards'. That 'its' may have been an accident, but, whether or not, it is, in its context, nothing but the most delicate compliment he could pay to his fellow humans. On the other hand, his pilgrim toad, 'with yellow eyes on the summit of his head', is, needless to say, 'he' throughout 'his' journey.

And last: 'There is', says Hudson, 'a sense of the *super-natural* in all natural things. . . . We may say, in fact, that unless the soul goes out to meet what we see we do not see it; nothing do we see, not a beetle, not a blade of grass.' It is this sense, above all others, that is the sign manual of all Hudson's writings. All beauty—and in spite of the horrors of life, in spite of the fleetingness of happiness, man has made this supreme discovery—all beauty appeals to our delight in mystery and wonder. Whereas with Fabre we are conscious of a faintly sardonic satisfaction in such phenomena, in Hudson's youth the discovery of the paralysed living larder of the wasp grubs tormented him with the question, How reconcile facts such as these with the idea of a beneficent Being who designed it all? And his Abel, in *Green Mansions*, in his misery cursed God. When, abandoned to a dreadful solitude, he kills the serpent, he dreams in his fantasy, that its 'icy-cold, human-like, fiend-like eyes' will for ever haunt him. 'Murderer! murderer! they would say . . . we two were together, alone and apart—you and I, murderer! you and I, murderer!' Then light falls on the body, revealing a lovely play of prismatic colours, and he muses that thus Nature loves all her children, and gives to every one of them beauty little or much, and he comforts himself with the assurance that Rima loved him. What Ariel is, not only to *The Tempest* but in all the Plays, so is the strange, half-earthly, demi-human Rima—'a thing divine, for nothing natural I ever saw so noble'—in all Hudson's writings. And in no chapter in *The Book of a Naturalist* dwells her influence so strangely and magically as on the four concerned with the serpent.

Its manner of progression, the marvellous cryptogrammic patterns of its skin, its fabulous history, its venom, its flickering forked tongue and its enchantments are considered with that closeness of attention and brooding which this observer in a varying degree expended on every other living creature.[1]

---

[1] Every species (says Charles Waterton) in the great family of animated nature is perfect in its own way, and most admirably adapted to the sphere of life in which an all-ruling Providence has ordered it to move. Could we divest ourselves of the fear which we have of the serpent, and forget for a while the dislike which we invariably show to the toad, both these animals

Naturalists

Nothing to him in Nature was common, nothing was unclean except the evil aberrations of mankind. But there haunts here also a peculiar intensity, as if a profoundly concealed innate voice of memory, rather than a novel earthly experience, were struggling to express a secret knowledge. It may seem strange to us that the hoary foe and tempter of Eve, the Serpent, should be thus befriended. But it is the music of the voice of Rima which clear as vibrant glass resounds in this prose, and it is her presence that confronts us at every turn with the conviction of the supernatural. The old Adam, the happy prehistoric child, in every one of us, in response to this incantation harks back in spirit to the garden of his banishment; wherein the divine awaits him, and he can be once more happy and at peace, the veil withdrawn, all old enmities forgiven and forgotten, amid its natural and praeternatural wonders, its abounding life. There is nothing on earth or in Nature that with the voice of Rima will not thus confide its prehistoric call-note to him that hath ears to hear, nothing— no dewfall-hawk or furtive hedgehog, no 'dare-gale skylark', no 'toning of a tear', no 'rope of sand which petty thoughts have made', no 'loaf of bread', nor even so forlorn and so ludicrously un-magical a thing as Hardy's 'last chrysanthemum'.

> I talk as if the thing were born
> With sense to work its mind;
> Yet it is but one mask of many worn
> By the Great Face behind.

would appear beautiful in our eyes; for, to say nothing of the brilliant colours which adorn the snake, there is wonderful grace and elegance in the gliding progress wherein this reptile's symmetry appears to such great advantage. The supposed horribly fascinating power, said to be possessed by the serpent, through the medium of the eye, has no foundation in truth. We give the snake credit for fixing his eye upon us, when in fact he can do no such thing; for his eye only moves with his body, and ... the toad, that poor, despised, and harmless reptile, is admirable in its proportions, and has an eye of such transcendent beauty, that when I find one, I place it on my hand, to view it more minutely.

CHILDHOOD IN POETRY

1. *'And then in Eden's paradise,*
He placèd him to dwell'.

Milton, as we have seen, attributes his headaches and the injury to his eyesight not to his father's 'forcing' but to his own 'impetuosity in learning'. How much his poetic imagination and his poetry itself were affected in later years by this glut of book-learning is clear in a positive sense. It became at last a magic mirror in his hands, reflecting with his own supreme and substantial splendour, the gods and goddesses, the demigods and heroes, cities, palaces and classic landscapes that as a child he had imaged in it.

But negatively, who can say? As with Swinburne, whose roses and lilies seldom affect us as things seen vividly and at a certain actual moment in the mind's eye, but rather as abstractions, so too Milton's rathe primrose and pale jessamine, his pansy freaked with jet, his twisted eglantine and daisies pied, even his fresh-blown roses 'washed in dew', do not *appear* to have been derived as directly from nature as—one might hazard—almost invariably do similar and no less lovely references in Shakespeare. *His* and Perdita's daffodils, that come before the swallow dares, and take the winds of March with beauty; their violets dim, and pale primroses seem to proclaim that at need he himself might even have dated and placed them! He, like Oberon, *knows* a bank whereon the wild thyme grows—even though what in writing he had in mind was only a memoried image of it. Ophelia's pansies and rosemary, Perdita's violets, her streaked gillyvors, hot lavender, and early bedding marigold, like the 'ruined choirs' of autumn, strutting chanticleer, the icicles that hang

by the wall, the frozen milk in pail, and the green fields of
which Falstaff babbled (if of green fields babble he did), are
almost as vivid in the reading of them as are our own remembered, sharp-seen glimpses of the actual and the real.
The flowers in the plays are cold with rain, sweet with their
nectar, and of the earth earthy. We might at any moment see
a butterfly flitting between our eyes and the printed page.
Wordsworth's daffodils too, though less utterly made his
own perhaps than Shakespeare's, are scarcely distinguishable
from the remembrance of some nodding, multitudinous drift
of them such as we have seen for ourselves in an English
valley. Milton's 'bells and flowerets' have a beauty all their
own—and his; resembling with their 'quaint enamelled
eyes' the most delicate embroidery 'inwrought with figures
dim'.

They are uniquely touched in, made personal—treasure
trove. It is their place of origin that differs. And in Shakespeare's case was not this place in his childhood called not
'human letters', but Out-of-doors?

Similarly with the English poets and the children whom
they present to us in their poems. Some of these children are
wholly natural. Others are idealizations. Others—viewed in
the light of the imagination—are as unique and isolated as

> *the daisy in Noah's meadow*
> *On which the foremost drop of rain fell warm*
> *And soft as afternoon. . . .*

On the whole the poets tend, like the hymn-writers, to
emphasize the littleness of childhood, and, following modern
views, to 'juvenate' their children. Any attempt to make up—
in a story, let us say—apt and natural talk for a child of five
or three years old will prove how very easy it is to fall into
this trap.

If indeed we compare poems about children written by
the poets of the sixteenth and seventeenth centuries—their
grave and lovely epitaphs, for example, or for that matter

those in prose in the eighteenth, with similar poems written during the last century, the contrast is apparent. There are exceptions. Andrew Marvell's 'nymphs' on the one hand—one might assume from what he tells us of them—resemble children even though they are well into their teens. It is their beauty, however, like that of flowers, that is ageless, rather than themselves. The children of Landor, Whittier, Whitman, Prior, Robert Bridges, are both in looks and character un-littled and natural. Wordsworth swings from one extreme to the other, with 'his sister Emmeline', 'a little prattler among men', his H.C., 'a fairy voyager', the child he seems to refuse to understand in *We are Seven*, and the child in *The Pet Lamb*, in which the evening colours and every syllable are exquisitely in keeping with the youth and innocence of both of them.

'Alice Fell' is another exception; but if anything Wordsworth tends to under-age his children. Another Alice, Lewis Carroll's, is at least as dignified as the queens she meets. But his dedications and some of his poems range from the sentimental even to the mundane. When, on the other hand, in some of his poems Mr. William Davies speaks of a child, a child itself, in its own natural kind, comes to life in his words. He sees what he sees; not merely the 'hell-born childishness' of war, but the half-closed eye of the 'love infant' in 'The Inquest', 'leering' that it may have been murdered. He tells also of

> *a boundless prairie, when it lay*
> *So full of flowers it could employ the whole*
> *World's little ones to pick them in a day. . . .*

and lo, there the world's little ones are: we see them picking the flowers. And these, like the children, seem to have suffered no darkening, no sullying, no loss of beauty and 'virtue', or greenness, sweetness and life; when he looks, the buttercup looks back, a bird twinkles in the tree, the water sings an instant louder: he and they have been in an immortal

Childhood in Poetry

conspiracy together for over fifty years. His own poems are
his children.

> *The world may call our children fools,*
> *Enough for us that we conceive.*

Most modern verse—and this folk-rhymes and proverbs
(and Dr. Heinrich Hoffman) all but never do—is apt to pret-
tify its children, dream or real; to patheticize them, scattering
its lines with such words as tiny, guileless, girlish, tomboy,
tears, angels, death and Heaven. If we attempt to translate, so
to speak, their verbal portraits into the pictorial we shall see
how widely they differ from the children of Durer, Velas-
quez, Botticelli, and even of Gainsborough and other painters
of his time. Robinettas, if rare in the nursery, are very welcome, but there are also young falcons, butcher-birds, jays.
'She has eyes as blue as damsons, She has pounds of auburn
curls'. That is natural; but Longfellow's 'Those heavenly
Zingari' is a bad second-best even to his 'blue-eyed banditti'.
And the 'heaven' to which these poets so frequently banish
the beloved one is apt to *look* as vacant if not as unrealized as
the conception of the angel the child has become. It is not at
any rate the heaven, vague even though that may be, referred to by John Beaumont in these solemn lines:

> *Dear Lord, receive my son, whose winning love*
> *To me was like a friendship, far above*
> *The course of nature, or his tender age,*
> *Whose looks could all my bitter griefs assuage.*
> *Let his pure soul, ordained seven years to be,*
> *In that frail body, which was part of me,*
> *Remain my pledge in heaven, as sent to show*
> *How to this port at every step I go.*

When childhood itself rather than children is the poet's
theme, and particularly the poet's own childhood, his outlook
and imaginative treatment are seldom sentimental. Such poems

251

as these are usually concerned not with any definite age in childhood, or its physical and intellectual characteristics, or even its earthly surroundings, but with a state of being. How far can we accept their witness? Can we trust the evidence of *any* human creature who has fallen in love? Or may not this be the kind of evidence which, with due provisos, is the most valuable? To describe such poets as mystics is to elude the question. It may isolate their attitude, but hardly explains or justifies it. In any case a freshness and radiance enter their words, as of dew and daybreak in April.

'Happy those early days when I Shined in my angel infancy!' says Vaughan. 'Before I understood this place'. What precise age, ancestry and cultivation does this statement imply? And again:

> *Were now that Chronicle alive,*
> *Those white designs which children drive . . .*
> *Quickly would I make my path even,*
> *And my meer playing go to Heaven. . . .*

'designs', I gather, meaning aims and intentions; 'drive', pursue; and 'go', go back. With Vaughan's 'meer playing' we shall be concerned later. Wordsworth laments not only the loss of childhood but the inward blindness of age: 'The things which I have seen I now can see no more', while yet treasuring

> *those first affections,*
> *Those shadowy recollections,*
> *Which, be they what they may,*
> *Are yet the fountain light of all our day,*
> *Are yet a master light of all our seeing. . . .*

And again—in *The Excursion*:

> *thou, who didst wrap the cloud*
> *Of infancy around us, that thyself,*
> *Therein, with our simplicity awhile*
> *Might'st hold, on earth, communion undisturbed. . . .*

How clear-coloured and actual a picture too is that of his
'curious child', and how like Vaughan's:

> *I have seen*
> *A curious child, who dwelt upon a tract*
> *Of inland ground, applying to his ear*
> *The convolutions of a smooth-lipped shell;*
> *To which, in silence hushed, his very soul*
> *Listened intensely; and his countenance soon*
> *Brightened with joy; for from within were heard*
> *Murmurings. . . .*

The mere beauty of this 'curious child', though not a word
definitely refers to it, recalls Coleridge's 'lovely boy':

> *Encinctured with a twine of leaves,*
> *That leafy twine his only dress,*
> *A lovely Boy was plucking fruits,*
> *By moonlight, in a wilderness.*
> *The moon was bright, the air was free,*
> *And fruits and flowers together grew*
> *On many a shrub and many a tree:*
> *And all put on a gentle hue,*
> *Hanging in the shadowy air*
> *Like a picture rich and rare.*
> *It was a climate where, they say,*
> *The night is more beloved than day.*
> *But who that beauteous Boy beguiled,*
> *That beauteous Boy to linger here?*
> *Alone, by night, a little child,*
> *In place so silent and so wild—*
> *Has he no friend, no loving mother near?*

This serene light and transparent colour resembles that of
the *Songs of Innocence*, even though the beauteous Boy is
wandering far from the haunts of the Piper. It may be said
that the children in such poems as these are to ordinary
children what physically the young horsemen on the frieze of

the Parthenon are to ordinary young men. But William Blake was not *only* 'imagining' with the insight that divines the hidden; he was also remembering. As a child himself, he had visions, now of the face of God at a window, filling him with terror; now of the prophet Ezekiel in the fields, for telling of whom he was beaten; now of a tree filled with angels, their wings 'bespangling every bough like stars'. And again, of angelic figures walking among haymakers at their work—who themselves little resemble the haymakers that we ourselves usually observe in our country walks, simply because they shared, like his angelic figures also, Blake's *mind*.

2. '*And how a littling child mote be*
   Saint er its nativitie'.

Traherne, too, is recalling not a dream but an actual experience in his 'Meditations' when he says:

'Certainly Adam in paradise had no more sweet and curious apprehensions of the world than I when I was a child. . . . I knew by intuition those things which since my apostacy I collected again by the highest reason. . . . All tears and quarrels were hidden from my eyes. Everything was at rest, free and immortal. . . . So that with much ado I was corrupted, and made to learn the dirty devices of the world, which I now unlearn. . . . The riches of nature are our souls and bodies, with all their faculties, senses and endowments. . . .'

There came a time when he accepted the 'thoughts' of others and forgot his own:

'So I began among my playfellows to prize a drum, a fine coat, a penny, a gilded book, etc., who before never dreamed of such wealth. Goodly objects to drown all the knowledge of Heaven and Earth!'

Lord Herbert of Cherbury in the following argument goes even further afield:

'When I came to riper years, I made this observation, which afterwards a little comforted me, that as I found myself in possession of this life, without knowing anything of the pangs and throes my mother suffered, when yet doubtless they did not less press and afflict me than her, so I hope my soul shall pass to a better life than this without being sensible of the anguish and pains my body shall feel in death. For as I believe then I shall be transmitted to a more happy estate by God's great grace, I am confident I shall no more know how I came out of this world, than how I came into it. . . .'

He continues this thesis in two Latin poems, *Vita* and *De Vita Coelesti conjectura*, and resumes:

'And certainly, since in my mother's womb this plastica, or formatrix, which formed my eyes, ears, and other senses, did not intend them for that dark and noisome place, but, as being conscious of a better life, made them as fitting organs to apprehend and perceive those things which should occur in this world; so I believe, since my coming into this world my soul hath formed or produced certain faculties which are almost as useless for this life, as the above-named senses were for the mother's womb; and these faculties are hope, faith, love, and joy, since they never rest or fix upon any transitory or perishing object in this world, as extending themselves to something further than can be here given, and indeed acquiesce only in the perfect, eternal, and infinite.

'I confess they are of some use here; yet I appeal to everybody whether any worldly felicity did so satisfy their hope here, that they did not wish and hope for something more excellent; or whether they had ever that faith in their own wisdom, or in the help of man, that they were not constrained to have recourse to some diviner and superior power than they could find on earth, to relieve them in their danger or necessity; whether ever they could place their love on any earthly beauty, that it did not fade and wither, if not frustrate or deceive them; or whether ever their joy was so consummate in any thing they delighted in, that they did not want much more than it, or indeed this world can afford, to make them happy. The proper objects of these faculties, therefore, though framed, or at least appearing in this world, is God only, upon whom faith, hope, and love were never placed in vain, or remain long unrequited'.

Blake's visionary angels may have been (no less 'experience' even if they were), a pure fantasy of the imagination, but we can produce no proof of it. And to dismiss or disdain Traherne's 'apprehensions' merely because we have never shared them is rather too easy a way out of a difficulty. It is in unusual minds that we expect unusual events, the fruit of unusual powers of perception. Even when he was a child of four, Traherne tells us, he used to speculate and wonder how 'the earth did end'. With walls or sudden precipices? Or perhaps did the face of Heaven lap down so close upon its margins that a man could 'hardly creep under'? Or was it upheld by pillars or by abysses of dark waters; and, if that were so, what upheld these? It is with conjectures of this *nature* that the modern astronomer is busy, his optic glass ranging stellar universes a myriad light-years away. One 'lowering and sad evening', he being alone in a field, the wilderness terrified the child: 'I was a weak and little child and had forgotten there was a man alive in the earth'. And Coleridge's words echo this forlornness: 'It was a climate where, they say, The night is more beloved than day'.

What Thomas Hood tells in rhyme in 'I Remember' Thoreau repeats in prose :

'If thou art a writer, write as if thy time were short, for it is indeed short at the longest. . . . The spring will not last for ever. . . . Again I say, Remember thy Creator in the days of thy youth. Use and commit to life what you cannot commit to memory. Why did I not use my eyes when I stood on Pisgah? . . . Ah, sweet, ineffable reminiscences!'

And John Clare, looking back out of the darkness and misery of his last asylum, becomes a poet in the rarest of senses:

> . . . *I long for scenes where man has never trod;*
> *A place where woman never smiled or wept;*

Childhood in Poetry

There to abide with my Creator, God,
*   And sleep as I in childhood sweetly slept:*
Untroubling and untroubled where I lie,
*   The grass below—above the vaulted sky.*

To be a child, these witnesses gravely declare, is to be an exile, an exile haunted with vanishing intimations and relics of another life and of a far happier state of being—of a lost Jerusalem to which it is all in vain (by the waters of Babylon) to pine to return. Consciousness itself, they declare, resembles the awakening out of a dream of innocence, serenity and bliss.

Father, O Father! what do we here,
In this land of unbelief and fear?
The Land of Dreams is better far
Above the light of the morning star.

Its very radiance and peace may continue awhile to shine on our young heads and to transmute the things of a world as yet 'not realized', but it fades quickly into the light of common day. Every man, in Jeremy Taylor's words, to take the other side of the account,

'is born in vanity and sin; he comes into the world like morning Mushromes, soon thrusting up their heads into the air and conversing with their kindred of the same production, and as soon they turn into dust and forgetfulnesse; some of them without any other interest in the affairs of the world, but that they made their parents a little glad, and very sorrowful: others ride longer in the storm; it may be until seven years of Vanity be expired, and then peradventure the Sun shines hot upon their heads and they fall into the shades below, into the cover of death, and darknesse of the grave to hide them. But if the bubble stands the shock of a bigger drop, and outlives the chances of a childe, of a carelesse Nurse, of drowning in a pail of water, of being overlaid by a sleepy servant, or such little accidents, then the young man dances like a bubble, empty and gay, and shines like a Dove's neck or the image of

R   257

a rainbow, which hath no substance, and whose very imagery and colours are phantastical; and so he dances out the gaiety of his youth. . . .'

Transitory glimpses of the lost may be recovered:

> . . . *I sought no more that after which I strayed*
>   *In face of man or maid;*
> *But still within the little children's eyes*
>   *Seems something, something that replies,*
> *They at least are for me, surely for me!*
> *I turned me to them very wistfully;*
> *But just as their young eyes grew sudden fair*
>   *With dawning answers there,*
> *Their angel plucked them from me by the hair. . . .*

And even the seemingly past-recall, if we accept George Macdonald's statement, is neither inactive nor beyond a far-deferred recovery:

> . . . *I think that nothing made is lost;*
> *That not a moon has ever shone,*
> *That not a cloud my eyes hath crossed*
> *But to my soul is gone.*
>
> *That all the lost years garnered lie*
> *In this Thy casket, my dim soul;*
> *And Thou wilt, once, the key apply,*
> *And show the shining whole. . . .*

The mind in the act of creation, said Shelley (who 'never learned to sit with folded wings'), is a fading coal. So to these poets was the state of early childhood, even although for them its ardour and light had not yet faded wholly out of remembrance. Our days, then, in childhood as in later life, in the words of William Drummond, 'are not to be esteemed after the number of them but after their goodness'. The flowers 'made of light' shine no more in their primal loveliness, though this may be revealed again and again as if by reflection

—an experience described by Mr. Frank Kendon in *The Small Years* when he first chanced on the blue succory:

'The flower was a miracle to me, something rich and strange, and I had to register my discovery (I suppose) on a mind not my own to be sure it was credible. But before I found [this witness] my flower had faded quite out of its beauty by the heat of the summer afternoon. . . .'

That fading reminds me of a similar experience when I was myself about seven. My flower was not the celestially blue succory, but a colourless convolvulus (a species which Edmund Gosse when he was six informed his father he was raising in a salt cellar). But its cool dark heart-shaped leaves and waxen vase-like simplicity awoke in me a curious wonder and delight, and I remember it as vividly and with the same peculiar intensity as I remember the shimmering seeding grasses bowing in the windy sunshine when I lay rapturously watching them one morning in a later June. I plucked the flower out of the hedge to take it home to my mother. But when I came into the house it had wreathed itself into a spiral as if into a shroud. And when I realized it would never more be enticed out of it again, I burst into tears!—'burst into my mother's arms', as a little boy of three the other day described the consequences of seeing in motion at a circus a Mechanical Man!

3. *'In the silence of the morning the song of the bird'.*

'So the child of whom I am writing', runs Walter Pater's tale of the hawthorn, 'lived on there quietly; things without thus ministering to him, as he sat daily at the window with the birdcage hanging below it, and his mother taught him to read, wondering at the ease with which he learned, and at the quickness of his memory. . . . How insignificant, at the moment, seem the influences of the sensible things which are tossed and fall and lie about us, so or so, in the environment of early childhood. How indelibly, as we afterwards discover, they affect us. . . . The realities and passions, the rumours of the greater world without, steal in upon us, each by its own special little passage-way, through the wall of custom about us; and never afterwards quite detach themselves from this or that accident, or trick, in the mode of their first entrance to us. . . .'

Among the most vivid of these in Mr. Romilly John's early childhood was a fountain, and the beauty of its falling waters; the luminous bright red too of a glass of grenadine. But even commonplace objects and very familiar ones have the power to whisper this secret *Sesame*, and may keep it far beyond the years of childhood—a bird seen very close; or held, its bead-like unspeculative eyes shining, in the hand; condensed mist on a grass-spider's web, the cheeping of a midnight mouse in the wainscot, the sickle of the new moon, the first splinters of ice in winter frost, the first snow—as in this description of it from *The Small Years*—no less true to nature than that in Ascham's *Toxophilus*, but filled with a rapture known only to a child: '. . . If the snow were wet, or still falling, so that we knew we could not go out, we would lean all together on the low nursery window-sill, staring out across the road to the orchard, our eyes made dizzy by the constant snow flakes as they floated down and by to settle. Four pairs of eyes were not enough to notice all, nor four excited voices enough to announce all the novelties, the birds that flew down, the solitary waggon that drew by, the depth of the snow in the wheel-tracks, or in the scoop-shaped laurel leaves immediately underneath us, or how it piled up against the window-glass, or how the millions of grey specks fought one another in the sky above the elm tops. We lived then, except for our mere bodies, in the world outside; games and books and fire were all forgotten while we gave our souls over to the snow. . . . The wonder of it, the nearness now, the whiteness, the brightness, the way you screwed your eyes up, the tidyness of the world! At first it was pleasure enough just to walk on it, feeling your feet sink in, and the squeak and crunch of your steps; then to run, careless whether you were on path or grass, the great delight being to make your tracks in snow that had not been imprinted before, to run scattering and then to stop and look back at the way you had written in the snow. Once, I remember, we looked over a gate with a great sloping field as white as a giant's sheet of notepaper, and we climbed into this field and ran wildly, writing our names with our feet in giant letters for the sky to read. . . .

'The sky was darker than the land; indoors through windows the light struck upwards to the ceiling instead of downwards to the floor; out of doors our hands and faces looked brown and rosy in contrast with the whiteness of the snow; our voices had no echoes, our games, our world, our characters were all necessarily different from those of the ordinary week-day world. There was nothing that the miracle did not change, and nothing, however trivial, which was not impressed with twice its normal significance upon minds intoxicated with the white excitement. So it was then, and so it is to-day; for if the truth be told there is a child in everyone when snow is about, and the word *snow* is richer in youthful association than almost any other English word. . . .'

And the snow may be London snow, as in Robert Bridges' poem, which itself transports memory into the wilds of childhood again.

> . . . *And all woke earlier for the unaccustomed brightness*
> *Of the winter dawning, the strange unheavenly glare;*
> *The eye marvelled—marvelled at the dazzling whiteness;*
>   *The ear hearkened to the stillness of the solemn air;*
> *No sound of wheel rumbling nor of foot falling,*
> *And the busy morning cries came thin and spare.*
>
>   *Then boys I heard, as they went to school, calling,*
> *They gathered up the crystal manna to freeze*
> *Their tongues with tasting, their hands with snowballing;*
>   *Or rioted in a drift, plunging up to the knees;*
> *Or peering up from under the white-mossed wonder,*
> *'O look at the trees!' they cried, 'Oh look at the trees!'*

Childhood in Poetry

To dismiss as pure illusion what poets such as Vaughan and Traherne and Blake attest because any such experience in childhood as theirs is, we assume, rare and extraordinary is merely to measure life by a home-made foot-rule. Their poetry is itself rare and extraordinary. Must that also go by the board? 'For my owne part', writes Vaughan, who was by profession a doctor of medicine, 'I honour the truth wherever I find it, whether in an old or a new Booke, in *Galen*, or in *Paracelsus*; and Antiquity (where I find it grey with errors), shall have as little reverence from me as *Novelisme*'. And where shall we begin and end our incredulity?

' "My love", said my mother, looking up from her work . . . "shan't we call him Augustine?"

' "Augustine", said my father dreamily, "why, that name's mine."

' "And you would like your boy's to be the same?"

' "No", said my father, rousing himself. "Nobody would know which was which. I should catch myself learning the Latin accidence or playing at marbles. I should never know my own identity, and Mrs. Primmins would be giving me pap." . . . '

He is eventually given the name of Pisistratus.

' "Pisistratus christened! Pisistratus! who lived six hundred years before Christ was born. Good heavens, madam! you have made me the father of an Anachronism".'

Shall we then dismiss these particular poets with their 'golden-age-of-childhood stuff' as *Anachronisms* and have done with it?

Well and good, but many other poets, who after all are human beings and so as likely to be at odds one with another in other respects as the prosaic and matter-of-fact may be, have volunteered their own variants of the same fantastic legend—Lamb, Lowell, Longfellow, Stevenson, Thomas Moore, Elizabeth Barrett Browning, Tennyson, Father Tabb. To ignore their evidence would fall a good deal short at least of being 'scientific'. Shelley is even persuaded to discover not only innocence and bliss in such recollections, but a goddess full-grown—Intellectual Beauty:

> ... *While yet a boy I sought for ghosts, and sped*
> > *Through many a listening chamber, cave and ruin,*
> > *And starlight wood, with fearful steps pursuing*
> *Hopes of high talk with the departed dead.*
> *I called on poisonous names with which our youth is fed;*
>
> > *I was not heard—I saw them not—*
> > *When musing deeply on the lot*
> *Of life, at that sweet time when winds are wooing*
> > *All vital things that wake to bring*
> > *News of birds and blossoming—*
> > *Sudden, thy shadow fell on me;*
> *I shrieked, and clasped my hands in ecstasy!*
>
> > *I vowed that I would dedicate my powers*
> > *To thee and thine—have I not kept the vow? ...*

and he, ineffectual angel of a remarkable energy of mind, never completely learned

> *To look on nature, not as in the hour*
> *Of thoughtless youth; but hearing oftentimes*
> *The still, sad music of humanity. ...*

It has been left to our own enlightened day to discover the secret of laughing at *everything* that is tainted with the transcendental—and so doing unto others as they may be tempted to do unto us.

Ah, yes, whispers Common Sense, but wait a little longer until these early ecstasies have ebbed or gone flat or turned cheat, what then? Shelley himself can preach his own funeral sermon on this trite text. When he was twenty-two, and the father of Ianthe, he writes to Hogg: 'My friend, you are happier than I. You have the pleasures as well as the pains of sensibility. I have sunk into a premature old age of exhaustion, which renders me dead to everything. . . .' This apparently was in part because Harriet, though 'a noble animal', could, like most of Shelley's schoolfellows at Syon House Academy and Eton, neither 'feel poetry' nor understand philosophy. A few months later the sixteen-year-old daughter of William Godwin darted into his life. He caught up a bottle of laudanum, says Peacock, who had come to call on him, and said: 'I never part from this'. And yet, urged Peacock, ' "it always appeared to me that you were very fond of Harriet".' 'Without affirming or denying this he answered: "But you did not know how much I hated her sister".'

And this—written on 4th March 1812, was what his worldly-wise father-in-law thought of him:

'My good friend—I have read all your letters (the first perhaps excepted) with peculiar interest, and I wish it to be understood by you unequivocally that, as far as I can yet penetrate into your character, I conceive it to exhibit an extraordinary assemblage of lovely qualities not without considerable defects. The defects do, and always have arisen chiefly from this source, that you are still very young, and that in certain essential respects you do not sufficiently perceive that you are so. . . .'

Which might have been a still more crushing summary if Godwin had been able to follow it up with a calculation showing how many centuries 'younger' a boy of twenty is than a baby of three.

'BENIGHTED'

As for us two, lest doubt of us yee have,
Hence far away we will blindfolded lie . . .

We surveyed one another a little ruefully in the starry air—and it is many years ago now, that quiet evening—then turned once more to the darker fields around us.

'Yes,' she said; 'there isn't the least doubt in the world. We are lost. Irretrievably. Before that owl screeched there seemed to be just a remote chance for us. . . . But now: not a house, not a living being in sight.'

'Not one,' I said.

'Not even Mrs. Grundy,' she said, and sighed. 'Poor dear—she has sipped her posset, tied on her nightcap, and gone to bed.'

Baa! cried a faintly lachrymose voice out of the stony pasture beyond the rough flint wall.

'It's all very well to say "Baa",' she replied, accepting the challenge. 'But it makes us all, you see, look a little sheepish.' There was silence; we trudged on.

Nights of summer-time remain warm with day, and are seldom more than veiled with a crystalline shadowiness which is not darkness, but only the withdrawal of light. Even at this midnight there was a radiance as of pale blue glass in the north, though east to west stretched the powdery myriads of the Milky Way. Honeysuckle, bracken, a hint of hay, and the faint, aromatic scent of summer lanes saturated the air. The very darkness was intoxicating.

'I could walk on like this for ever,' I managed to blurt out at last.

'Those "for evers"!' mocked a quiet voice.

'Benighted'

The lane ran deeper and gloomier here. Beneath heavy boughs thick with leaves gigantic trees were breathing all around us. The vast, taciturn silence of night haunted the ear; yet little furtive stirring sounds kept the eyes wide open. Once more we paused, standing stock still together.

'Let's just go on up—a little way,' I pleaded. 'There *might* be a house. You look so sleepy—and so lovely—my dear. A sort of hawk-like look—with that small head in this dim blur; even though your eyes *are* full of dreams.'

She laughed and turned away. 'Not sleepy, only a little drugged. And oh, if only I could be lovely *enough!*'

We did go up, and presently, out from under the elms. And we came to many houses, low and squat and dark and still—roofing the soundest of all sleepers. We gazed slowly from stone to stone, from tiny belfry to distant Vega.

'Well, there they are,' I said. 'And they appear to have been there for some little time. What a silence!'

'Why, so!' she answered. 'And such is life, I suppose—just the breaking of it.'

'And you forgive me?'

'I try.'

'I could have sworn we were on the right road.'

' "She trusted in him, and there was none to deliver her!" But of course', she said, 'the road *is* right. There is no other way than the way once taken. And especially this. Besides, my dear, I don't mind a bit; I don't indeed. It's still, and harmless, and peaceful, and solitary. We are all alone in the world. Let's sit down in there and talk.'

So we entered the old graveyard by its tottering gateway and seated ourselves on a low flat tombstone, ample enough in area for the Sessions of all the Sons of Israel.

The wakefulness of long weariness had overtaken us. The dark air was translucently clear, sprinkling its cold dew on all these stones and their overshadowing boughs. We ravenously devoured the fragments left over after our day's march. And we talked and talked, our voices sounding small and hollow even to ourselves, in this heedful solitude. But at last we too fell silent; for it began to be cold, and that hour of the night was coursing softly by us when a kind of inhumanity seems to settle on the mind, and words lose the meanings they have by day; just as the things of day may be transformed by night —ranging themselves under the moon like phenomena of another world.

'I wonder', I said at last, 'when we—or just you, or I, come to a place like this: I wonder, shall we forget—be forgotten— do you think? Nearly all these must be.'

'In time,' she answered.

'Yes, in time; perhaps. Not exactly "forget", though—but remember; with all the hopelessness, the helpless burning and longing gone. Isn't that it?'

'I wonder,' she said gravely. 'Life's an abominably individual thing. We just *live* on our friends.'

'And what would you say about me—if you had to? On my stone, I mean? *Before* forgetting me?'

But her face gave no sign that she had heard so fatuous a question. I somehow refrained the sigh that offered itself.

'Let's see—if we can—what *they* did,' I suggested instead.

So, no moon yet shining, I took out my matchbox and counted out its contents into her left hand.

'Twenty-one,' I said dubiously. 'Not *too* many for so much to do!'

'Riches!' she replied. 'You see, even if we have to use two for a tombstone, that would be ten altogether, and a little stone over. And surely there should be, say, *three* epitaphs among them. I mean, apart from mere texts. It's a little odd you know,' she added, peering across the huddled graves.

'What's odd?'

'Why, that there are likely to be so few worth reading— with such lots to say.'

'Not so very odd,' I said. 'Your Mrs. Grundy hates the sight of them. They frighten her.'

'Well, I don't somehow think,' she answered, peering

through the shadowiness at me, 'I don't somehow think anybody else ever was here but you and me. It's between real and dream—like Mrs. Grundy herself.'

I held out my hand; but she smiled and would give me no proof. So we began our scrutiny, first stooping together over the great stone that had seated us to supper. And all that it surrendered for our reward was the one vast straddling word —'M.O.R.S.'

The dark, flat surface was quite unbroken else. The flame (screened between the shell of my hands) scarcely illumined its margins. The match languished and fell from my fingers.

'"M O R S",' she spelt it out. 'And what does MORS mean?' inquired that oddly indolent voice in the quiet. 'Was it his name, or his initials, or is it a charm?'

'It means—well, sleep,' I said. 'Or nightmare, or dawn, or nothing, or—it might mean everything.' I confess, though, that to my ear it had the sound at that moment of an enormous breaker, bursting on the shore of some unspeakably remote island; and we two marooned.

'Well, that's one,' she said. ' "MORS": how dull a word to have so many meanings! You men are rather heavy-handed, you know. You think thinking helps things on. I like that Mors. He was a gentleman.'

I stared blankly into the darkness: and my next match flared in vain on mouldering illegibility. The third lasted us out, however, stooping side by side, and reading together:

> *Stranger, where I at peace do lie*
> *Make less ado to press and pry!*
> *Am I a Scoff to be who did*
> *Life like a stallion once bestride?*
> *Is all my history but what*
> *A fool hath—soon as read—forgot?*
> *Put back my weeds, and silent be,*
> *Leave me to my own company!*

We hastened to do as we were bid, confronted by phantom

eyes so dark and piercing, and groped our way over a few markless grassy mounds to the toppling stone of 'Susannah Fry, who after a life grievous and disjointed, fell asleep in a swoon'.

> Here sleep I
> Susannah Fry,
> No one near me,
> No one nigh:
> Alone, alone
> Under my stone,
> Dreaming on,
> Still dreaming on:
> Grass for my valance
> And coverlid,
> Dreaming on
> As I always did.
> 'Weak in the head?'
> Maybe. Who knows?
> Susannah Fry
> Under the rose.

Under the rose Susannah lay indeed—a great canopy of leaves and sweetness looming up palely in the night darkness. 'That's six,' I said, turning away from a tomb inscribed with that prosaic rendering of 'Gather ye rosebuds'—'Take care lest ye also be called early'; and the victim a Jeremiah of seventy-two! The tiny flame spluttered and hissed in the dewy grass.

But our seventh rewarded us:

> Here lies my husbands; One, Two, Three:
> Dumb as men ever could wish to be.
> As for my Fourth, well, praise be God
> He bides for a little above the sod.
> But his wits being weak and his eyeballs dim,
> Heavn'd speed at last I'll wear weeds for him.
> Thomas, John, Henry, were these three's names
> And to make things tidy, I adds his—James.

'Benighted'

'If it would not in the least prejudice matters, might I, do you think, be Thomas?' I said. 'The unsuspecting?'

She laughed out of the darkness. 'The pioneer!' she said. 'Hope on.'

Our next two matches burned over a stone which only the twisted roots of a rusty yew tree had for a little while saved from extinction. The characters were nearly extinct on its blackened lichenous surface:

> *Here restes ye boddie of one*
> *Chrystopher Orcherdson.*
> *Lyf he lived merrilie;*
> *Nowe he doth deathlie lie:*
> *All ye joye from his brighte face*
> *Quencht in this bitter place.*
> *With grateful voice then saye,*
> *Not oures, but Goddes waye!*

With grateful voice I counted out yet another six of the little store left into a hand cold and dim. And we took it in turn to choose from among the grassy mounds and stones. Two matches were incontinently sacrificed: one to a little wind from over the countryside, smelling of Paradise; and one to a bramble that all but sent me crashing on to the small headstone of the 'Shepherd', whose mound was a positive mat of fast-shut bindweed flowers. Oddly enough, their almond-like smell became more perceptible in the vague light we shed on them.

> *A Shepherd, Ned Vaughan,*
> *'Neath this Tombstone do bide,*
> *His Crook in his hand,*
> *And his Dog him beside.*
> *Bleak and cold fell the Snow*
> *On Marchmallysdon Steep,*
> *And folded both sheepdog*
> *And Shepherd in Sleep.*

'Benighted'

Our next two matches gleamed on a tomb raised a little from the ground, with a damp-greened eyeless head on each panel that must once have been cherubim:

> Here rest in Peace Eliza Drew and James Hanneway
>   whom Death haplessly snatched from Felicity.
> Eliza and James in this sepulchre tarry
> Till God with His trumpet shall call them to marry.
> Then Angels for maids to the Bride shall be given,
> And loud their responses shall echo in Heaven.
> And e'en though it be that on Paradise Plains
> A wife is no wife; spinster spinster remains;
> These twain they did tarry so long to be wed
> They might now prefer to stay happy instead.
> Howe'er it befall them, Death's shadows once past,
> They'll not laugh less sweetly who learnt to laugh last.

And we spent two more on a little old worn stone couched all askew, and nearly hidden in moss:

> Poor Sam Lover,
> Now turf do cover;
> His Wildness over.

It was obviously a sacred duty to clear at least of sow-thistles and nettles the grave of one once loved so kindly. 'There! Sam Lover,' exclaimed a rather breathless voice at last, ' "nettles shall not sting this year".'

And at that moment the first greenish pallor of the fast-waning and newly-risen moon peered out on us from between the yews.

Distant and companionable, cock answered cock across the drowsy acres. But even when it had ascended a little into its brightness the moon shone but wanly, casting the greyest of faint shadows from the fretted spire over the tombs of a Frenchman, Jules Raoul Dubois, and the Virgin on his left hand.

'Benighted'

Here sleeps a Frenchman: Would I could
Grave in his language on this wood
His many virtues, grace and wit!
But then who'd read what I had writ?
Nay, when the tongues of Babel cease,
One word were all sufficient—Peace!

Thick English grasses waved softly over him beyond the faint moonlight, and covered as deeply the grave of one left nameless:

Blessed Mary, pity me.
Who was a Virgin too, like Thee;
But had, please God, no little son
To shower a lifetime's sorrows on.

Just a message out of nothingness, for the words summoned no picture, scarcely even the shadow of a human being, into the imagination. Not so those over which the last of our twenty-one battled feebly against the moon:

J.T.
Here's Jane Taylor,
Sweet Jane Taylor,
Dark,
Wild,
Dear Jane Taylor.

Silence, dense as the milky mist that wreathed the neighbouring water-meadows, now enwrapt us. Cold and cheerless, we sat down once more to await the coming of the dawn. And it was the sun's first clear beams, putting to shame all remembrance of night, that, slanting in palest gold, lit up for us a little odd stone at our feet, almost hidden in brambles:

Be very quiet now:
A child's asleep
In this small cradle,
In this shadow deep!

Words have strange capricious effects. *Now*, it was as if I could actually recall in memory itself the infant face in its white frilled cap—icily still, stonelike.

And then I raised my eyes and looked into the face of the living one beside me. Hers were fixed as if absently on the broken inscription, the curved lids fitting them as closely as its calyx the rose. The face was cold and listless; her hands idle in her lap. It was as though the beauty of her face were lying (like a mask) dead and forgotten, the self within was so far away.

A thrush broke into song, as if from another world. Conscious at last of my silence perhaps, she slowly lifted her head into the gilding sunshine. And as if with a shrug of her slender shoulders, 'Now for the rest of our lives,' she said.

PHYSIC

Emilia and William had been keeping one another company in the kitchen. Mary, her trusty substantial cook-general, was 'out', and would not be knocking at the door until half-past ten. After that there might be another hour to wait. But then Emilia would be alone. Meanwhile, just like man and wife, William and she would soon be having supper together at two corners of the kitchen table, and William would have an egg —with nine bread-and-butter fingers.

This, once fortnightly, now weekly, Wednesday-night feast had become a kind of ritual, a little secret institution. They called it their covey night. Not even Daddie ever shared it with them; and it was astonishing what mature grown-up company William became on these occasions. It was as if, entirely unknown to himself, he had swallowed one of Jack's bean-seeds and had turned inside into a sort of sagacious second-husband. All that Emilia had to do, then, was merely to become again the child she used to be. And that of course needs only a happy heart.

He was a little dark-skinned boy, William—small for his age. A fringe of gilt-edged fair hair thatched a narrow fore-head over his small, restless eyes. His sister Sallie—poor gaunt Aunt Sarah, whom she had been called after, having departed this life when less than a month had passed since the gay chris-tening party—little Sallie, after a restless and peevish afternoon and a wailful bath, was asleep now, upstairs, in her crib. You could tell that almost without having to creep out every now and again to listen at the foot of the stairs.

William had been even more lively and hoppity than usual. He and Emilia had been playing Beggar-my-Neighbour, and he had become steadily more excited when with something

very like sheer magic, every sly knave in the pack had rapidly
abandoned poor Emilia and managed to slide into his hand.
And when—after an excited argument as to where the Queen
of Hearts had best be hidden—they changed the game, he
laughed and laughed till the tears came into his eyes to see her
utter confusion at finding herself for the third time an abject
Old Maid! And when supper-time came—plates, spoons,
forks—he had all but danced from dresser to table, from table
to dresser again. They had borrowed Mary's best blue-check
kitchen tablecloth; he had said it looked cooler. 'Don't you
think so, Mummie?' And every now and again he had ejacu-
lated crisp shrill remarks and directions at Emilia, who was
looking after the cooking in the outer room, a room she had
steadfastly refused to call the 'scullery'. Merely because she
disliked the word! Though one day in a sudden moment of
inspiration she had defended this priggishness by exclaim-
ing, 'Well, spell it with a *k* and then see what you think
of it!'

It was a little way Emilia had. As tenaciously as she could
she always put off until to-morrow even what it was merely
difficult to put up with to-day. Never trouble trouble till
trouble troubles you, was her motto when driven into a corner. She hated problems, crises, the least shadow of any
horror, though they would sometimes peer up at her out of
her mind—and from elsewhere—when she wasn't looking,
like animals at evening in the darkening hills. But when they
actually neared, and had to be faced; well, that was quite
another matter.

For some minutes now, busied over her sizzling pan at the
gas stove, she hadn't noticed that William's galvanic sprightly
conversation piped up from the kitchen had been steadily
dwindling, had almost ceased. He had decided to have his
supper egg fried, though 'lightly boiled' was the institution.
And Emilia had laughed when, after long debate, he had declared that he had chosen it fried because then it was more in-
digestible. She was dishing it up from the smoke and splutter

—a setting sun on a field of snow, and with a most delicate edging of scorch.

When she came back into the kitchen William was standing by the table, gazing across it at the window. He couldn't be looking *out* of the window, for although there was a crevice a few inches wide between the flowered chintz curtains that had been drawn over it and where the blue linen blind had not been pulled down to the very bottom, it was already pitch dark outside. Yet even at this distance she saw that he couldn't also be staring solely at his own reflection.

He stood motionless, his eyes fixed on this dark glassy patch of window, his head well above the table now. He had not even turned at sound of her footsteps. So far as Emilia's bird-like heart was concerned it was as if a jay had screeched in a spinney. But best not to notice too much. Don't put things into people's heads. 'There!' she exclaimed. 'Well now, you *have* cut the bread and butter thick, Mr. Stoic! *I'm* going to have that scrap of cold fish. Eat this while it's hot, my precious!'

But William had continued to wait.

'I don't think, Mummie,' he said slowly as if he were reciting something he had been learning by heart, 'I don't *think* I'll have my egg after all. I don't think I feel very hungry just now.'

All his eagerness and excitement seemed to have died down into this solemn and stagnant reverie; and for a child to have the air and appearance of a sorrowful old dwarf is unutterably far away from its deliciously pretending to be a sedate grown-up.

'Not to have it!' cried Emilia. 'Why, look, blessing, it's cooked! Look! Lovely. You wouldn't know it wasn't a tiny half of a peach in cream. Let's pretend.'

'I couldn't like even that, Mummie,' he said, glancing at it, a slight shudder ending in a decisive shake of the head as he hastily looked away again. 'I don't think, you know, I want *any* supper.'

Emilia's eyes widened. She stood perfectly still a moment, the hot plate in her hand, staring at him. Then she hurriedly put it down on the table, knelt with incredible quickness beside him, and seized his hand.

'That's what it is,' she said. 'You don't feel very well, William. You don't feel very well? Your hands are hot. Not sick? Not sore throat? Tell mummie.'

'I'm *not* ill,' wailed William obstinately. 'Just because I don't want the egg! You *can't* like that horrid cold fish, and if I did feel sick, wouldn't I say so? That's only what *you* say.' He paused as if the utmost caution and precision were imperative, then added, nodding his head mournfully and sympathetically in time to the whispered words, 'I *have* got a teeny tiny headache, but I didn't notice it until just now.' His mouth opened in a prodigious yawn, leaving tears in his eyes. 'Isn't it funny, Mummie—you can't really see anything out of the window when it's black like that, yet you needn't look at your*self* in the glass. It's just as if. . . .'

His eyes came round from examining the window, and fixed themselves on her face.

'That's what it is,' said Emilia, raising herself abruptly from the floor. 'That's what it is.' She kept squeezing the thin, unresponsive fingers of his hand between her own. 'You're feverish. And I knew it. *All* the time. Yes—*how* stupid of me.' And instantly her voice had changed, all vain self-recriminations gone. 'I'll tell you what we'll *do*, William. First, I'll fill a hot-water bottle. Then I'll run up and get the thermometer. And *you* shall be the doctor. That's much the best thing.' And she did not even pause for his consent.

'I expect you know, Dr. Wilson,' she had begun at once, 'it's something that's disagreed with my little boy. I expect so. Oh, yes, I expect so.'

William, pale and attentive, was faltering. 'Well, yes, Mrs. Hadleigh, p'raps,' he said at last, as if his mouth were cramfull of plums. 'You *may* be right. And that depends, you know, on what he has been *eating*.'

'Yes, yes, I quite understand, doctor. Then would you perhaps wait here just for one moment, while I see if my little boy is ready for you. I think, you know, he might like to wash his hands first and brush his hair. And *pray* keep on your overcoat in case you should feel cold.' She took a large dry Turkey towel that was airing on a horse near by, and draped it over William's shoulders. 'I won't be a moment,' she assured him. 'Not a moment.'

Yet she paused to glance again at his shawled-in pale face and fever-bright eyes, as if by mere looking she could bore clean through his body; and stooping once more, she pressed her cheek against his, and then his hand to her lips.

'You said,' half tearfully chanted the little boy, 'that I was the doctor; and now you are kissing me, Mummie!'

'Well, I could often and often kiss lots of doctors,' said his mother, and in a flash she was gone, leaving him alone. She raced up the dark staircase as if she were pursued by twenty demons, not even waiting to switch on the light. And when she came to her bedroom it was as if everything in it were doing its utmost to reassure her. The shining of the street lamp was quietly dappling its walls with shadow. The whole room lay oceans deep in silence; the duskily mounded bed, the glass over the chimney-piece, the glass on the dressing-table. They may until that very moment have been conferring together, but now had, as usual, instantly fallen mute, their profound confabulations for the time being over. But she did not pause even so much as to sip of this refreshing stillness. Her finger touched the electric switch, and in an instant the harmless velvety shadows—frail quivering leaf-shadows—the peace, the serenity, had clean evaporated. It was as if the silence had been stricken with leprosy, so instantaneous was the unnatural glare—even in spite of the rose-pink lamp-shades. For now Emilia was staring indeed.

How, she was asking herself, how by any possibility could that striped school tie of her husband's have escaped from its upper drawer on to the bedspread? How by an utter miracle had she failed to see it when she had carried Sallie into the room only an hour or two ago? Ties don't wriggle out of top-drawers across carpets and climb up valances like serpents in the tropics. Husbands miles away cannot charm such things into antics like *these*!

Mary had been out all the afternoon. She herself had been out for most of it with the children, and she could have vowed, taken her oath, *knew*, that *that* couldn't have been there when she had come up to put on her hat. In the instant that followed before even she could insist on raising her eyes from this queer scrap of 'evidence', her mind suddenly discovered that it was dazed and in the utmost confusion. It was as if, like visitors to a gaudy Soho restaurant, a jostling crowd of thoughts and images, recollections, doubts, memories, clues, forebodings, apprehensions and reiterated stubborn reassurances had thronged noisy and jostling into consciousness—and then were gone again. And at that, at once, as if by instinct and as unforeseeably as a night moth alights on one out of a mul-titude of flowers, her stricken glance had encountered her husband's note.

At sight of it her heart had leapt in her body, and then cowered down like a thing smitten with palsy. Novels told you of things like these, but surely not just ordinary life! The note had been scribbled on a half-sheet of her own notepaper, and hastily folded into a cocked hat—perhaps the only old-fashioned device she had ever known her husband to be capable of. It seemed that she had learned by heart the message it contained before even she had unfolded the paper and read it. Indeed, it did not matter what it had to say. It hardly even mattered *how* it had said it. So considerately, yet so clumsily, so blastingly. 'She'—that alone was enough. When shells ex-plode why be concerned with fuse or packing? Edward was gone. That was all that mattered. She had been abandoned—she and the children.

So far, so inevitably. You can in vile moments of suspicion, incredulity and terror foresee things like that. Just that he was gone—and for good. But to have come stealing back in the afternoon into a vacant house, merely for a few clothes or a little money, and she out, and Mary out, and the children out —and everything else out; well, that seemed a funny, an unnecessary thing to do!

'I wouldn't have so much minded . . .' she began to mutter to herself, and then realized that her body was minding far too much. A thin acid water had welled into her mouth. Unlike William, she felt sick and dizzy. She had gone stiff and cold and goose-flesh all over. It was as if some fiendish hand were clutching her back hair and dragging the scalp from her forehead taut as the parchment of a drum over her eyes. It was as if she had swallowed unwittingly a dose of some filthy physic. Her knees trembled. Her hands hung down from her arms as though they were useless. And the only thing she could see at this instant was the other woman's face. But it wasn't looking at her; on purpose. It was turned all but three-quarters away —a becoming angle for the long, fair cheek-bone, the drooping eyelashes, the lips, the rounded chin—Clara. And then, suddenly, she saw them both together, stooping a little; at a railway station, it seemed; talking close. Or was it that they had just got out of a cab?

Emilia might as well have been dreaming all this, since although these picturings, this misery, this revulsion of jealousy, and the horror of what was to come persisted in a hideous activity somewhere in her mind, she herself had refused for the time being to have anything to do with it. There was something infinitely more important that must be done at once, without a moment's delay. Husbands may go, love *turn*, the future slip into ruin as silently and irretrievably as a house of cards. But children must not be kept waiting; not sick children. She was already clumsily tugging at the tiny middle drawer of the old mirror, one of their first bargains, on the dressing-table, and she caught at the same instant a glimpse of the face reflected in its glass; but so instantaneously that the eyes of the image appeared to be darkened and shut, and therefore blind.

What a boon a little methodicalness may be. What a mercy that in this world *things* stay where they are put; do not hide, deceive, play false, forsake and abandon us. Where she always kept it, *there* lay the slim, metal, sharp-edged case of the thermometer. It was as if it had been faithfully awaiting this very reunion—ever since she had seen it last. In the old days, before she was married and had children, even if she had possessed such a thing, she might have looked for it for hours before discovering it. She had despised thermometers. Now, such a search would have resembled insanity.

She hesitated for scarcely the breadth of a sigh at the door, and then with decision switched off the light. Stuffing her husband's scribbled note into her apron pocket, she flew into the next room, put a match to the fire laid in the grate, pushed the hot-water bottle between the sheets of the bed, and hastened downstairs. Her legs, her body, her hand flitting over the banisters, were as light and sure again as if she had never experienced so much as an hour even of mere disappointment in her life. Besides, for some little time now, that body had been habitually told what it had to do. And so long as her orders came promptly and concisely, it could be trusted to continue to act in the same fashion, to be instantly obedient. That was what being a mother taught you to become, and even taught you to try within limits to teach a young child to become—an animated automaton.

'Dr. Wilson' stood where she had left him beside the table and in precisely the same attitude. He had not even troubled to sit down. He had, apparently, not even so much as moved his eyes.

'Now, Doctor,' said Emilia.

At this, those eyes first settled on her fingers, then quietly shifted to her face.

'You were a long time gone, Mrs. Hadleigh,' he remonstrated in a drawling voice, as if his tongue were sticking to the roof of his mouth. 'A very long time.' He took the thermometer and pushed it gingerly between his lips, shutting them firmly over the thin glass stem. Then his blue and solemn eyes became fixed again, and, without the faintest stir, he continued to watch his mother, while she in turn watched him. When half a minute had gone by, he lifted his eyebrows. She shook her head. In another half-minute he himself took the thermometer out of his mouth, and, holding it between finger and thumb, gravely scrutinized it under the light. 'A hundred and forty-seven,' he announced solemnly. 'H'm.' Then he smiled, a half-secret, half-deprecatory smile. '*That's* nothing to worry about, Mrs. Hadleigh. Nothing at all. It looks to me as if all you did was to worry. Put him to bed; I will send him round a bottle of very nice medicine—*very* nice medicine. And . . .' his voice fell a little fainter, 'I'll look in again in the morning.'

His eyes had become fixed once more, focused, it seemed, on the far-away. 'Mummie, I do wish when Mary pulls down the blinds she would do it to the very bottom. I *hate* seeing— seeing myself in the glass.'

But Emilia had not really attended to this fretful and unreasonable complaint. She herself was now examining the thermometer. She was frowning, adjusting it, frowning again. Then she had said something—half-muttered, half-whispered —which Dr. Wilson had failed to catch.

'I'd give him,' he again began wearily, 'some rice pudding and lemonade, and——' But before the rest of his counsel could be uttered she had wrapped him tighter in his bath towel, had stooped down to him back to front so that he could clasp his hands round her neck, pick-a-back; and next moment he was being whisked up the dark staircase to the blue and white nursery. There she slid him gently down beside the fender, took off his shoes, smoothed his fringe, and tenderly kissed him.

'You have very bright eyes, Dr. Wilson. You mustn't let them get too bright—just for my sake.'

'Not at all, Mrs. Hadleigh,' he parroted, and then suddenly his whole body began to shiver.

'There,' she said, 'now just begin to take off your clothes, my own precious, while I see to the fire—though *that*, Dr. Wilson, should have been done *first*. Look, the silly paper has just flared up and gone out. But it won't be a minute. The sticks are as dry as Guy Fawkes' Day. Soon cosy in bed now.'

William with unusually stupid fingers was endeavouring to undo his buttons. He was already tired of being the doctor. 'Why,' he said, 'do your teeth chatter, Mummie, when you are very hot? That seems funny. And why do faces come in the window, horrid faces? Is *that* blind right down to the very bottom? Because I would like it to be. Oh dear, my head does ache, Mummie.'

It was extraordinary with what cleverness and dexterity Emilia's hands, unlike her son's, were now doing as they were bidden. The fire, coaxed by a little puffing in lieu of bellows, in a wondrous sheet of yellow, like crocuses, was now sweeping up the chimney as if to devour the universe. A loose under-blanket had been thrust into the bed, the hot bottle wrapped up in a fleecy old shawl, the coal scuttle had been filled, a second pair of small pyjamas had been hung over the fender to air, a saucepan of milk had been stood on the stove with its gas turned low—like a circlet of little blue wavering beads; and William himself, half-naked for less than the fraction of a second, had been tucked up in his bed, one of her own tiny embroidered handkerchiefs sprinkled with lavender water for company. There, he had instantly fallen asleep, though spasmodic jerks of foot and hand, and flickering eyelids showed that his small troubles had not wholly been left behind him.

So swiftly and mechanically had her activities followed one upon the other that Emilia had only just realized that she was still unable to make up her mind whether to telephone at once to the doctor or to venture—to dare—to look in on Sallie.

Blind fool! *Blind* fool!—foreseeing plainly every open or half-hidden hint and threat of to-night's event, smelling it, tasting it, hearing it again and again knocking at the door of her mind, she had yet continually deferred the appalling moment when she must meet it face to face, challenge and be done with it, and accept its consequences. The mere image in her mind of her husband's school tie left abandoned on the bed had made the foreboding of looking at Sallie a last and all but insupportable straw. The futility, the cowardice! What needs most daring must be done instantly. There had not been the least need to debate such a question. You can't do twenty-*one* things at once!

Having stolen another prolonged scrutiny of William's pale dream-distorted face and dilating nostrils, she hastened into her own bedroom again, groped for the tiny switch-pull that dangled by the bed-rail, stooped over the cot beside it, and, screening its inmate's face as much as possible from the glare, looked down and in. The small blonde creature, lovelier and even more delicate to the eye than any flower, had kicked off all its bedclothes, the bright lips were ajar, the cheeks flushed —an exquisite coral red. And the body was breathing almost as fast and shallowly as a cat's. That children under three years old should talk in their sleep, yes; but with so minute a vocabulary! Still, all vocabularies are minute for what they are sometimes needed to express—or to keep silent about.

No sickness, no sore throat; but headache, lassitude, pains all over the body, shivering attacks and fever—you just added up the Yes's and subtracted the Noes; and influenza, or worse, was the obvious answer. Should she or should she not wheel the cot into William's room? Sallie might wake, and wake William. Whereas if she remained here and she herself lay down in the night even for so much as an hour—and began to think, she wouldn't be alone, nor hopelessly alone. It was the fear of waking either patient that decided the questions. She very gently drew blanket and counterpane over Sallie's nakedness, draped a silk handkerchief over the rose-coloured shade, switched on the electric stove in the fireplace, and ran downstairs. There for a few moments, eyes restlessly glancing, she faced the stark dumbness and blindness of the mouthpiece of the telephone.

Dr. Wilson *was* in. Thank Heaven for that. Incredible, that was his voice! There might have been a maternity case—hours and hours. He might have had a horde of dispensary patients. But no, he would be round in a few minutes. Thank Heaven for that. She put back the receiver with a shuddering sigh of gratitude. All that was now needed—superhuman ordeal—was just to wait.

But this Emilia was to be spared. For midway up the staircase, whose treads now seemed at least twice their usual height, she had suddenly paused. Fingers clutching the banister rail, she stood arrested, stock still, icy, constricted. The garden gate had faintly clicked. There could be only one explanation of that—at least on a Wednesday. Edward's few friends and cronies, every one of them, must have discovered long ago that Wednesdays were now *his* 'evenings out'. And she—she hadn't much fancied friends or company recently. It was he himself, then. He had come back. What to do now? A ghastly revulsion took possession of her, a gnawing ache in the pit of her stomach, another kind of nausea, another *kind*, even, of palpitation.

If only she could snatch a few minutes to regain her balance, to prepare herself, to be alone. Consciousness was like the scene of a fair—a dream-Fair, all distortion, glare, noise, diablerie and confusion. And before she was even aware of her decision—to make use of a deceit, a blind, a mere best-thing-for-the-time-being—she had found herself in her bedroom again, had somehow with cold and fumbling fingers folded the note into its pretty cocked-hat shape again, and replaced it where she had first set eyes on it, beside the charming little travelling clock, the gift of Aunt Sarah, in the middle of the mantelpiece.

What light remained in the room behind the blinded and curtained windows could not possibly have been detectable outside. That was certain. In an instant she was in William's room once more—listening, her heart beating against her ribs like the menacing thumping of a drum. She had not long to wait. The latch of the front door had faintly squeaked, the lower edge of the door itself had scraped very gently across the coarse mat within, had as softly and furtively shut.

'Is that you, Edward?' she heard herself very gently and insidiously calling over the banisters from the landing. 'How lovely! You *are* home early. I didn't expect you for—for hours and hours!'

And now she had met and kissed him, full in the light of the hall-lamp. 'Why, what's the matter, darling. . . ? You are ill!' She was peering as if out of an enormous fog at the narrow, beloved, pallid countenance, the pale lips, the hunted, haunted, misery-stricken light brown eyes in those pits of dark entreaty and despair.

'Is it *that's* brought you home?'

He continued to stare at her as if, spectacles lost, he were endeavouring to read a little book in very small print and in an unfamiliar language. His mouth opened, as if to yawn; he began to tremble a little, and said, 'Oh, no; nothing much. A headache; I'm tired. Where *were* you?'

'Me?' But her lips remained faintly, mournfully, sympathetically smiling; her dark eyes were as clear and guileless and empty of reflections as pools of water under the windless blue of the sky. 'I was in William's room. It's hateful to say it now, Edward—now that you are so tired yourself—but—but I'm rather afraid, poor mite, he's in for another cold—a little chill—and I shouldn't be surprised if Sallie. . . . But don't worry about that—because, because there's nothing of course at all yet to worry about. It's you I'm thinking of. You look so dreadfully fagged and—what a welcome! . . . There's nothing . . . ?'

Her vocabulary had at last begun to get a little obstinate and inadequate, 'You don't mean, Edward, there's anything *seriously* wrong? I fancy, you know'—she deliberately laid her hand for an instant on his, 'I fancy *you* may be the least little bit feverish yourself—you too. Well. . . .' She turned away, flung up a hand as if to flag off a railway train, 'I'll get you something hot at once.'

'And Edward'—she turned her head over her shoulder, to find him as motionless as she had left him, in almost as stolid and meaningless an attitude as 'Dr. Wilson's' had been in the kitchen, as he stood brooding on the nightmare faces in the darkness of the glass. 'There is just one thing, if you could manage it. Just in *case*, would you in a moment or two first wheel Sallie's cot into William's room. I've lit the fire—and I *had* to ask Dr. Wilson to come. I'm so dreadfully stupid and anxious, when—even when there's no reason to be.'

The two faces had starkly confronted one another again, but neither could decipher with any absolute certainty the hitherto unrevealed characters now inscribed on them. Each of them was investigating the map of a familiar country, but the cartographer must now have sketched it from an unprecedentedly eccentric angle. The next moment she had turned away, had whisked upstairs and down again, leaving him free, at liberty, to dispose of himself—and of anything else he might be inclined to. In every family life there are surely potential keepsakes that would be far better destroyed; and perhaps a moment *some* time might come. But now. . . .

When she returned with her tray and its contents—a steaming tumbler of milk, a few biscuits and a decanter containing a little whisky—she found him standing beside William's bedroom fire. He watched her, as with the utmost care she put down her burden on the little wicker table.

'Millie,' he said, 'I'm not sure. . . . But, well—it was, I suppose, because of William's being ill that you haven't yet been into—into the other room, our bedroom. And so'—he had gulped, as if there was some little danger of producing his very heart for her inspection—'you have not seen *this*?' He was holding towards her the unfolded note, and with trembling fingers she found herself actually pretending to read its scribbled lines again.

Her face had whitened; she had begun to despair of herself, conscious beyond everything else—the tumult in her mind, the ravaging of her heart—that she could hardly endure the mingled miseries, remorse, humiliation in his eyes, in the very tones of his voice, yet listening at the same time to a message of ineffable reassurance. He has not then deceived me again! At last she had contrived to nod, her chin shaking so stupidly for a while that she could scarcely utter a word. 'Yes. I *have* read it. I put it back . . . couldn't face it when I heard you. The children—I had to have time. I'm *sorry*, Edward.'

' "*Sorry!*" ' he echoed.

'I mean—it *was* an awful, well, revelation; but I was stupid; I ought to have seen . . . I did see. But we won't—I *can't* go into that now. You are tired, ill; but you are back . . . for the present.'

Her eyes had managed at last to glance at him, and then to break away, and to keep from weeping. And, as if even in his sleep his usual tact and wisdom had not deserted him, William had suddenly flung back his scorching sheet and in a gasping voice was muttering to an unseen listener in some broken, unintelligible lingo that yet ended with a sound resembling the word faces. 'There, darling,' she answered him, smoothing back his fair fringe from his forehead. '*I* know. They are gone; all gone now; and the blind *is* down—to its very last inch.'

She stayed watching him, couldn't look back just yet.

'You see, Millie. . . . She'—her husband was trying to explain—'that is, *we* had arranged to meet. It's hopeless to attempt to say anything more just now. . . . I waited. She sent. . . . She didn't come.'

'I see. And so?'

'Millie, Millie. It wasn't, it wasn't *you*. Oh, I can't bear it any longer. If I had dreamed—the children!' He had flung himself into a pretty round basket chair and sat shuddering, his face hidden in his lean, bloodless hands.

The few minute sounds in the room, the peevish creakings of the chair, William's rapid, snoring breathing, the fluttering of the fire, were interrupted by the noise of brakes and wheels rasping to a standstill in the street below. A brisk yet cautious knocking had followed, awakening an echo, it seemed, in the very hollow of her breast bone.

'Look,' she said, 'that's where *that* goes. There's no *time* now.' The scrap of paper, more swiftly than a vanishing card in a conjuring trick, had been instantly devoured by the voracious flames, had thinned to an exquisitely delicate fluttering ash, and then, as if with a sudden impulse, wafted itself out of sight like a tiny toy balloon into the sooty vacancy of the chimney.

'Listen. Must *you* see the doctor, to-night? Unless it's not—you know—well *bad* 'flu? Wouldn't it be better not? I'll tell him; I could find out; I could say you had gone to bed. Quick, I must go.' Every nerve in her body was clamouring for motion, action, something to face, something to do.

He nodded. 'And you'll come back?'

'Yes. . . . I'll try. Oh, Edward, I'm sorry, sorry. If only there were words to say it. It must have been awful—awful!' She hesitated, gazing at his bent head, the familiar hands. . . .

And now the doctor, having deftly packed up Sallie again, burning hot but seemingly resigned to whatever fate might bring, and having carefully wiped his thermometer on the clean huckaback towel Emilia had handed him, was stuffing his stethoscope back into his little brown case. An almost passionate admiration filled her breast at his assured, unhurried movements, and with it a sort of mute, all-reconciling amusement to see how closely, deep within, behind these gestures, and the careful choice of words, he resembled his small and solemn understudy, William.

She was returning earnestly glance for glance, intently observant of every least change of expression in his dark decisive face, of timbre in his voice. Practically every one of the hungered-for, familiar, foreseen, all-satisfying assurances—like a tiny flock of innocent sheep pattering through a gateway—had been uttered and sagaciously nodded to: 'It may be just a feverish attack; it might, it *might* be 'flu.' 'Don't forget, Mrs. Hadleigh, they are down one moment and up the next!' 'I'll send round a bottle of medicine to-night, almost at once, and some powders.' 'I'll look in again first thing in the morning.' Then he had paused, little leather case in hand, his eyes fixed on the fire.

Some day, she told herself, she *must* retaliate in kind: 'You must understand, Dr. Wilson, that at this hour of the night it would be utterly stupid of you to breathe the word *pneumonia*, which takes weeks and weeks and weeks; may easily be fatal; and one has just to wait for the crisis!' Or, 'Don't be mistaken, Dr. Wilson, even if you were at death's door yourself I shouldn't hesitate to ring you up if their temperatures go over 103'—that kind of thing.

'You know, Mrs. Hadleigh,' he was beginning again, 'it just beats me why you mothers—quite rational, sensible, almost cynically practical creatures some of you, simply wear yourselves out with worry and anxiety when there's scarcely a shred of justification for it. Quite uselessly. Getting thin and haggard, wasting away, losing all that precious youth and beauty. I say I often *think* these things—wish I could express them. You simply refuse to heed *the* lesson in life: that really great Englishman's, Mr. Asquith's—"Wait and See". *Condensing*, don't you see, and not squandering all energy, impulse and reserves. "Never trouble trouble until trouble troubles you." Isn't *that* good sense? It's what's called an old wives' saying, of course—not a mother's. But I could have saved dozens of precious lives and bodies and all but souls, if only . . . well, literally saved them, I mean, a deuce of a lot of wear and tear.'

She was drinking in his words, this delicious lecture, these scoldings; devouring them, as if they were manna dipped in honey, the waters of life. They were a rest and peace beyond expression. A ready help in time of trouble. He shall lead his flock like a shepherd. Yea, though I walk. . . . Why all this Bible? Dr. Wilson was not a parson; he was just a doctor.

And then another Dr. Wilson had piped up in memory again,
' "You *said* that I was the doctor; and now you are kissing
me, Mummie!" . . . "I could often kiss lots of doctors!" '

'I know, I know,' she heard herself meekly assuring him.
'I'm utterly stupid about these things. And of course if we
were all sensible savages or gipsies there wouldn't be. . . .
Even—oh, but you can't think what a comfort it is to—to
be reassured.'

He was eyeing her now more closely, totting up and sub-
tracting yes's and noes, it seemed, on his own account, and on
hers. It was with difficulty she met the straight clear scrutiny.
'Well, there we are,' he decided. 'Just look what lovely babies
you have. Everything a woman could wish for! Gipsies be
dashed. There are, I assure you, my dear Mrs. Hadleigh, spinsters galore in this parish who. . . . How's your husband?'

Her dark shining eyes had now at last quivered in their
sockets, if only for the fraction of a second.

'It sounds very silly,' the words were squeezing out like
cooing turtle doves through too narrow an exit, 'but *he's* not
very well either! It's, it's almost funny, ridiculous—all three
at once. Isn't it? He came home rather late from—from the
office, and he's gone to bed.' It seemed a pity that one's cheeks
should flatly refuse not to flame up, when one's eyes were
hard as brass. 'The fact is, Dr. Wilson, he refused to see you.
You know what men are. But could it be, do you think', a
little nod towards William's bed had helped her out, 'that
too?'

'I think', Dr. Wilson had replied drily, a scarcely perceptible forking frown between his eyebrows, 'it might very well
be that too. But listen, Mrs. Hadleigh. Husbands, of course,
are not really of much importance in life—not really. Necessities perhaps; but here to-day and gone to-morrow. *Children*
are what the kernel is to the nut; the innermost part of it. And
so must be taken great care of. *Therefore*—and this is not advice; this is *orders*: I forbid you to worry; forbid it. I shall
throw up the case! If you *must* stay up—you have a maid, a

good solid, stolid one too. Wake up her and chance it; she'll love you all the better. And you can share the night-watch between you. Otherwise—unless of course you need me again, and you won't, though I should be *easily* handy—you are not only not to worry (more than you can help) but you are on no account to get up more than twice until the morning to look at your patients—at *our* patients, mind you. It's bad for them, worse for you. When they've had their dose, they'll soon quieten down—unless I'm *wrong*. And—imagine it!—I sometimes am.' He was holding out his hand, a look of unadulterated, generous, wholly masculine admiration on his vigilant, assured features.

'By gad!' he said. 'All three! But then *you* know *I* know what you can manage when hard pressed. So that's all right.' He was plunging downstairs into the night, and Emilia was trying in vain to keep up with him.

'And after the first dose and the powders, Dr. Wilson, I shouldn't, I suppose, wake either of them up to give them any *more* medicine—not until the morning?'

'As a general rule, Mrs. Hadleigh,' replied the doctor, carefully putting on his hat and glancing as he did so into the strip of looking-glass on the wall, 'it's wiser never to wake *anybody* up, merely to give them physic—and certainly not mere doctor's physic.'

THOMAS HARDY'S LYRICS

If devotion and love are the happiest flowers that can inter-twine a poet's laurels, then the wreath upon Mr. Hardy's brows is indeed burdened with sweetness. It is impossible to read him with indifference or in mere admiration. We blow either hot or cold; a fact that may in part explain why, years ago, he was compelled to surrender verse for prose, and long afterwards to forswear the writing of fiction. That dead past has now prudently buried its dead. To-day our proud affec-tion may even veil his rarest qualities. In heart as well as in time we stand too close to his work to appraise its complete achievement, to see it in true perspective and in relation to that of the great masters.

In reading again, and in reading steadily through, his lyrical poems we can realize, at any rate, the abundance and variety of his work, its homogeneousness and originality. No other English novelist has, in a chosen context, written prose that in effect, in feeling and atmosphere is nearer to poetry. No other English dramatist has written an historical play which more closely resembles than does *The Dynasts* a vast panoramic fiction, wherein real men and women so strangely reflect the idiosyncrasies of a distinct personality and imagina-tion. So with these poems. They are, one and all, haunted with the presence of their writer. Every line of them—best and worst—is sealed with his own hand. We share an intense solitude of the spirit. We are as close to actual experience as words can bring us.

But even the most lyrical and individual of them is touched with the dramatic. A score of diverse disguises conceal (and betray) the one wearer; and ever to and fro glides the shuttle of wizardry, weaving make-believe out of the actual. More than once Mr. Hardy has warned us that his lyrics are dramatic or impersonative in conception, even when not obviously so. He has bidden us make allowance for widely differing moods and circumstances. He deprecates, that is, an arraignment of himself as A for what another self utters as Z. None the less—Alpha to Omega—all there is his, and all is himself. Nor should the inherent apparent contradictions be cancelled out as in a sum of arithmetic. They are light and colour from the facets of one multi-angled consciousness, that makes a various and chequered beauty of the white ray that is the infinite reality.

The simplest of poets may, it is true, drape himself in more than one domino. Herrick is Ariel in his songs, Caliban in his epigrams; the bacchanalian of the Mermaid and of the Triple Tun at one moment, the pious vicar of Dean Prior the next. But Mr. Hardy in his lyrics not only plays countless parts (from Prospero's to Trinculo's), and will squander on three brief stanzas the nucleus of a novel, but he is untrammelled by the incapacity to make poetry of the commonplace. In the Sala delle Muse, in Rome, he once kept tryst with one (surely a distant cousin of Sue Bridehead's) who was 'an essence of the Nine'—'a pensive smile on her sweet, small, marvellous face'. He lamented his fickleness, his inconstant love for Form also, and Tune, Story, Dance, and Hymn. She consoled him:

> Nay, wight, thou sway'st not. These are but phases of one;
>   And that one is I; and I am projected from thee,
> One that out of thy brain and heart thou causest to be—
>   Extern to thee nothing. Grieve not, nor thyself becall,
>   Woo where thou wilt; and rejoice thou canst love at all.

So well has he obeyed her that anywhen, anywhere that ghostly face may smile on him in still regard, and make of every working day exactly four-and-twenty timeless hours. Certain themes may recur again and again; but he is not confined to any particular region of thought, experience, or of the imagination. Self-forgotten, he lives in the created. Absorbed in characters of his own making, he none the less fashions them in his own protean image. Never was the tinder of the mind more hospitable to the feeblest of actuality's sparks. The merest glimpse—a boy in a railway carriage with a key hung round his neck, a skeleton parasol, a tapping moth, a cheval glass, a fly bestraddling his midnight manuscript, a candle-lit face, a tottering tombstone, a church clock, a gargoyle, a fiddle, the wind in the chimney, dying daylight —and the poet in him answers as to a decoy. It may be convenient to call him a realist—though what poet, if reality is the habitation of the spirit as well as of the body, can be anything else is a nice question. A more precise term would be realizationist.

But if, apart from mask and domino, his scope, his multifarious range of theme, differentiates Mr. Hardy's lyrical poetry, no less does his treatment of it, the thought with which he complicates and deepens it, and the intensity, less of impulse than of elaboration, with which he constrains it to his will. The poet whose nut-tree bears silver nutmegs and gold pears would only scare his Spanish princess if he plucked for her also crab-apples and sloes. Fruits as tart and acrid abound in Mr. Hardy's orchard; and however gladly we may feast our eyes upon their vivid and sombre clusters, they are as bitter to some stomachs as was the honey-flavoured book to St. John. Lyrical poetry in general makes its own lovely paradise, fresh and sweet with dews of Lethe. Its airs blow rare from the intense inane. Much of Mr. Hardy's poetry limes our wings and tethers us close indeed to a God-forgotten 'tainted ball'. Mutes attired in dead black, their eyes submissive though preternaturally active, their ears exquisitely 'on the *qui vive*', stand on either side of the portals of its philosophy. Poem after poem reiterates that this poor scene of our earthly life is 'a show God ought surely to shut up soon', the 'unweeting dream-work' of some vast Imbecility, that spends eternity in passive reverie or remorse, that framed this planet in jest and abandoned it to hazardry. 'That I made the Earth, and life, and man It still repenteth me.' As for Nature—she is naught more pitiful than a sleep-walker. 'Busy in her handsome house known as Space', she has fallen a-drowse; and man's only sure reward for all his hopes and aspirations is that 'storm-tight roof' which 'earth grants all her kind'; his only comfort that, though he must at last fall a prey to the 'iron daggers of distress', twice he cannot die. If this, and scores of kindred maledictions, were the final, unalleviated message to humanity of 'One who, past doubtings all, Waits in Unhope', then the poet in Mr. Hardy would have died in the arms of the philosopher, as might have Heine in those of Schopenhauer. But Mr. Hardy is too imaginative a philosopher to venture a final answer to the great riddle. He asks and asks:

> *Thy shadow, Earth, from Pole to Central Sea,*
> *Now steals along upon the Moon's meek shine*
> *In even monochrome and curving line*
> *Of imperturbable serenity.*

> *How shall I link such sun-cast symmetry*
> *With the torn troubled form I know as thine,*
> *That profile, placid as a brow divine,*
> *With continents of moil and misery?*
> *And can immense Mortality but throw*
> *So small a shade? . . .*

No God, it is true, could loom more phantasmal and remote from our trivial and agonizing affairs than the 'all-Immanent Will' that drives us into the world in 'rabble rout', mutters in slumber, or mocks, or sighs out of his tenebrous abiding-place in consciousness, as 'the monotonous moil of strained hard-run Humanity'. But anthropomorphic deities are usually flattering reflections of their creators. *This* deity is infinitely less compassionate, tender, magnanimous, and faithful than the poet whose workmanship he is, and who in every word he writes is present with us. Wherefore relenting and tenderness often steal into the limning of this Divine conception, and pity smiles from the eye-holes of the cold mask of the ironic:

> *Thou shouldst have learnt that Not to Mend*
> *For Me could mean but Not to Know. . . .*

It takes two to make either a quarrel or a friendship. 'Dazed and puzzled 'twixt the gleam and gloom', the only human hope is honesty.

> *Yet would men look at true things,*
> *And unilluded view things,*
> *And count to bear undue things,*
> *The real might mend the seeming,*
> *Facts better their foredeeming,*
> *And Life its disesteeming.*

And in *The Spell of the Rose*, another story is told to us:

> *But I was called from earth—yea, called*
> *   Before my rose-bush grew;*
> *   And would that now I knew*
> *What feels he of the tree I planted,*
> *   And whether, after I was called*
> *   To be a ghost, he, as of old,*
> *   Gave me his heart anew!*

> *Perhaps now blooms that queen of trees*
> *   I set but saw not grow,*
> *   And he, beside its glow—*
> *Eyes couched of the mis-vision that blurred me—*
> *   Ay, there beside that queen of trees*
> *   He sees me as I was, though sees*
> *   Too late to tell me so!*

That rose-bush is love—'long-suffering, brave . . . sweet, prompt, precious', even though 'cruel as the grave'. Not ours the arrogance to reconcile on his behalf a poet's contradictions. Yet there is a bloom upon this Dead Sea fruit that is more inviting and even more sustaining than the milky juices of that of the mere optimist. Beyond this, simply because the faithful and unflinching presentation of a philosophy, however Spartan, darkened or forlorn it may be, is poetic, it confers light, energy, and even peace on us. *Worse* tidings cannot reach us, nor can Truth wear a colder, harsher, more sardonic grin (and assuredly in the 'Fifteen Glimpses' she displays her dog teeth to some purpose). But we have fallen in love with her ambassador; and like ambassador, the heart argues, like Queen.

Beneath this heaven, indifferent or hostile, Mr. Hardy sets up his stage, the panorama of mortal existence, calls up his characters, peoples his solitude:

> *Listen: I'll tell the tale,*
> *It may bring faint relief.*

Our company, it must be admitted, is not that of 'the winged seraphs': or of alien divinities as lovely as they are inexacting; or of a society urbane, at ease, immune in its Palace of Art. There are not many 'ladies' in this volume—the majority of them are haplessly jilted, or helplessly wed. There are fewer perfect gentlemen. One such buys an enemy's portrait intent on the joy (of which he is cheated) of destroying it; another is the husband of the unfortunate bride in *A Conversation at Dawn*:

> *'I'm a practical man, and want no tears;*
> *You've made a fool of me, it appears;*
>   *That you don't again*
> *Is a lesson I'll teach you in future years.'*

> *She answered not, lying listlessly*
> *With her dark dry eyes on the coppery sea,*
>   *That now and then*
> *Flung its lazy flounce at the neighbouring quay.*

A third 'gentleman' affrighted even a wagtail.

Thomas Hardy's Lyrics

In a world indeed wherein, if closely examined, the guise of life is less 'fell' only when it is realized that cold, sickness, gloom, death are but 'subalterns', passively subject to the higher command, class distinctions seem of trivial import, and 'the courtesies of the bland' a mere veneer. It is little wonder then that poor Mrs. Grundy cuts a sorry figure in it; that the conventions and conformities are left to take care of themselves, as they very well can; and that 'Order-keeping's rigorous control' resembles that of a foolish and embittered nurse in a rebellious nursery. Moonshine or noonday, and whether its stage be thronged or deserted, this is a world also, whose borders are astir with the spectral. How could it be otherwise, seeing that of any man's friends so large a number are in the grave? It is here, if anywhere, that literary company looks in on Mr. Hardy, and come to sup with him Emily Brontë and the author of *The Duchess of Malfi*. Barham, too, when the port is on the table, will rap at the door; and neighbour Burton lug in a folio on the Pleasures of Melancholy. His phantoms and revenants are for the most part the wistful evocations of misgiving or regret. Some of them are more lovely, and all are more understandable, even when inclined to the satirical, than when in the real. Many are earthily jovial, 'clay-cadavers', with their mugs and pipes, their lutes and viols, touched by lights of midnight, under willow and yew. And amid their revelries from among the deeper shadows leers out the sinister-grotesque.

Thus freed from the artificial, thus haunted, thus aroused, we share the company of Mr. Hardy's wayfaring men and women, intent on their all-absorbing share in the egregious drama, and part-perfect. Entangled in the webs of circumstance, the majority of them are the prey of their desires, their aspirations or their folly, racked, cheated by mischance, victims of age or affliction, or of a tender and lively charm and innocence that is but a mockery in its transitoriness. Their happiest stories are overcast with the precarious (and at the mercy of an ironic appendix!); but even the most tragic are such as our own experience can ratify, however hastily a self-defensive memory may have strown her poppy.

Like the figure which we discern in the poems that are not obviously impersonative or dramatic, these characters are mysterious, and touched with a kind of strangeness or romance, as indeed all humanity is mysterious when, viewed searchingly, it is off its guard, or when the scales of habit or prejudice have dropped from our eyes. Unobserved, we watch them as closely as in mind we can watch the faces of friends with whom long ago we were in intimate and earnest colloquy; but seldom, indeed, as watches Peeping Tom when the vivisectionist is busy. So passionately intent is Mr. Hardy's 'visionary power' on the naked truth of things in their changing aspects that he seems designedly to reject in his record of them the refinements of art and beauty.

But since beauty and significance are debts which no living imagination can evade paying to reality, his poetry is drenched with them. Even if these figments of humanity were absent from his pages, we might almost guess his portraits from their frames. No other poetry is richer in scene, within doors or without; in landscape—its times and lights and seasons, in Englishness. To present a true account, debit and credit, between Mr. Hardy and his Wessex would make the fame of a literary accountant. But what of that further west of the most passionate of his poems, where in 'chasmal beauty' roars the Atlantic, and swing the surges over sunken Lyonesse?

Yet, for pure melody, the music of this verse is unlikely to redden with envy the cheeks of the Sirens. The style is often crustacean. Occasionally it is 'an irk no local hope beguiles', and as if 'smitten by years-long wryness born of misprision'.

The thought, too, may be as densely burdened in its expression as the scar of a tree by the healing saps that have enwarted its surface. But what rare and wondrous clumps of mistletoe bedeck the branches. Stubborn the medium may be, but with what mastery is it compelled to do this craftsman's bidding. Let the practised poet borrow but a score of

Mr. Hardy's latinities and vernaculars—hodiernal, receptivity, deicide, a senior-soul-flame, his mindsight, naysaying, eyesome, potent appraisements, smugger, years-haired, forefolk, and the rest, and then invoke his own Muse! Difficulty, seeming impossibility, is the breath of Mr. Hardy's nostrils as a craftsman. He makes our English so much his own that a single quoted line, lifted at random, betrays his workmanship. He forces, hammers poetry into his words; not, like most poets, charms it out of them. He disdains the 'poetical', yet will redeem the veriest commonplace; and will so encrust his chosen theme that it shines the brighter for the roughness and uncouthness of its setting. His argument winds in and out of his congested, complex stanzas, keeping a low pitch, and, by emphasizing rather than by suddenly escaping its monotony, wins this effect.

When indeed life and energy pour their visionings of truth and reality into the mould of form, poetry cannot but be their reward. This imagination, accepting the world, even while renouncing the 'Impercipient' that set it in the void, redeems its mischances, and of the sorriest disaster makes a memory for our comfort and understanding. Charm, grace, delicacy seem idle terms in the presence of this genius. Bare, uncompromising, mocking, pitiful, and utterly human, Mr. Hardy has gone his way, aloof, impassioned, watching life, living it, sharing it with man and nature; and, above all, loving its seared, suffering, heroic face that smiles on at grief, and is indomitable in happiness in a world that seemingly cheats to destroy.

A poem entitled *In the Seventies*, having for motto 'Qui deridetur ab amico suo sicut ego', tells, in retrospect, of the starry thoughts that in those far days shed their magic light on this poet's 'worktimes' and his 'soundless hours of rest'; tells, too, of 'the vision';

> *In the seventies naught could darken or destroy it,*
> *Locked in me.*

Thomas Hardy's Lyrics

Though as delicate as lamp-worm's lucency;
Neither mist nor murk could weaken or alloy it
In the seventies!—could not darken or destroy it,
Locked in me.

Upwards of forty years have passed since that day, and all but a fraction of the work in this volume is of the last two or three decades. Mr. Hardy, once and for all, set up as a poet, then, at an age when Shakespeare left our mortal stage. This book, for that reason alone, is an unprecedented achievement. Apart from that, to read steadily through it—and what severer test of lyrical poetry could be devised?—is to win to the consciousness, not of any superficial consistency, but assuredly of a 'harmony of colouring'; not, however keen the joy manifest 'in the making', of an art become habitual, but of a shadowy unity and design. In the seventies Mr. Hardy could not have foreseen that full design, nor can he have consciously traced it out. But laborious days and an unfaltering constancy have set free those starry thoughts, that secret wondrous vision, and have thrown open one of the most hospitable doors in English literature in welcome to all.

Thomas Hardy's Lyrics

MAPS IN FACT AND FICTION

It is a mournful thought that every explorer, since Adam was exiled from the Garden of Eden and the brighter stars were called by name, has ultimately only succeeded in contracting the human conception of the universe. The world as conceived by Homer was but a small blot on the world known to Ptolemy, and the world of Ptolemy merely a fraction in area of that mapped out by Martin Behaim. And yet the centuries in driving back the frontiers of *terra incognita* have somehow apparently cramped the fancy. For it is in the vaguely dreamed of and in the wholly unknown that the imagination takes its ease and delight. The present generation has experienced the treacherous novelty of having first the North Pole and then the South served up with its breakfast. It danced round them for a while as eagerly as children used to dance round a Jack-in-the-Green. But these May days will never dawn again. Does any unknown sea remain into which a yet-to-be-astonished mariner shall be the first to burst? Ought not the civilized world to have saved a few such, as children save a *bonne bouche* or sweethearts the last page of a love-letter? To muse indeed on a piece of water or mountains never seen by mortal eye, blind, can we say, even to its own being, and known only by an inconceivable Creator to be good, is to muse on a mystery past divining. To-morrow, flight across the Atlantic will make but a three days' journey, a nine days' wonder. And though it would be a dull mind that could find no romance in a modern atlas, that atlas contests with the dictionary the claim to be a record of comparative finality. Neither flowers into guesswork or hearsay. They are concerned with all but finished achievement. There is even less chance (and all hail to Mr. Roosevelt!) of adding a new river or mountain or race to the one than there is of enriching with an endurable neologism the other.

Use and wont, then, as well as rather abject adoration of the practical, make maps of things-as-they-are dullish documents. Nimble spirits may, of course, entertain themselves as pleasantly with Mercator's Projection as with an Ordnance Survey imprint of six inches to the mile, in which one's neighbouring haystack and brook make as fair a show as Baghdad and the Amazons. But the spectacular pens and vivid surmises of the past are things of the past. Utterly out of fashion now are the beautiful old hues and designs, the brilliant banners above the tiny miniature cities, the winds and half winds and quarter winds, in black and green and red, of the portolan skin charts of the fifteenth and sixteenth centuries, with their seas of generous blue and emerald, lavishly edged with gold. And we should hardly even ourselves venture to huddle into the uppermost corner of Europe, as once the map-maker did, an amateur representation of the earthly paradise. Few latter-day travellers, perhaps, would envy Scylax of Caryanda, the author of the oldest known Greek periplus, his coast-wise voyage of 153 days in circuit of the Mediterranean; but the most prosaic grown-up would rub his eyes in pleasure (mingled with scorn) at a geography chequered with such dream-wide suggestions of infinity as 'Beyond the Pillars of Hercules, which are in Europe, there are many trading stations of the Carthaginians, also mud, and tides, and open seas.'

It is, indeed, the generous credulity, the childlike wonder, the independence of spirit (all excellently disguised as a passion for accuracy) in the ancient cartographers that are the fascination of their work. One can pore over the Cataläner Map, for instance, for hours together, and rise refreshed as with the waters of Hippocrene. Why does the City of Lop, 'leagues south of the route of the caravans which pass from Sarra to Catayo across a great desert', so intrigue the fancy?

And the Island of Chis? Has perchance Lord Dunsany trodden the echoing courts of the one, the yellow sands of the other? Why, for quite other than obvious reasons, does Regio Feminarum, tucked securely away in the remote, clear-cut oblong of the Island of Jaua, so cordially 'invite the soul'? Names as outlandish and bizarre throng every gazetteer, but the effect is by comparison sterile.

> *Whither is fled the visionary gleam?*
> *Where is it now, the glory and the dream?*

There are, of course, more succulent sops to the imagination even than these: 'Here reigns K. Stephen, a Christian. In this land lies St. Thomas. Look for the City Butifilis.' We look for the City Butifilis; and there it is. Cook's being our guide, we will pack up to-morrow! Up in the N.E. corner, again, sprawls the princedom of Gog and Magog, securely confined amid delicious mountains, as well as 'shut up by Alexander of Macedon'. Gog must have yearned northwards over those impregnable hills for the islands where abound 'many good Gerfalcons which are taken for the Great Can', and Magog have turned hungry eyes due south towards the '7, 548 Islands' in the seas of the Indies 'where grow the spices', where dwell 'naked savages', and southwards still, towards Tapbrobana, 'last in the East', called by the Tartars Great Cantij, wherein flourish not only cannibals, negroes, etc., but wherein also falls into ceaseless ruin a nameless 'City destroyed by serpents'.

But the Catalan Map is of 1375. Gog and Magog have been reduced to a tavern sign, and the Great Kahn's immortality is inextricably bound up with Samuel Taylor Coleridge's. Traveller's tales must grow leaner and leaner. But since there are ghosts in men's bodies, the desire for adventure will never perish. We shall seek other means for travel, dare lands beyond land's end and Thules still more ultimate. Mars shines for conquest. Far, far better—the gradual awakening of a sixth sense may renew and transmogrify the whole habitable globe!

Meanwhile there remains a way out of possible stagnation and ennui that has as yet attracted few adventurers. Neither Columbus nor Cabot, Vasco da Gama nor Vespucci ever set sail for the regions of Romance. Yet romance has always edged into, only to be as pertinaciously banished from, man's record of his earthly voyagings. Castles in Spain may have a poor reputation; yet their ruins, viewed through the perspective of time, wear a winning aspect. And to give to airy nothing a habitation and a name is the office not only of love but also of fiction. The song the sirens sang everybody knows the tune of, though nobody may remember the words. But we can only guess at the sandy trysting-place of Man Friday and Robinson Crusoe, and we are unlikely to explore on Shank's mare the fabulous island of Monte Cristo. The whole problem, indeed, of the where, the how, and the when of the imaginative novelist is still obscure.

Modern story-tellers for the most part lap their creatures in the luxuries of a real Mayfair, or people with phantasms the streets-in-being of an actual Five Towns. They only thinly disguise their Wessex, their Dartmoor. Chaucer's imaginary pilgrims trod a tangible Watling Street. Scott was a patriot, George Eliot was a *genius loci*. The journey of Little Nell and her grandfather may be traced from London up to Tong. And Borrow, Kingsley, and Dumas could swear pretty straitly by the map. Houses are another matter. And, though by some elusive wizardry we realize that in *that* particular corner of her boudoir our heroine flung herself upon a prie-dieu to weep, that our heedless hero slammed a door to the left, and that the wicked old uncle died in his fourposter with his face to the ivied window, it would often puzzle us to fit in the floors and storeys of an otherwise admirable mansion of the fancy; while to descend from attic to cellar in some dream-houses would be an experience of the purest nightmare. It is a nice question whether a novelist should actually call in an architect before he sets to work, a still nicer whether he should preface his story with a practicable plan—bathroom and porch, pantry and embowered arbour. The indefatigable Watson at times traced Sherlock Holmes's footprints in the snows as it were, of Scotland Yard; adding a twinge of horror to crime by indicating the locale of a corpse with a cross. But then these little conscientiousnesses were rare. No less rare was a clear, precise North-East-South-West sketch to scale of a province, countryside, city, or village that never was on sea or shore. Mr. Conrad has told how a fair and inquiring visitor one workaday morning shattered the whole universe of his *Nostromo*. He built it up again, but he did not map it out with compasses and Indian ink. Such a feat is the entertainment and device of a more ingenious, a less grave and creative mind. One can see a Robert Burton absorbedly recording every gulf, morass, creek, and quicksand in the sad and mighty realms of Melancholy; but hardly a Milton, quill in hand, tracing out the frontiers of Paradise. The sport is a childish fantasy, but none the less precious for that.

Precious now and then, at any rate; and even to the tune of £44. For that was the sum squandered only last week on the original of the chart prefixed to *Treasure Island*. Even though it represented the stockinged hoardings of a lifetime, the buyer made a bargain. The map is a little masterpiece. The story goes that it was designed to beguile a youthful stepson. For youth's sake alone the thumbed and perishing chart was sewn up together with Billy Bones's nefarious ledger and sealed with a thimble. So be it, but we know our Louis Stevenson. 'It is about nine miles long and five across, shaped, you might say, like a fat dragon standing up, and had two fine land-locked harbours, and a hill in the centre part marked "The Spy Glass".' 'Methinks it is like a weasel'—but fat dragon will serve. No fancy-itching detail has been overlooked in that 'facsimile struck out by J. Hawkins'. (The original of that is probably in the possession of the heirs of Flint's quarter-master, 'along of his timber leg'.) It has been lovingly done—the rayed compass, the ships in bellying sail, solemn dolphin, spouting whale, and somewhat lamentable sea-nymph, swamp and spring, tide and cove and sounding, and above all, in bright red, in dingy red, in greeny-blue, the scripts of 'J.F.', of 'W.B.' ('this twenty July 1754') and of the bright as fortunate Jim.

'We had run up the trades to get the wind of the island we were after—I am not allowed to be more plain' ; for there is still treasure—silver—not yet lifted! It is odd that, in spite of definite description—'. . . General colouring uniform and sad . . . grey melancholy woods and wild stone spires . . . odd outlandish swampy trees . . . the fog had now buried all heaven . . .'—that island remains, in one faraway vision of it at least, ablaze with emerald and sunshine. Was it 'the nutmeg and azalea', 'the poisonous brightness' of the foliage that led fancy astray, or did the brass buttons *thick* on the unctuous, the sly, the murderous, and impossible John Silver's coat cast a reflected and unfading glamour of light upon that 'sweet pretty place'? Jim may write (with artful finish) of 'our dark and bloody sojourn', and in these outspoken days we may cordially admit the bloody. But that dark was surely for ever dissipated by the doubloons and double guineas and moidores and sequins, stamped with the pictures of all a century's kings of Europe, and the shores of Treasure Island (save only where that victim of chuck-farthen and of his brass-hearted shipmates, Ben Gunn, ran doubled-up down the hill) remain radiant with gold and coral, lit only not with a tropical sun, but by the lamp left by Israel Hands, still burning in broad daybreak in the cabin of the Hispaniola, and by the wasteful fires of the mutineers. Forty-four pounds! It was a bagatelle for such a memorial of a genius that will for many a long day lure childhood back from the wreckage of the years and once at least kept the austere Dean Church out of bed.

A chart designed by a characteristically evil Chinaman is mentioned though not represented in Mr. Wells's *Treasure of the Forest*. Poe reproduces Captain Kidd's cryptogram (written probably in a solution of regulus of cobalt in spirit of nitre), but, alas! supplies no chart in tints of Legrand's heaven-sent scarabæus. *King Solomon's Mines*, however, is handsomely prefaced by the old Dom José de Silvestra's map, scratched down in his last trickle of blood (before he was frozen cold as mutton) on a fragment of linen (? his shirt) 'in the little cave on the north side of the nipple of the southernmost of the two mountains I have named Sheba's Breasts'. It is written in Portuguese, and the bare route stretches from the River Lukanga to the mountains at the end of King Solomon's Road. 'I know not', writes Alan Quatermain, 'how to describe the glorious panorama which unfolded itself to our enraptured gaze.' And we must take his word for it. But he makes reiterated play with Sheba's Breasts and refers to a scene 'like Paradise'. This is vague, but there is beauty less vaguely paradisical in his record, that of 'the young ladies', 'like arum lilies', for instance, who danced the dance of death before the one-eyed Twala, and 'the snowy loveliness' of Good's bare legs. Detail would not have come amiss regarding 'the five miles round of fertile ground' of the palace at Loo— 'unlimited Loo', according to the facetious owner of the legs. But Alan makes up with thrills what he lacks in the picturesque and (with *Treasure Island* in mind) in style.

William Morris's chart of the course of the Sundering Flood is a very different thing. It is the work of an artist—not apparently of Osberne himself—and so outside the story. And the decorative rather than the vividly imaginative was its inspiration. It is, if anything, too definite, if not too rich, and perhaps a little literary and artificially elaborate. We read of dromonds and roundships, but the salt sea wind of the Hispaniola does not pluck at their shrouds. We read of far countries and outlandish folk, of dread and unknown tongues, of dwarfs and landwights, of 'a little cot somewhat kenspeckle'. But Morris is not bent on waking terror or trying our nerves, the little cot *remains*—somewhat kenspeckle. And *The Wood Masterless* is somehow less woody that poetic. In one thing, too, narrative and chart are in quarrel. So long as in a series of pictures serene and pure the little carle, Osberne, meets and talks with Elfhild on the Bight of the Cloven Knoll, with fifty feet of roaring water sundering each from each, the romantic dream remains unstirred, unbroken. The arrowing of the boy's gifts across the gulf, those two loving faces whose nearest approach is in a steadfast gaze—all this is gay and tender and charming. And Elfhild's 'O thou beauteous creature, what art thou?' is no less lovely an impulse than her 'But what else canst thou do, Champion?' is an arch and womanly piece of naïveté. But chance and circumstance separate the children. The supernatural machinery creaks a little. Steelhead is a hard nut to crack. And then, disappointment of disappointments, when the lovers meet again, Elfhild has long since crossed the magic waters of Sundering Flood, and by a ferry! The idea, the symbol has been betrayed. The very essence of the romance has fainted into air.

Inspired schoolmasters there may be who set their scholars not the vast cutlet of Africa, sea-fretted Scotland, or the hundreds-and-thousands of the Grecian Archipelago to map out on paper, but a fantastic country of their own contriving, crammed with strange beasts and wildernesses, and precipices and virgin streams and valleys. One such contraption was devised far too many years ago by a certain small boy now small no longer. Outlined in cloudy blue, hedged about with tottering, ungainly print, the shores of his isles—of *Goats*, of *Ba* and *Be*, of *Rags* and *Riggerbar*—are washed by the tides of the *Graca Ocean* and the *Sea of Rega* (with the S back side before). 'Here is a Forest' (green as green), 'Here is the Rem Mountains', 'Here is a great Castle', run his legends. And an indulged and indulgent uncle ventured on the letterpress:

'. . . Now to speak of the Islands that we went in rowboats to visit before our ship set sail thither (a N.W. point near the River Dum), the weather remaining calm and fair for three days till the fourth morning, first we landed on the *Isle of Butter* which lieth alongside of the *Isle of Ray*. In this isle is an

exceeding steep high Mountian [*sic*] capped with frozen ice
that doth marvellously gleam and twinkle when the sun by
day doth fall upon it, sending forth beams far and near of
divers colours like to a great Lantern. Also at night the moon
gloateth upon the ice and it is like the Opal, for I did look
upon it as I lay in my bunk, ashipboard. But to scale this
Mountian it were a thing impossible by reason of its steepness
and the slipperiness of its perpetual ice. In the *Isle of Butter* is
great store of little pebbles that are round and smooth as
marbles (that children be accustomed to play with), also in
its waters lurketh a little fish called the butter-fish—it is so
greasy in the broiling. . . . And hearing strange shrill cries, we
lifted our wagging heads and espied a company of dwarfmen,
with naked skins grey as the crocus, riding upon shaggy flat-
footed beasts after the manner of our mules. But though we
threw up our hands and besought them dumbly, our tongues
being swollen beyond speech, they galloped away from us.
And, when we looked, we counted only seven men left of us,
with the boatswain. And I conjecture two men namely,—
Benjamin and Robert Small, were taken in their sleep and
devoured by these grey people; for such is their barbarous
custom to eat man's poor flesh, having dried it in the sun.
And we asleep. But Heaven being pitiful to us that remained,
we toiled on, the boatswain alone sitting down with coura-
geous face to the west, unable longer to continue, his body
being puffed out nigh double through chewing of a root he
had found. And he died there looking towards his own
country and asking mercy on his sins. . . .'
What, after all, is the great globe itself but undiscovered
country to every newcomer? Who even can deny us the
privy conviction that we walk and slumber, not, as it might
appear, on a silly giddy ball in space, but on an endless sea-
ridden plain whose furthermost bourne is breathed of as
'Death'? Our jaded, sated sense of fact is all a fallacy. A green
meadow may be El Dorado and all the Indies to a simple and
unexacting heart. Thou art—what thou dost gaze upon. To a

tortured imagination the homely Thames may wander black as Acheron; to a happier, not Jordan itself is a more miraculous stream. And if, possibly, one sometimes wearies of the old familiar places, of Greenwich time and down-trodden longitudes, how easy to take pencil and brush in hand and idly map out that place where one would be—Life's Courage, Heart's Ease. It would not be necessary to write a book about it. It would fetch not forty-four farthings in open auction. It would be a poor thing, but one's own.